VALLEY OF THE SHADOW OF DEATH

CAVES OF PAGAN AND POPE

FAIRSPEECH
Birthplace of By-Ends

Christian Meets Faithful

The Encounter with Talkative

Here Faithful was Martyred

VANITY FAIR

Hopeful Joins Christian

VAIN GLORY
Birthplace of Formality and Hipocrisy

Lot's wife

DEMAS' SILVER MINES

The Shepherds

DELECTABLE MOUNTAINS

W GATE

DOUBTING CASTLE

Giant Dispair Dwells Here

HILL CALLED ERROR

Little-Faith was Robbed Here

The Flatterer Led Them Far From the Way

Christian and Hopeful Meet Ignorance

ENCHANTED GROUND

THE CELESTIAL CITY

Beulah Land

River of Death

The Sojourner's Adventure Through Pilgrim's Progress

C.J. Lovik

www.lighthouse.pub

Visit our website
to purchase books and preview
upcoming titles.

Contact us at:
feedback@lighthouse.pub

Design by Sergio E. León
Sergio was born and raised in Mexico City where he studied Design and Arts in the National Autonomous University of Mexico (UNAM). For more than 20 years, Sergio has worked in a variety of positions, primarily acting as Art and Design Director for major brands and publications. Today Sergio is the Art and Design Director for Lighthouse Gospel Beacon, where he is responsible for all digital and print media. Every day Sergio is growing in Christ while continuing to produce art and media to help illustrate the love of the Savior. Sergio is married to his wonderful wife, Monica, and they have two amazing children.

DEDICATION

As I approach the end of my pilgrimage here on this earth, I am all the more aware of the great debt that was paid in order that I might be welcomed into the Celestial City. There has been much in my unsteady pilgrimage to forgive, and if it were not for the great FORGIVER, where would I be? The Redeemer's love for poor sinners has been lavished on me with outrageous abandon. His mercy is a gift, which, even given eternity to consider, can never be fully comprehended. His blood so precious that my heart quakes at the thought of what would happen to me if I failed to bend the knee and humbly receive its efficacy.

There is only one who is deserving of my praise—only one who provokes everlasting gratitude. I dedicate this book as a humble offering to the King of Kings, the Lord of Lords, and my best friend and Savior, Jesus the Christ!

ACKNOWLEDGEMENTS

Can two walk together, except they be agreed?
Amos 3:3

I would like to acknowledge the tireless efforts of Wayne, Buck, and Josh Keely as we labored together on this timeless allegory. The time spent together in front of a fireplace with these men, the Holy Scriptures, the Holy Spirit, and the manuscript for this book will not soon be forgotten. This time of joyous fellowship resulted in well over 1000 verses of scripture added throughout the chapters in this book, anchoring it firmly to the Word of God. We claim the promise made by the Matchless Revelator that whenever His Word goes forth it will find a home in the hearts of men.

It is our prayer that the reader experiences a personal visitation from the Son of God who contemporizes Himself whenever His Word is read in faith believing.

Wayne Keely, CJ Lovik, Buck Keely and Josh Keely

Tina Miller and Susan Keely

I would also like to acknowledge the diligent editing of Tina Miller and Susan Keely. Round after round, revision after revision, week after week. Thank you for your tenacity and patience. This work would not be what it is without you, my fellow saints in the LORD, and I am thankful for you.

I would like to thank my wife, Jo Ann, for her Christ-like example, for her encouragement during this long, wonderful journey, and for the invigorating and inspiring illustrations incorporated into this work. Her contributions to this effort simply cannot be enumerated. Her knowledge of the Word of God is both humbling and challenging. Thank you, Jo Ann, for your manifold contributions.

I would like to thank my friend and brother in Christ, Josh Keely, whose magisterial reign over my publishing business—and more specifically this project—has been exemplary and inspiring. Thank you, Josh, for all the hard work and untold hours you have put into The Sojourner's Adventure Through Pilgrim's Progress.

And finally, a very special thank-you to Sergio León, a pilgrim who was once a citizen of the City of Destruction himself, but, by the grace and mercy of the King, has been granted entrance through the Narrow Gate, and is on his way to the Celestial City. Sergio's invaluable creative efforts in coloring, illustrating, designing, and laying out this book cannot be overstated. May his testimony be a light for those who still take up residence in the City of Destruction, and may they seek the same path he is on. Sergio, keep that light in your eye!

FOREWORD

ilgrim's Progress has been, until just recently, a perennial favorite among those who are followers of Jesus Christ. Bunyan's allegorical tale has touched the hearts and minds of countless millions in the past 350 years, and it is not surprising that, second only to the Holy Scriptures, it has been the most distributed and published book of all time. When it was written in the late 17th century, England was well on the way to becoming the most biblically-literate nation in the entire world. Sadly, no longer is this the case for England or for America.

The Post Modern/Post Truth/Post Christian Age is upon us with a vengeance that can hardly be exaggerated. The biblical underpinnings of our country have all but crumbled under the unrelenting assault that has ushered in the seismic shift Christians now find themselves facing every day. Truth that only gave way by a fraction of an inch just a couple of generations ago is now disappearing with the ginned-up speed of a hurricane or tsunami. The results are clearly evident as we witness the night-fall darkening the souls of men. The once vibrant, biblical heartbeat which influenced our culture and restrained the pagans, skeptics and unbelievers has flat-lined.

John Bunyan wrote his classic allegory while suffering the consequences of his decision to ignore both King and Parliament who took it upon themselves to regulate the Anglican Church of England, licensing *only* the pastors who met their approval. With that sad condition came all the other restrictive edicts which were clearly outside of Christ's mandate to preach the true Gospel to all men. Bunyan would not bend to the tyranny of men and chose rather to obey the Lord as he preached the gospel without the permission of the state. For his obedience to God he suffered at the hands of men.

It was from a dank, moist prison cell built under a bridge in Bedford England that Bunyan went to work, pouring out his grieving heart onto the pages of books and poems. These precious works have survived him in order that millions might be blest by the gracious grace and providence of God.

Who would have ever predicted the outcome of Bunyan's pitiable circumstances? Who, *but God,* seeing the end from the beginning, chose to sequester Bunyan so that the Gospel of Jesus Christ might be glorified in ways unimaginable to humble Bunyan.

My love and respect for Bunyan and his allegorical legacy is evident in the work I was asked to produce almost a decade ago, and I am humbled by the response of Christian leaders and laity alike who have praised the work.

The challenge I faced in writing the edited translation of Pilgrim's Progress was to retain the voice of Bunyan, strictly adhere to the allegorical storyline, and bring clarity to the modern reader who would have trouble untangling the 17th century English metaphors and patterns of dialogue. The greatest compliment I have received for my effort in editing is that Bunyan's original work was "lightly edited," when in fact over 35% of his work was altered and edited without doing damage to the antiquity or character of the book.

C.J. Lovik with The Sojourner's Adventure through Pilgrim's Progress (2019) and The Pilgrim's Progress (2009)

So why write another version of Pilgrim's Progress?

Any obvious alteration or addition to Bunyan's original work is going to be greeted with a woeful outcry from some of those that love Bunyan and are suspicious of anyone who attempts to improve on his masterpiece.

Over the years, there have been many efforts to repackage Pilgrim's Progress in both print and film, including, most recently, a dramatized animation of the work, in an attempt to reintroduce this jewel to a new generation.

The problem is that many of these new adaptations, although loosely following Bunyan's allegorical framework, are so "seeker friendly" that the deep truths of the everlasting Gospel of Jesus Christ are lost or discarded in exchange for whimsical entertainment. In short, these valiant attempts are sorely missing the beating heart of biblical truth, the very reason and foundation of Bunyan's original work.

Can Bunyan's Pilgrim's Progress be improved upon? To be clear I am not asking if it can be made more understandable to the English-speaking audience. This has already been accomplished. Rather, the question stands, can it be improved?

I believe the answer to this question is yes and amen! The Sojourner's Adventure through Pilgrim's Progress is clearly a tribute to Bunyan, as half the book is dedicated to the faithful retelling of his original work. The other half is my own original storyline which uniquely meshes with Bunyan's work in a way designed to captivate the reader and increase understanding of the gospel of Jesus Christ. This is accomplished using the same literary device used by Bunyan, *the allegory*. The purpose is to clarify, untangle when necessary, and relentlessly proclaim the everlasting gospel of Jesus Christ.

There have been hundreds of commentaries on The Pilgrim's Progress. However, to my knowledge, this is the first time a work has been produced incorporating the same literary device used by Bunyan to expand on the biblical truths revealed in Pilgrim's Progress, while staying within the boundaries and architecture of Bunyan's original work.

I love Bunyan and have never stopped relishing the reading of Pilgrim's Progress. The same Lord that is the inspiration of Bunyan's work that has blessed millions, is the inspiration for this expanded version.

The Sojourner's Adventure through Pilgrim's Progress will never have the reach of Bunyan's original work, but that does not dampen my joy or alter my purpose in writing this book. If even one person comes to trust in Christ as a result of this book, it will have been worth all the treasure and time I have invested in writing it.

May God bless you and the Lord draw you nearer to himself as you read this book.

If you're trusting in Christ, my friend, then look up; our salvation is nearer than it was when we first believed!

See you in the Celestial City!

CONTENTS

CHAPTER 1
The Dire Condition of Graceless

As I walked through the wilderness of this world, I came to a place where there was a cave; and I lay down in that place to sleep. As I slept, I dreamed a dream.

This dream was so vivid and clear that I was, upon waking, both perplexed and amazed.

Perplexed because I was sure the dream, unlike any other I had ever dreamed, held mysteries— mysteries that beckoned me to search the matter out.

Amazed that this dream, unlike all the other dreams I have ever dreamt, did not slip away from my memory or escape my reasoning when I awoke.

The dream, upon my reflection, yielded up pictures and voices so crisp that it pressed against my mind in such a way as to form a memory as if it were not a dream at all but rather a recollection of a great unfolding adventure.

As I trekked back home, I began to try and make good sense out of the drama that now echoed in my head.

What did it all mean?

My path home passed the cottage of a man that was considered by many in the city, in which I dwelt, to be a peculiar man with ideas that were as compelling as they were unpopular.

I had made the gentleman's acquaintance and formed my own good opinion of him, despite the rude opinions of some of my neighbors.

He was an elderly man who was both fair and tall, and as fit as most men half his age.

He was a man who had assisted many who were troubled by the policies and practices that flourished in the City of Destruction—my place of birth.

Perhaps, I reasoned, he can help me understand my dream.

On the other hand, he might think me an idle fantasizer and my dream such a trivial matter of such dubious origins that it would not be worth his consideration.

Just then, I came up the little hill that gave me a view of Great-Heart's cottage, for Great-Heart was his name. As I walked over the brow of the little incline, I spied Great-Heart and his daughter Fidelity weeding their small garden.

Great-Heart, as if he knew I was coming, stood up and waved me forward.

This is where my adventure begins.

Great-Heart: My dear friend, come and tell me how it goes with you!

 1 Peter 3:15

That was all the invitation he needed, and within the space of half an hour, Faithless found himself in his spacious cottage, comfortably seated. He was being served hot tea with cinnamon, accompanied by a small piece of freshly baked bread, generously lavished with honey.

Great-Heart: Welcome to the King's Cottage. How does this fine day find you?

Faithless: Well, I am, that is to say...I would like to...

Faithless could not find the words and so he just sat, stopped and stared into the face of Great-Heart. His countenance was so warm and reassuring that he wondered why he hesitated, but he did.

He will find this to be too fantastic and silly, Faithless thought to himself.

Perhaps this is just an idler's dream after all and will fade away....he will think me a child if I share my dream with him.

This is how Faithless reasoned for a space of time until he was shaken out of his confusion by a gentle thump.

Great-Heart: Something is weighing heavy on your mind, my dear friend.

Great-Heart reached out his large callused hand, bent forward and tapped Faithless on the shoulder.

Great-Heart: Out with it, before your tea goes cold.

Faithless: I had a dream!

Great-Heart moved back into his chair as if half amused and half surprised. He then smiled and slowly stroked his salt and pepper graying beard.

Great-Heart: A dream, you say?

Faithless: Yes, but not just any ordinary dream, a dream like Daniel's dream, a dream that one is meant to remember. A dream...

Faithless stopped abruptly as he was at a loss for any further words to carry his thoughts forward. He simply bowed his head and stared at the rough-hewn pine plank floor.

Great-Heart: You imagine this to be an important dream?

Faithless lifted his head relieved that Great-Heart had responded.

Faithless: Yes, a dream like no other dream!

Faithless halted, not knowing exactly what he would say next. Faithless felt he needed some grand eloquent words to convince Great-Heart that this was not some whimsical vision but a dream worth investigating as it was filled with wonders, terrors, delights, adventures and mysteries.

Great-Heart: And you have come here to ask me what this dream means?

Faithless: I was hoping you might have some knowledge of the things that I dreamt, as they seem in some manner I am now unable to describe — not of this world.

Great-Heart paused as if something important had arrested his attention. He looked into the eyes of Faithless and smiled.

Great-Heart: A dream of the world to come?

Faithless: I think so.

Great-Heart: If this is a "Daniel's dream," then I need to add one more visitor to the great conversation we are about to have.

Great-Heart stood up and went to the small shelf pegged to the inside partition of his cottage, picked up a large book and put it in his lap.

Faithless' mouth fell open and his eyes widened to the size of robin eggs as he looked with amazement at the Book Great-Heart carried with such care back to his chair.

It was a big leather-bound book, ragged at the edges, dog-eared with a large black smudge in the top right-hand corner.

The great book looked as if it had been plucked from a fire.

Jude 1:23

Faithless: That's the book!

Faithless was so amazed that he rose out of his chair.

Faithless: That's the book I saw in my dream.

Great-Heart lifted the book up and held it up in front of Faithless

as if he were a court magistrate who would have nothing but a true confession from the witness.

Great-Heart: You saw this book in your dream, not just a book like it?

Faithless: Yes, that is the very book!

Faithless reached up and touched the charred leather corner that had been blackened as if pulled out of a flame.

Great-Heart's countenance changed from light-hearted to grave and contemplative as he gently laid the great leather-bound book in his lap, looked up at Faithless and gestured with his tilted head and a little quick nod as if to say, *you have my full attention.*

A small space of time was filled with silence that strangely did not seem uncomfortable but rather a void filled with thoughtful anticipation.

Without a word of encouragement, Faithless knew that Great-Heart was waiting for him to share his dream, and so he began at the beginning.

Faithless: In my dream, I saw a man clothed in rags, standing in a place with his face turned away from his own house. He had a book in his hand, the very book you now have in your hand, and a heavy burden upon his back.

 Isaiah 64:6, Luke 14:33, Psalm 38:4

Graceless awakened to his lost condition outside the gates of the City of Destruction

Great-Heart looked down at the book in his lap and then just as quickly looked up again and gave Faithless a nod as if to continue, which he did.

Faithless: I saw the man in my dream open the book and begin to read; and as he read, he wept and trembled. Not being able to contain himself, he cried out in a loud voice, *What shall I do?*

 *Habakkuk 1:2-3, Acts 2:37, Acts 16:30*

Faithless paused for a moment as if to ask what it all meant.

Great-Heart: What to do indeed!

Great-Heart put his hand on the Book in his lap as if to open it.

Great-Heart: Do you know what this all means, Faithless?

Faithless: I am not sure.

Great-Heart: You have been given a vision of something both fearsome and wonderful.

Faithless: Pray tell.

Great-Heart: I know the man in your dream, as I would recognize him anywhere.

Faithless: What is his name?

Great-Heart: I am surprised you have not met him before as he is a close neighbor of yours.

Faithless: I have never met this man before.

Great-Heart gave him a reassuring look.

Great-Heart: Well, you have probably never met him in the condition you found him in your dream, but you have made his acquaintance, I am sure.

Faithless was puzzled but determined not to be put off.

Faithless: Can you tell me his name?

Great-Heart answered without hesitating.

Great-Heart: This man presently is named GRACELESS and he is the eldest son of Fit-For-Wrath, one of the founding fathers of the City of Destruction—the very city in which you yourself now dwell.

 Romans 9:22

Faithless: You say this man is *"presently"* named Graceless?

He asked this, as he was puzzled by the inference.

 Ephesians 2:1-2

Great-Heart: Yes, but that is something I believe we have yet to discover. You say he was clothed in rags?

Faithless: Oh, yes. They were not only soiled and tattered, but they were covered with something dark and filthy. His attire was not fit for any good company and I hardly think any amount of washing could make them respectable. They were not just rags, they were loathsome rags.

Great-Heart fixed his gaze on Faithless.

Great-Heart: Can you figure out the meaning of the filthy rags?

Faithless: I imagine that Graceless has found himself in some sort of trouble—perhaps a debtor who has lost all his living and livelihood and has been cast out of good society. Or, perhaps he has committed some great offense against the ordinances and laws of my city and must flee to escape punishment.

Great-Heart smiled.

Great-Heart: Graceless is a debtor indeed but he has not lost his livelihood or his standing in what you call *good society*. At least not yet. No, indeed, what you are seeing is the true condition of Graceless. The filthy rags are a picture of his own righteousness.

 Matthew 18:32, Romans 5:6

Faithless: And what of the burden on his back?

Great-Heart: Can you not guess?

Faithless: If his tattered and ragged clothes are his unrighteous acts, then I suppose he has done some terrible deed and his burden is the consequences of those sins.

Great-Heart looked at Faithless carefully as if examining a newly hatched chick.

Great-Heart: If the great burden on his back were his sins, then why are not all the citizens of the City of Destruction, the home of Graceless and all the kinsmen of Fit-For-Wrath, not so burdened? For all have sinned and there is none since Adam that can escape sin's influence.

 *John 16:8-10*

At this point, Faithless found himself in a **Grubble,*** as he had no answer.

Great-Heart, sensing his confusion, offered up the solution to the mystery of the great burden that weighed down Graceless.

Great-Heart: Graceless is a sinner indeed, and for the moment at least he has come under the conviction of his own sin and unrighteousness. The burden on his back is his awakening sense of this true condition, not the condition itself. For all are sinners, but few are burdened by the sense and crushing weight of it.

 Isaiah 64:6, Romans 3:23

Faithless: And what about the great book in his hand? The one the poor fellow reads as he cries out, "What shall I do to be saved?"

 *Acts 16:30-31*

Great-Heart smiled as he lifted up the very book.

Great-Heart: Do you know what book this is?

Faithless: I suppose it is a great book of wisdom and guidance.

Great-Heart cradled the book in his lap tightly as he prepared his answer.

Great-Heart: This book is the best of all books as there is no other book in the world that is its equal, nor ever will be.

Faithless: I remember the poor man, Graceless, saying that he perceived, by the book in his hand, that he was going to die.

Great-Heart: We are all going to die, I doubt Graceless did not know that death is the destiny of all Adam's race.

---

* **Grubble** — *To feel or grope around for something you cannot see.*

Faithless: Well then, I wonder why Graceless seems to be so full of fear and confusion since in my dream I see him often reading the book, and then weeping.

Faithless asked this, not wanting to offend, but wondering why such a great book should cause so much anguish in Graceless as the reading of it seems to trouble him greatly.

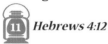 *Hebrews 4:12*

Great-Heart smiled.

Great-Heart: Now that is a mystery you may one day experience yourself.

Faithless was not so sure he wanted to read a book that would cause him to lose all sense of his own good offices, put him in a condition of poverty and cause him to fear and tremble.

Faithless, again not wanting to offend, and desiring to know what other mysteries Great-Heart might reveal, held his peace.

 John 3:16-19, Romans 10:8-10

Great-Heart, sensing his confusion, answered the question Faithless was asking without him having to ask it.

Great-Heart: You see Faithless…

Great-Heart spoke in a low measured voice that was meant to be soothing.

Great-Heart: This Book…

Great-Heart lifted the book up as he spoke.

Great-Heart: …is full of precious promises that you find in no other book in the world. I know the promises are true because this book was written by HIM who cannot lie.

 *Numbers 23:19*

Faithless: Why then is Graceless so alarmed by reading about these great promises found in this book?

    Great-Heart smiled again as he answered Faithless.

Great-Heart: Because there are also great warnings in this book that are alarming and filled with judgment and wrath.

 *Romans 11:22*

Faithless: So, Graceless has not yet read the promises that are contained in this great book?

Great-Heart: Graceless has read them but cannot yet see them because he is condemned in his mind and spirit and blinded by fear. He has read the awesome threats and charges that God has written against all the citizens of the City of Destruction that sin from sunup to sundown and transgress His righteous law as regularly as the pounding of the human heart within.

 Psalm 34:16, Psalm 6:2-3, Psalm 7:11, Romans 6:23

    As Faithless thought about what Great-Heart said, he began to sense he was somehow connected with the dream and its interpretation, as he was a citizen of the City of Destruction with some standing and good reputation.

Instead of protesting the implications of Great-Heart's interpretation of the dream, he was overwhelmed with the sense that some work of providence or some hidden hand had led him to the very man who could unfold the mysteries which were now hidden from him in the Great Book with the brand of fire on its leather cover.

 Acts 8:29-31

As he thought about all which
had been revealed, Fidelity
tapped him on the shoulder and
offered to refresh his cup of tea
while placing another honey-
soaked biscuit on the white
saucer that held his teacup.

Great-Heart: Now Faithless, you
must tell me what happened next.

Faithless thought for a
moment as he found his place
back in the dream that had now
become something of great importance in both his mind and in the
mind of Great-Heart who was anxious for him to continue his story.

Faithless: In my dream, I saw Graceless journey back to his home where
he tried to keep himself hidden from his wife and children, since he did
not want them to see him in his great distress.

But after a short time, his anguish had so increased he could not
remain silent. So, he began to share with his wife and children what
was on his troubled mind.

Great-Heart: Did you hear what he told his wife and children in
your dream?

Faithless: Oh yes, I cannot forget what he said as it seemed so mysterious to me. I desire to know what great event has caused this
sorrowful condition to come upon him. I would like to know why he
prophesied with such certainty that a great calamity was going to
come upon his entire family, and not just his family but all the citizens of the City of Destruction, where I myself have my home and
make my livelihood.

Graceless, after a long period of solitary silence, finally gathered his
poor family together and said to them...

Graceless shares his anguish and fears with his wife and children

Graceless: *Dear wife and children, I am very troubled by this burden which torments me and grows heavier by the day. Moreover, I have received information that the city in which we live will be burnt with fire from heaven. When this happens all of us will be destroyed, unless (by a way I do not as yet see) some way of escape can be found, so that we may be delivered.*

 *Acts 2:37-39*

Great-Heart: And what did his family make of Graceless' announcement to them?

Faithless: I heard his wife say she was puzzled and concerned, not because she believed what he said to them, but because she thought that he was losing his mind.

 I Corinthians 2:14-16, Matthew 10:34-36

Great-Heart: What did the children of Graceless say?

Faithless: In my dream, I could not make out what they said, but what they did convinced me they thought their father was suffering from some ailment or fever of the mind.

As the evening approached, hoping that sleep might calm him down, they put him to bed.

But the night was as troublesome to Graceless as the day. Instead of sleeping, he spent the night in sighs and tears.

So, when morning came, his family arrived to find out how he was doing.

"Worse and worse," he told them.

He also started speaking to them again about his fears and concerns, but instead of listening they closed their ears and became cold toward him. They also tried to change his outlook by treating him rudely. Sometimes they would deride, sometimes they would chide, and other times they would just ignore him.

 1 Corinthians 1:18

Great-Heart: And what did Graceless do?

Faithless: He retired to his chamber to pray for his wife and family as if they needed pity and not him. Don't you think that is odd?

Great-Heart put his index finger to his lip as if to guard his tongue, thought for a moment and then replied.

Great-Heart: Faithless, I know it may appear a **Jargogle**,* that cannot be explained by the wisdom and customs of this world.

So, to answer your question, while I can understand your confusion, the fact is that I do not find it odd at all. In fact, I find it very hopeful.

Faithless: Hopeful?

Great-Heart: Very hopeful.

Faithless wanted to ask Great-Heart more questions about what seemed to him to be odd behavior and wondered why Great-Heart thought it quite the opposite. There was a mystery in this that he

---

* **Jargogle**— *To confuse or jumble.*

did not understand but as requested he reported the next account of what he had witnessed in his dream.

Faithless: Graceless kept reading the Great Book.

It seemed to me that he was trying to find consolation but it appeared there was no consolation to be found.

Faithless paused but received no comment from Great-Heart who seemed deep in thought as he considered his dream. Finally, after a few moments, Faithless continued the telling of his dream.

Faithless: In a word, it appeared to me the more Graceless read the book the more his misery increased.

In my dream, I saw him often walking alone in the fields, praying and reading. This continued in my dream for many days.

Graceless greatly distressed as he reads the warnings revealed in the Bible

One day, Graceless was walking in the fields reading in the Great Book and with great distress of mind. As he read, he burst out, as he had done before, crying, "What shall I do to be saved?"

 John 3:14-15, Acts 16:30

I noticed he looked this way, and then that way, as if he would run; yet he stood still because he could not seem to decide which way to go. Just then I looked and saw a man coming toward him but I could not make him out.

Graceless meets Evangelist

Great-Heart: And then what happened?

Faithless: Then I woke up from my dream.

What does it all mean? Is some great calamity about to befall my city?

Great-Heart closed the pages of the Great Book and stood up.

Great-Heart: It means that you and I will be meeting again very soon.

Faithless: How soon?

Great-Heart: Why, as soon as you have your next dream.

Faithless: But that was my dream.

Great-Heart: I doubt that very much.

Great-Heart put the Great Book back on the wooden shelf and rustled through the rest of his books. After a moment of searching, he pulled out another book with a leather cover and a black smudge on the right corner.

It was much like the Book Faithless saw in his dream, but much smaller.

This book also appeared to be dog-eared and well used.

Great-Heart: I want you to take this small book and begin reading it with reverence and great care.

Great-Heart handed the book to Faithless.

He took the book and opened it to the firstpage where it said...

"A true and faithful report of the King's Son, of things past, things that are now, things to come and things which are also profitable for instruction."

 21   *Revelation 1:1, Revelation 4:1, II Timothy 3:16*

He was about to turn to the next page when Great-Heart gently closed the book he now held. His large rough hand seemed to pass gently over the blackened leather cover in a way that reminded Faithless of the way a mother would stroke the cheek of a beloved infant child.

He could not help but gaze at the firebrand in the corner of the leather-bound book and could not keep himself from asking...

Faithless: What does this black smudge mean?

Great-Heart: I was wondering when you would ask me that question.

These Great Books, like the one you saw in your dream, have been used by the King of the country, of which I am a citizen, to pluck poor sinners out of the fire on too many occasions to count.

The words in the book are preserved by the King Himself but He has let the cover of the book be bruised and battered by wind, rain and fire as a reminder, to all who treasure it, that we will have tribulation in this world but we will, in the end, be preserved by the everlasting Word which is contained in this book.

 22   *John 16:33*

    Although Faithless really had no idea what Great-Heart was talking about, he did sense that he now had something precious in his possession and thought it best not to ask any further questions except for one.

Faithless: And when shall I return it?

Great-Heart: When you have your next dream, of course.

Faithless: What if I don't have another dream?

Great-Heart: Then come to see me anyway as I am anxious to talk to you about otherworldly and mysterious things.

Faithless thanked Great-Heart for his warm hospitality and for helping him understand a dream that had become even more mysterious than it was before. He said goodbye to Fidelity and made his way back to the City of Destruction.

After waving goodbye, both Great-Heart and Fidelity watched Faithless trudge toward the near horizon that was flush with blackberry bushes laced with three full-grown mulberry trees and one giant oak. They watched and prayed as the figure of Faithless entered the little lane which led back to the City of Destruction where Faithless made his home.

 Philippians 3:19, Micah 2:10

Fidelity held her father's hand and wondered out loud.

Fidelity: Do you think Faithless will return?

Great-Heart: Oh yes, my dear, we have only just begun a grand adventure that has been set in motion by the Prince of Glory Himself.

Fidelity squeezed her father's hand and smiled.

Fidelity: Father, why didn't you tell Faithless why it was important for Graceless to be fearful?

Great-Heart turned to his daughter.

Great-Heart: Fidelity, your cousin Constance will be arriving next week along with her father, you can ask her.

Fidelity clapped her hands with joy as she made a small leap in the air.

Fidelity: They are coming to visit?

Great-Heart: Oh yes!

Fidelity: When did you invite them?

She asked this, as she was wondering why she had not heard about this earlier.

Great-Heart: I did not invite them.

Fidelity knew when more questions would not provide any more useful information, and from past experience, knew this was exactly the right moment to give her father a quick embrace trusting that the LORD of King's Cottage, Who was in warm fellowship with her dear father, must have passed some message along by means which were as mysterious as they were certain.

The Burden of Grace

When Grace arrives to mark the Path
What first appears is fearsome wrath
No pleasant verse or sweet refrain
No joyful thoughts to light the lane
Yet terror, doubts and fear remain.

The soul awakened by God's Grace
Soon rises up, its sin to face
Thoughts of mercy quickly flee
All that's left is debt's large fee
Looming as far as eye can see.

The heart of man, thoughts and deeds
Increase the debt like seeds of weeds.
Thus every day, try as he might
Is one step further into night
As heaven's promise slips from sight.

What frightful terrors wait in store
For Graceless men who shun the door
All such men have sealed their fate
Unless sped on by Grace so Great!
A Grace that leads to Christ the Gate.

CJL 2018

CHAPTER 2
EVANGELIST DIRECTS GRACELESS

The summer days passed with little commotion and soon the days became weeks. The King's Cottage stirred with the constant motion of Great-Heart, Fidelity and dozens of neighbors who arrived each Sunday and Wednesday to study the King's Book, sing psalms and earnestly pray for their own improvement. They also prayed for the citizens of the City of Destruction, including the newest addition to the prayer list, Faithless.

 Hebrews 10:25, Acts 2:42

It was early in the morning and a stiff breeze that rustled the leaves of a large Maple tree lightly grazed up against the cottage.

Then there was a gentle tap, tap, tap at the door.

Fidelity wrung out the mop and leaned it into the corner of the kitchen. She then made her way briskly to the front entry as she brushed her long, flowing hair back behind her ears and over her shoulders.

As soon as the door was opened there was a shriek of delight from both inside and outside the cottage as Fidelity and her favorite cousin, Constance, embraced each other.

The two danced a little jig that put them both squarely in the middle of the living room. It was then Fidelity's uncle's turn to be enthusiastically greeted, as he was hugged and kissed on the cheek without mercy or complaint.

Uncle: Fidelity, it is good to fix my eyes on you again and where, may I inquire, is my brother?

Fidelity: I don't know where he is.

Fidelity swept through the house looking for her father but he was nowhere to be found.

Fidelity: He must be out in the backwoods collecting kindling to heat up the tea kettle and the rabbit stew we have planned for our midday meal.

Uncle: You two cousins catch up with each other while I go scout around until I find him.

Fidelity's uncle was a tall, fair, vigorous man who had reached his 50th year without an ache or pain worth mentioning.

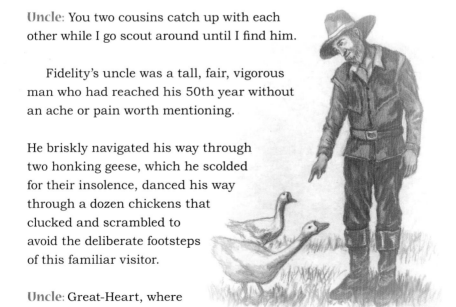

He briskly navigated his way through two honking geese, which he scolded for their insolence, danced his way through a dozen chickens that clucked and scrambled to avoid the deliberate footsteps of this familiar visitor.

Uncle: Great-Heart, where are you?

A moment later the reply came and within a couple of minutes the two brothers embraced.

Uncle: Did you know I had been sent to see you on some urgent business of the King?

Great-Heart: Urgent business indeed, the best kind of business. Oh yes, I have been expecting you.

Uncle: Pilgrim business?

Great-Heart: Yes, and very urgent as the Lord has once again visited a citizen of the City of Destruction by way of a most amazing dream.

 John 6:44

Uncle: A dream?

Great-Heart: A dream and a dreamer.

As the two made their way back to the King's Cottage, the conversation turned to serious matters as both shared the victories and sorrow that had unfolded since they last met.

The next day and well into the afternoon was spent in lively conversation about the King's business and all the news that was fit to repeat. Some of it was sad and some of it was glad.

The two brothers sat at the hefty oak table graced with a large **Tuzzy-Muzzy**.* Each nursed a hot cup of tea, dunking stale bread into the steaming brew in hopes of somewhat reviving a treat what should have been offered to the chickens days ago.

Suddenly they heard a knock at the door.

---

* **Tuzzy-Muzzy** — *A collection of flowers, a bouquet.*

Great-Heart: Our friend Faithless has arrived. Now I want you to stay here until I beckon you.

Great-Heart's little brother cocked his head as if a little puzzled.

Uncle: That all sounds a wee bit mysterious.

Great-Heart: Yes, indeed it is.

Great-Heart patted his brother on the back and wound his way to the front door.

As the door opened, there stood Faithless clutching the leather-bound book with the blackened scar on the right-hand corner of the cover, while fidgeting with his hat nervously.

Faithless: I have had another dream, another dream!

Great-Heart smiled, extended his hand in friendship, gently grasped Faithless' elbow and escorted him into the living room.

Great-Heart: Welcome my friend, please come in.

Constance quickly introduced herself to Faithless.

The two cousins went about making him feel welcome and comfortable. A fresh cup of tea showed up with a large muffin smothered in blackberry jam. A napkin was provided along with a cheery smile.

Great-Heart took his place across from Faithless and sat silently waiting for Faithless to begin the conversation.

Faithless: I have come to return your book.

Faithless held the book out with his right hand expecting Great-Heart to retrieve it and put it back on the rough shelf on the partition wall that was just yards away from where they were sitting.

Great-Heart held his hand up in a gesture that clearly meant he was not ready to collect his book.

Great-Heart: Have you been reading it?

Great-Heart leaned forward to receive his answer.

Faithless: Oh yes, it has been my constant companion these many weeks and I have read it from cover to cover twice and am now reading it again for the third time.

 II Timothy 2:15

Great-Heart: Do you understand what is written in the book?

 John 16:13, Acts 8:31

Faithless grimaced and squinted a little as he ever so slowly squeezed out an answer that was meant to be truthful but not offensive.

Faithless: Some of it is clear and plain but most of it is hard for me to understand.

Great-Heart was not disappointed by the answer as he smiled at Faithless and responded with a short, quick request.

Great-Heart: Faithless...

Great-Heart pointed at the book.

Great-Heart: I would like you to write down your

questions and when next we meet, we will try and unravel those matters that are presently a mystery to you.

Faithless: And the book?

Great-Heart: The book is yours for as long as you treasure it.

Faithless was happily surprised by the gift and clearly pleased with the answer as it gave him joy to think that he would be invited back again into the home to enjoy the companionship of the great man that sat before him.

Faithless: Yes, I will do as you have asked.

Great-Heart: And now tell me the rest of your dream.

Faithless: Do you remember where my dream ended?

Great-Heart: Oh yes, I do remember it well.

Let me see, Graceless was out in the field walking, reading the King's Book and praying when he spied a tall, fair and fit fellow coming his way.

Faithless: How did you know he was tall and fair and fit?

Great-Heart: He was tall, fair and fit, was he not?

Faithless: Well yes, but I wonder how you might know that.

Great-Heart: And do you know who that fellow is?

Faithless: I think he is a messenger sent from the King of the Country in which you reside, and I am certain as to his name...

Great-Heart: Before you reveal the name of this stranger, let me introduce my little brother to you.

Great-Heart and Faithless stood up in order to greet the latest visitor to the King's Cottage.

The tall, fair and fit man that entered the room created quite the commotion. Faithless stammered and then took a deep breath as he opened his mouth in wonder.

Faithless: Your name is Evangelist! You are the man I saw in my dream.

 Ephesians 4:12

Great-Heart's younger brother—whose name was Evangelist—was stunned.

Evangelist: You saw me in a dream?

Faithless: Yes, a dream.

Great-Heart took charge of the temporary confusion and seated his brother, Evangelist, at the right hand of Faithless while he took his seat squarely in front of his bewildered brother and Faithless.

After a few moments filled with half-finished sentences, as both Evangelist and Faithful were attempting to come to terms with this remarkable and bewildering circumstance, Faithless finally sighed.

Faithless: So that's how you knew he was tall, fair and fit.

Great-Heart looked at his brother with a wry smile that Evangelist knew the meaning of without a word being spoken.

Great-Heart: Tall, fair and fit, hmm?

Evangelist sat up straight and tall as he chuckled at his brother's jesting and then his countenance suddenly changed to sober and serious as he considered the circumstances he now found himself in.

To find yourself in someone else's dream is a curiosity but to find yourself in a dream that may be a vision of something that has actually happened or may happen in the future was all the notification Evangelist needed to alert him that a sacred drama was unfolding before his very eyes.

 *Romans 8:28*

Great-Heart and Evangelist had never experienced anything like this. They had heard of such things from other servants of the King but never expected to find themselves so curiously situated.

Great-Heart: Now please, dear friend, tell us your latest dream.

Evangelist: Latest dream?

Great-Heart: Yes, the second dream that I suppose is a continuation of the first.

Faithless: That is true.

Faithless gave both Great-Heart and Evangelist a passing glance as he prepared to recount the events that unfolded in the dream that had taken on a life outside of his mind and imagination by circumstances too curious to ignore and too precise to pass off as a coincidence.

Faithless: In my dream the man who approached Graceless as he walked in the open field outside the City of Destruction was Evangelist.

Faithless looked at Evangelist with a tight smile that was informed by a sense of wonder. Evangelist was silent and slightly shaken by what he was hearing.

Faithless: In my dream, Evangelist came up to Graceless and asked...

Faithless stopped and looked at Evangelist with a piercing gaze that begged a question.

Evangelist cleared his throat and wiped away the mist from his eyes. The circumstances he now found himself in seemed to be less and less a curiosity and more and more a miracle.

Faithless continued to look at Evangelist who finally realized that he was being asked a question.

Evangelist: Oh, as I recall, I asked Graceless why he was crying out. And do you remember what Graceless told me?

Evangelist instructs Graceless to keep reading the Bible "Keep that light in your eye"

Evangelist gazed at Faithless not really expecting that he would know.

Faithless: I remember quite well. The conversation between you and Graceless went as follows:

Graceless: *Sir, I understand from reading the book in my hand that I am condemned to die and after that to come to judgment.*

I am not willing to do the first, nor able to do the second.

 Hebrews 9:27, Ezekiel 22:14

Evangelist: *Why are you not willing to die since this life is attended with so many evils?*

 Job 10:21-22

> **Graceless**: *Because I am afraid that this burden that is on my back will sink me lower than the grave; and I shall fall into Hell and if I be not ready to die, then I am not prepared to go to judgment and from there to execution. Thinking about these things distresses me greatly.*

 Isaiah 30:33, Hebrews 10:27

Evangelist was amazed as the mist in his eyes became waterfalls as he wept at the exact summary of the conversation he had previously had with Graceless just a week ago to the very day.

Evangelist: I remember asking Graceless, *"If this is your condition, why are you standing still? Flee from the wrath to come."*

Faithless: In my dream, I heard Graceless tell you that he did not know where to go.

I saw you give Graceless a parchment. You unrolled it so that he could read it.

Seeing that his brother was momentarily so overtaken by the miracle that was unfolding in front of his eyes, Great-Heart entered into the conversation.

Great-Heart: And do you remember what the parchment scroll said?

Faithless: No, but I am curious as to its contents since it seemed to alarm Graceless and stiffen his resolve to flee the City of Destruction.

 Psalm 19:11

I do remember one thing that Graceless read out loud from the parchment.

Great-Heart: And what was that?

Faithless: Graceless, reading the scroll said, *"O generation of vipers, who hath warned you to flee from the wrath to come?"*

 Matthew 3:7

In my dream I saw Evangelist, pointing with his finger over a very wide field, asking Graceless, *"Do you see the narrow gate?"*

 Matthew 7:13-14

Great-Heart: What did Graceless reply?

Faithless: Graceless replied that he could not see the Small Sheep Gate.

    Evangelist was listening in amazement to the conversation as he prayed for wisdom from on high in order that he might know what part he was to play in this extraordinary drama.

Evangelist: Do you remember what I asked Graceless next?

Faithless: You asked Graceless if he could see the shining light.

 Psalm 119:105, 2 Peter 1:19

Evangelist points Graceless to the Narrow Gate which is Christ Jesus

Evangelist: Do you remember his answer?

Faithless: Oh yes, I remember Graceless straining to see the light and then reporting that he thought he saw it.

Faithless: Then you told Graceless, "Keep that light in your eye and go up directly toward it, and soon you will see the narrow Sheep Gate." Then you instructed him that when he finally came to the gate that he should knock on it and then he would be told what to do.

 Mark 10:21

There was a long pause.

Great-Heart: Is that the end of your dream?

Faithless: No, but I have for many days now been curious and puzzled by the two questions that Evangelist asked Graceless.

It is a mystery I was in hopes you might unravel. But since by some great act of providence I do not yet understand, the very man that asked Graceless the two questions is now here before me.

Evangelist: You would like me to answer the riddle?

Evangelist lifted his head from between his hands where he was silently praying and weeping, overcome by what was clearly a visitation with some holy purpose designed by his King. After a few moments, he regained his composure as he looked up and gazed at Faithless.

Evangelist had led many pilgrims out of the City of Destruction under circumstances that were clearly ordained and by some accounts very strange. Evangelist had never been so miraculously called to minister as a messenger of the Great King.

Evangelist: Faithless, let me unravel the riddle so that you may understand it, just as I revealed it to Graceless. You may also find yourself more than just curious as to the answer I revealed to Graceless.

The narrow gate is the Small Sheep Gate by which all those who put their trust in the King's Son, the Good Shepherd, must enter in order to be set on the path to eternal life. It is a narrow gate that is only seen by those who have heard and understood the Glad Tidings regarding the Son of God Who came to rescue vessels that were fit for wrath; clay vessels that all dwell in the City of Destruction and its surrounding towns and villages.

Faithless cringed as he listened to the indictment of all his neighbors and kinsfolk. Faithless considered all his kinsmen and neighbors who, by all accounts, were happily and profitably living in the City of Destruction.

 Romans 3:10

Determined to find out the meaning of his dream, he held his tongue and reserved his own judgment concerning the matters Evangelist was disclosing. Faithless reasoned that it was not the time to quibble over matters he clearly did not fully understand. So, determined to reserve his own counsel until he learned more, Faithless continued to listen without comment.

 Proverbs 18:13

Evangelist: The sheep gate can only be seen through eyes of faith. It is the small gate that leads to the narrow way which transports all those who enter therein to the Celestial City. It is the gate of forgiveness purchased at great expense by the King of the country I now dwell in. It looks to all the world to be a humble and lowly way, but its value cannot be estimated. It is worth more than all the wealth the world could heap up in a thousand millennia. It is an offense and stumbling block to many as it was purchased by a means that is horrible, bloody, violent and cruel.

 1 Corinthians 2:9-10, John 10:9

Faithless was mystified by the answer as it raised more questions in his darkened mind than he could in its present state consider. But it was the answer he sought and so he nodded as if he did understand at least some of what Evangelist had said.

Faithless: And what is the Light that Graceless is to keep in his eye?

Evangelist pointed to the book that Faithless had nestled on his lap.

Evangelist: It is God's Holy Word written for pilgrims who desire to dwell eternally in the Celestial City.

Faithless: In my dream, I heard you tell Graceless to keep reading the book he was holding. It was the very book that was causing him to weep and tremble.

Evangelist sat up straight.

Evangelist: Yes I did!

Faithless: I saw Graceless reading the book and as he read he wept, looking this way and that, not knowing which way to go.

Great-Heart: And then, what did he do?

Faithless: He prayed continually.

Great-Heart: And who do you suppose he prayed to?

Faithless: I suppose Graceless prayed to the One who wrote the Great Book that troubled

his soul and caused him to tremble?

Evangelist: You have answered well.

Great-Heart: And what happened next?

Faithless paused and bit his lower lip as he considered all that had happened since he was visited with the dream. Clearly, thought Faithless, this is a dream like no other, a Daniel's dream. A dream of things both past and a vision of things to come.

Faithless: As to what happened next, I remember that just before Evangelist came upon Graceless in the field just outside the City of Destruction, Graceless was reading in the Great Book and seemed to be greatly distressed.

I remember him falling down on one knee as he gazed intently at the Great Book, as if he had found a verse or passage that had wounded him and pierced his heart. Then he looked up to the heavens and with tears he burst out in a loud voice, *"What shall I do to be saved?"*

18 *Acts 2:37, Acts 16:30-31*

Faithless paused for a moment and then turned to Evangelist with a quizzical look on his face.

Faithless: Were you sent to answer the questions asked by Graceless?

Evangelist: The answer is yes. Now let me ask you a question. Do you know what questions Graceless was asking?

Again, there was a space of time given to Faithless to pull the plow through the rough hard soil of his mind and heart in order to uncover the answer.

Faithless: I know he was very distressed and I heard him cry out with a loud lament, "What must I do to be saved?" Is that the question you seek?

Evangelist: Yes, as it is the only real question worth asking. Can you think of a more important question?

Faithless cleared his throat as he felt the first pangs of conviction.

Faithless was not ready to yield himself up to the obvious implication of his part in this drama and so he took a deep breath and answered the question as if he were a school boy answering a question about history or geography.

Faithless: I suppose it is an important question.

Evangelist knew when to give a sinner space, especially since it was the job of the King Himself to awaken the heart of man to their true condition.

Evangelist: Yes, I was sent to answer the most important question anyone in this present world can ask.

Faithless pricked up his ears to hear the answer once more.

Great-Heart interrupted the short silence that followed with an invitation. He handed his Great Book to Faithless and pointed to a verse that had been underlined.

Evangelist: Did you see me pointing out a passage to Graceless in the King's Book?

Faithless: Yes, I do remember you pointing out several passages in the Great Book.

Evangelist: Faithless, would you mind reading this verse?

Faithless shuffled his feet nervously on the hardwood floor, clearing his throat as he bent forward to read the text. Then he took a deep breath and read.

Faithless: *That if thou shalt confess with thy mouth the Lord Jesus, and shalt believe in thine heart that God hath raised him from the dead, thou shalt be saved. For with the heart man believeth unto righteousness; and with the mouth confession is made unto salvation.*

 Romans 10:9-10

After Faithless read the verses, he was quiet. Evangelist did not interrupt the silence, giving Faithless time to think about what he had read. What followed was a long patch of silence.

Evangelist: Do you have any questions about what you just read? Faithless did not say a word but just shrugged his shoulders. Another long silence followed.

Just then Fidelity came around the corner and entered the room.

She did not say a word but she signaled with a raised brow that lunch was ready to be served.

Great-Heart, sensing that Faithless needed time to think about all he had just learned, finally broke the silence.

Great-Heart: Faithless, would you like to join the four of us for lunch? I can smell the soup simmering and the fresh bread baking. Fidelity and Constance have prepared a lunch fit for a king and we would like you to be our guest.

Faithless was relieved by the chance to escape the uncomfortable silence and to reflect on what he had discovered. He immediately accepted the invitation with enthusiasm.

Fidelity: Lunch in 10 minutes.

The three men stood up and stretched their legs.

Great-Heart invited his brother and Faithless to join him in the orchard that was about twenty yards from the kitchen porch. Great-Heart had planted an assorted variety of fruit trees two decades earlier.

Fidelity and Constance were busy putting the final touches on the afternoon meal.

After arriving at the small orchard, Great-Heart plucked off a couple of **Scrogglings*** from the previous year and began looking for some ripe plums and apples to pick, hoping his efforts would result in a large slice of apple pie after lunch.

Evangelist mused as if reading his brother's mind.

---

* **Scrogglings** — *Small, worthless apples left hanging on a tree after the crop is gathered.*

Evangelist: I am sure that Fidelity and Constance would relish the challenge.

Great-Heart smiled as they meandered through the two-dozen fruit trees that were all laden with ripened and nearly-ripened fruit.

Evangelist snatched an apple from a low-hanging branch, polished it with his shirt tail and tossed it to Faithless who caught it and immediately began to eat it. The crisp snapping sound it made as Faithless bit down on it to its core alerted Great-Heart and Evangelist that Faithless had probably arrived at the King's Cottage without eating any breakfast. Since it was now nearly two in the afternoon, he was probably famished.

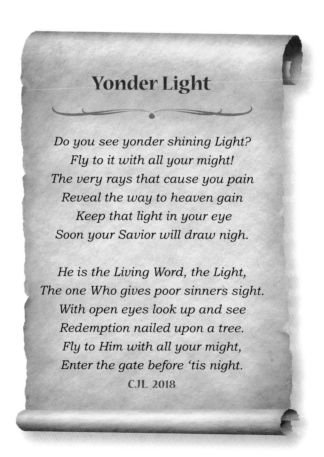

Yonder Light

Do you see yonder shining Light?
Fly to it with all your might!
The very rays that cause you pain
Reveal the way to heaven gain
Keep that light in your eye
Soon your Savior will draw nigh.

He is the Living Word, the Light,
The one Who gives poor sinners sight.
With open eyes look up and see
Redemption nailed upon a tree.
Fly to Him with all your might,
Enter the gate before 'tis night.

CJL 2018

CHAPTER 3
OBSTINATE AND PLIABLE

The sun shone directly over the King's Cottage announcing that the middle of the day had arrived. Faithless, having left the City of Destruction early that morning without a thought of eating because he was consumed with his dream, was now famished.

The aroma of a carefully prepared midday meal invited the three men into the kitchen where they all took their places with a lively anticipation of what was to come.

The midday meal was no **Maw-wallop*** but rather a delicious feast that was greeted with enthusiasm by Faithless who was the first to compliment the two cooks,
Fidelity and Constance.

The conversation was lively and the rabbit stew all but disappeared, except for a thin layer of gravy that Faithless rescued from the soapy wash basin with the heel of the freshly baked bread that was whisked around the inside of the cast iron pot twice in order to soak up every last tasty morsel.

 Acts 2:46

---

* **Maw-wallop** — *A badly cooked mess of food.*

Fidelity popped the apple crisp into the oven as Constance announced that desert would be ready to serve in a quarter of an hour.

The three men remained at the table, each nursing an after-dinner tea that was garnished with fresh cream and a spoonful of honey. They dipped and munched on the remaining **Fasels*** that were with the creamy goat cheese sauce that beckoned them from the dish in the center of the kitchen table.

After congratulating the cooks for the wonderful meal, the conversation once again turned to Faithless and his dream.

Evangelist was the most anxious to turn the conversation back to the vision that he believed his King had given to Faithless in order to rescue him from the soon coming calamity that would befall the City of Destruction.

 Hebrews 11:6

Evangelist: We are all eager to hear more of the adventures you witnessed in your dream.

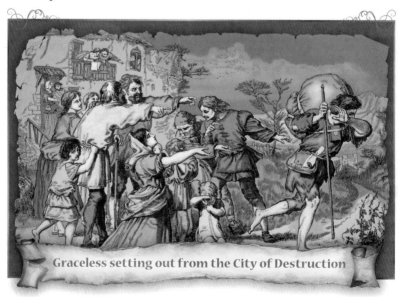
Graceless setting out from the City of Destruction

---

* **Fasels** — *Chick-peas, kidney beans.*

Great-Heart, Constance and Fidelity all chimed in with words meant to encourage Faithless to continue the recounting of his dream, something he seemed most anxious to do.

Faithless had been cordially included in the family meal and was by now somewhat relaxed and at ease with all the company that surrounded him. He folded his hands and took a deep breath, as if to give his following recitation of his remarkable dream a good long think.

Faithless: So, I saw in my dream Evangelist, while pointing to a destination far from the City of Destruction, asking Graceless if he saw yonder shining light. I watched Graceless squint and lean forward as if he was setting a course. Then with a shout, he ran toward the light as fast as he could, but not as quickly as he would have liked because of the great burden on his back.

Great-Heart: So, Graceless began to run?

Faithless: Yes, but he had not run very far from his home when his wife and children, realizing what was happening, cried after him to return.

Fidelity: What happened next?

Faithless: Graceless put his fingers in his ears and ran on while crying *Life! Life! Eternal Life!* So, without looking back, he fled toward the middle of the valley.

 Luke 14:26, Genesis 19:17

The neighbors came out to see what was going on. When they saw who it was that was running they became very agitated and noisy. Some called for Graceless to come back, others complained he had left and others mocked him for leaving so abruptly without so much as a thought for the luxury, companionship and safety famously offered within the sanctuary of the City of Destruction.

 Jeremiah 20:10, Luke 17:32

Constance: And what did the neighbors do?

Faithless: Besides yelling after him, threatening and censuring and mocking him, it appeared that they would do nothing. But after the din had died down, there were two men who decided to fetch him back by force. The one was Obstinate and the other was Pliable.

Now by this time, Graceless was a good distance away.

But Obstinate and Pliable were determined to pursue him, which they did. Soon they caught up to Graceless, who seemed dismayed that they were chasing him. After catching him, here is what I heard them say:

> **Graceless**: *Why have you run after me?*

> **Obstinate**: *To persuade you to go back with us.*

> **Graceless**: *That is not possible. You live in the City of Destruction, the place where I was born; and I believe that if you stay in that city you will die sooner or later and then you will sink lower than the grave, into a place that burns with fire and brimstone. Please consider, good neighbors, coming along with me.*

Obstinate and Pliable pursue Graceless

> **Obstinate**: *What! And leave our friends and comforts behind us?*

 Luke 14:26

Graceless: *Friends in peril and comforts that will soon fade like a plucked flower! All that you leave behind is not worthy to be compared with even a little of what I am seeking to enjoy; and if you will come along with me and not give up, we will both be blessed with treasure to spare, beyond anything we can imagine. Come along with me and see if what I am telling you is not true.*

 2 Corinthians 4:18, Luke 15:17-18, I Peter 4:4

Obstinate: *What are you looking for that is so valuable that you would turn your back on all the world to find it?*

Graceless: *I am looking for an inheritance that is imperishable, undefiled and unfading, kept in heaven. It is kept safe there to be given at the appointed time to those who diligently seek it. You can read about it in my book.*

 Hebrews 11:16, 2 Corinthians 4:17-18, 1 Peter 1:4

Obstinate: *Tush, Tush, hold your silly tongue and put away your book of myths and legends and come back home with us.*

Graceless: *No! I have started this journey and I must finish it.*

 Luke 9:62

Great Heart: What happened next?

Faithless: Obstinate grew more and more impatient with Graceless and called him an empty-headed ***Fopdoodle***,* a ***Lubberwort***,* and a ***Mumblecrust***.*

Great-Heart: And how did Graceless respond to these insults that were heaped upon his person?

---

* **Fopdoodle** — *Means a person of little significance.*
* **Lubberwort** — *Slow-witted.*
* **Mumblecrust** — *Toothless, comic beggar.*

Faithless: You might have thought that Graceless would have responded in kind and called Obstinate a ***Gobermouch***,* which is what I would have told him.

Evangelist: But what did Graceless say to Obstinate?

Faithless: That was the strange thing. Graceless bore the reproach without saying anything to Obstinate, who finally turned to Pliable and said, *"Let's go back to our home, the City of Destruction, since Graceless is obviously one of these mixed-up lunatics who, when they get a crazy idea in their heads, think themselves wiser than seven men that can render a reason. Let's be done with this **Whiffle-Woofer**.*"*

 I Peter 4:4

Faithless: I was miffed by the answer of Pliable who seemed to be under the heavy hand of Obstinate. I was surprised when Pliable stood his ground and told Obstinate not to be so harsh.

Great-Heart: Is that all Pliable said?

Faithless: No, he also said:

> **Pliable**: *The things Graceless is looking for are better than anything we have. I feel like I should go along with my neighbor.*

> **Obstinate**: *What! More fools still?*

Obstinate tried to bully Pliable by telling him:

> **Obstinate**: *Do what I say, and go back; who knows where this lunatic will lead you? Go back, go back and be wise.*

> **Graceless**: *Please Pliable, come along with me. Consider again all the things that are to be gained and many more glories besides.*

---

* **Gobermouch** — *A nosey person who takes an unhealthy interest in the affairs of other people.*
* **Whiffle-Woofer** — *A person who just wastes your time.*

Great-Heart: Did Pliable heed the words of Graceless?

Faithless: Only after some debate between the two neighbors. Obstinate insisted that the whole venture was a fool's errand that was destined to have an unhappy, tragic end.

Great-Heart: Did Graceless say anything else to try and persuade Pliable to come along?

Faithless: Oh, yes, he did. Graceless opened the Great Book and invited Pliable to read about it for himself adding that:

> **Graceless:** *The trustworthiness of this 'Best of Books' was confirmed by the blood of Him who made it.*

 Hebrews 9:17-21

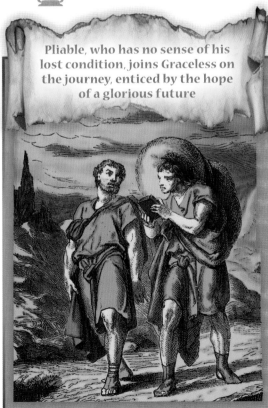

Pliable, who has no sense of his lost condition, joins Graceless on the journey, enticed by the hope of a glorious future

Faithless: Finally, after Obstinate had spent himself with bluster and insults, Pliable announced that he had come to the decision to cast his lot along with Graceless.

Great-Heart: Was that all Pliable said?

Faithless: No, in my dream I saw Pliable turn to Graceless and ask if he was sure he knew the way to the desired place. As I recall, this was the response:

Graceless: *I was given directions by a man whose name is Evangelist who told me to go as quickly as I could to the little gate that is just up ahead and once there we will receive instructions about the way before us.*

Pliable: *Come then, good neighbor, let's be going.*

Then they went along together.

Fidelity: What did Obstinate do?

Faithless turned around in his chair in order to speak directly to Fidelity who was holding a dish in one hand and a towel in the other.

Faithless: Let me tell you what I remember:

Obstinate: *I will go back to my home, I will not be a companion of such misled fanatical fellows.*

Faithless: Now I saw in my dream, after Obstinate returned to the City of Destruction, Graceless and Pliable began to talk as they walked together through the middle of the valley and this is what they said:

Graceless: *I am glad you were persuaded to come along with me. I am surprised that Obstinate returned so quickly to the City of Destruction. I think if he had felt the power and terror of the unseen, as I have, he would have been persuaded to come along with us.*

 Proverbs 26:11, Luke 13:3

Pliable: *Come, neighbor Graceless, since it is just the two of us, tell me more about the wonderful things that await us when we arrive at the place we are going.*

Graceless: *I can better conceive of them with my mind than talk about them. But yet, since you are interested, I will read about them in my book.*

Faithful: In my dream, I saw Pliable stop walking in order that Graceless might catch up with him. After a few moments, Graceless came alongside. Graceless was a little out of breath because he tried to keep the pace that Pliable had set.

Graceless was glad for the small rest as he stood before Pliable, caught his breath and asked again what concerned Pliable.

Pliable was a little stern with Graceless as he thought himself deserving of the answers that were suddenly coming into his mind.

> **Pliable**: *And do you think the words of your book are true?*

> **Graceless**: *Yes, very sure; for the words were written by the One who cannot lie.*
> *Titus 1:2*

Faithless: In my dream, I saw that Pliable seemed to be well satisfied with the answers to his questions.

Evangelist: How did Pliable respond?

Faithless: I heard Pliable say:

> **Pliable**: *Yes, yes, this is a good answer. Please tell me about the things that await us.*

Faithless: In my dream, Graceless paused for a moment to give it a good long think before beginning to share his vision of things yet to come with Pliable as the two walked on at the slower pace set by Graceless. This is what they said:

> **Graceless**: *There is an endless kingdom to be inhabited and everlasting life to be given to us so that we may live in that kingdom forever.*
> *Isaiah 65:17, John 10: 27-29*

Pliable: *Well said. What else?*

Graceless: *We will be given crowns of glory and clothing that will make us shine like the sun!*

 2 Timothy 4:8, Revelation 22:5, Matthew 13:43

Pliable: *This sounds very grand indeed. What else?*

Graceless paused a little and then said in tones somewhat lilting, as if it were half a song:

Graceless: *There shall neither be crying nor sorrow; for He that is the owner of the place will wipe all tears from our eyes.*

 Isaiah 25:8, Revelation 7:16-17; 21:4

Pliable: *And what sort of neighbors shall we have there?*

Graceless: *We will be with seraphim and cherubim and creatures that will dazzle your eyes when you look at them.*

 Isaiah 6:2, 1 Thessalonians 4:16-17, Revelation 5:11

Pliable smiled and impatiently prodded Graceless for more information.

Pliable: *And what else?*

Graceless: *We will meet with tens of thousands that have gone before us to that place; none of them are hurtful, but all of them are loving and holy, every one walking in the sight of God and standing in his presence with acceptance forever. In a word, there we will see the elders with their golden crown. There we will see the holy virgins with their golden harps. There we will see men who were cut in pieces by the world, burnt in flames, eaten of beasts, drowned in the seas, suffering all this and more for the love they have for*

*the Lord of the place. Everyone in that place is clothed with
immortality, as with a robe.*

 *Revelation 4:4, Revelation 14:1-5, 2 Corinthians 5:2, John 12:25,
Hebrews 11:37*

Pliable: *Hearing about all of this is enough to excite my heart but
are these things to be enjoyed by anyone? What do we have to do
to share in all these things?*

Graceless: *The Lord, the governor of the country, has recorded in
this book that if we are truly willing to have it, He will give it to us
freely. Would you like me to read it out loud from the Great Book?*

 John 6:37, 7:37, Revelation 21:6, 22:17

Faithless: And then I saw in my dream that Pliable took a quick look
at the book, shook his head no, paused for a moment and then said...

Pliable: *Well, my good companion, I am glad to hear about these
things. Come, let's hasten our pace.*

Graceless: *I am greatly hindered by this burden and unable to
walk as quickly as you.*

Faithless: I saw that Pliable obliged and slowed his pace in order that
he might hear more and more of the glorious place he fancied himself
soon inhabiting.

Now I saw in my dream, just as they had finished talking, that they
came near to a very miry swamp that was in the middle of the valley. Then suddenly, both Graceless and Pliable, who were not paying
attention to where they were walking, fell into the swamp.

Great-Heart: The Swamp of Despair?

Faithless: Yes, the name of the swamp was Despair. Well, as I
was saying, the two of them wallowed there until they were both

completely covered with mud and muck. Graceless, weighed down by the burden on his back, began to sink into the slime.

Great-Heart gave Evangelist a quick knowing look and shook his head as if he knew exactly what was going to happen next.

Graceless and Pliable are beset by unbelief, doubts and fears.

Great-Heart: Evangelist and I know this place very well.

Faithless: You know about the Swamp of Despair?

Evangelist: It has many names. Some have called it the Slough of Despond, others have called it the Sewer of Doubt. Most, these days, just call it the Swamp of Despair.

And what did Pliable say about the condition he now found himself in?

Faithless: Pliable was none too pleased and became uncivil in the space of one heartbeat. This is the conversation I heard between Pliable and Graceless, as best I can remember it:

> **Pliable**: *Where are we now Graceless?*

> **Graceless**: *Honestly, Pliable, I do not know.*

Great-Heart: Did this answer satisfy Pliable?

Faithless: Contrariwise, it seemed to put Pliable in an angry fever. He railed against Graceless in language I will not repeat in good company. The upshot of it was that if he was to have this much difficulty at the beginning of his journey then what might he expect in the end?

Soon Pliable's anger turned to mockery as he cursed Graceless (as if he was the reason he was stuck in the stinking mire) and blamed him for his carelessness and reproached him for being taken in by the myth of a brave country that he began to doubt even existed. In brief, he told Graceless that he could go on this fool's errand on his own.

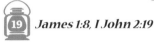 *James 1:8, I John 2:19*

Evangelist: How did Graceless respond to Pliable's abuse and rebuke?

Faithless: He bore it with humility and began talking to himself as if he had already lost the company of Pliable who, having pulled himself out the mire, shook the muck off himself with loads of complaints and began running back in the direction of the City of Destruction.

I did see Graceless turn his head for an instant as he wallowed in the slime and I witnessed Pliable as he began running as fast as he could. But that is not all. Pliable began muttering and then shouting insults and heaping more abuse upon the person of Graceless. When Pliable was about 50 yards from the edge of the swamp, he stopped, turned around and shook his fist at Graceless.

As I remember, Graceless did not see or seem to hear the insults as he was strangely, I thought at first, trying with all his might, although encumbered by the burden on his back, to reach the opposite edge of the swamp.

Fidelity: So, Graceless was left to struggle in the Swamp of Despair alone?

Fidelity seemed to be somewhat put out by the report that Pliable, once out of the mire, did not try and assist his neighbor, Graceless. Great-Heart smiled as he answered Fidelity with a soft answer.

Great-Heart: Pliable could not help Graceless as he was not trying to get out of the swamp on the side that faced the City of Destruction.

Fidelity: Yes, that is true but he could have tried to assist poor Graceless.

Evangelist: I think what your father is trying to say is that any help that Pliable offered, had his heart been so inclined, would have been no help at all since the pilgrimage of Graceless must go forward despite the difficulties, if he is to ever reach the Narrow Gate that opens to the path to eternal life.

Fidelity seemed satisfied by her uncle's explanation.

Fidelity: What happened next?

Faithless: Well, in spite of the difficulty, Graceless still tried to get to the side of the swamp that was the furthest from the City of Destruction and nearest the Narrow Gate. He finally reached the edge of the swamp but he could not, no matter how hard he tried, lift himself out of the swamp because of the heavy burden that was on his back.

So, I saw in my dream that Graceless was left to tumble in the Swamp of Despair, alone. I did notice that he still endeavored to struggle to that side of the slough that was farthest from his own house and nearest to the Narrow Gate that Evangelist had directed him to enter.

Evangelist: Did my cousin, Help, arrive on the scene to assist Graceless?

Faithless was again reminded that his dream was no ordinary dream, but rather a vision of things that were and things that were yet to come.

Faithful: Is Help a relative of yours?

Great-Heart: Oh, yes indeed.

Evangelist: My cousin, Help, was the eldest son of Mr. Steadfast. He was a rascal in his youth and made very bad choices in the companions he kept. His birth name was Rowdy and The City of Destruction has chronicled many of his missteps and notoriously corrupt exploits. It looked like he would come to ruin, but the King of our country had other plans for him.

Faithless: I would like to hear more.

Evangelist: At the point of his greatest need and after a life that only produced sorrow and heartache, Rowdy was rescued by our King Who ministered to him. He renamed him and then employed him to help other men who were sinking and wallowing in doubts and fears just as he had done at one time, almost sinking beneath the scum, never to rise again. Had it not been for his younger brother who was sent to rescue his elder brother at just the right time, Rowdy would have been just another sad epitaph to the consequences of faithless unbelief.

 II Corinthians 1:4-6

Graceless tried to reach the opposite edge of the swamp

Faithless: I did see a wiry, stout man come to the place where Graceless lay exhausted and unable to move. And I remember that when Graceless asked his name, he said it was *Help.*

Evangelist: Help is not for dainty company. No indeed, he is a valiant man who only cares about the good opinion of his King and has love mixed with pity for all those who are stuck in the place he unhappily once called his home.

Faithless: Home in the Swamp?

Evangelist: Yes. As a young man, his father, Mr. Steadfast, would clean his wayward son up and put him in the best clothes he could find. For all his best efforts he would soon discover that Rowdy would head for the Swamp as soon as he was untethered to wallow in the filth of it.

What once he loved he now detests. He serves the King best by reaching into the muck and filth that at one time almost consumed him. He pulls poor sinners like Graceless out and up where they can once again put their feet on the path of the solid ground that leads from the Sewage Pit to the Small Sheep Gate that all sinners must enter if they desire eternal life.

Constance: So, what happened next?

Faithless: As best I can remember here is what happened:

> **Help**: *What are you doing there?*
>
> **Graceless**: *Sir, I was asked to go this way by a man called Evangelist, who directed me also to yonder gate that I might escape the wrath to come. And as I was going there, I fell into this stinking mire.*
>
> **Help**: *Didn't you see the stone steps?*
>
> **Graceless**: *I am ashamed to say that I was careless and full of fear and could not see the steps.*
>
> **Help**: *Give me your hand dear fellow.*
>
> **Psalm 40:2, Psalm 40:17**

Help pulls Graceless out of the Swamp of Despair

Faithless: Graceless put forth his soiled hand and instead of recoiling at the sight and smell of it, Help gave him a manly grip and with a strength that I am sure must have surprised Graceless, judging by the look on his face. Help pulled him out of the Swamp with such force and speed that it caused the muck to boil over and fold upon itself like a whirlpool.

Fidelity was now sitting at the table having completely forgotten about the apple crisp which was being attended to by her cousin,

Constance, who was also listening while she busied herself cleaning up the kitchen.

Fidelity: Did he rush to the Narrow Gate and enter in?

Faithless: No, but I did see Help set Graceless upon sound and solid ground. He asked him to go to the Narrow Gate, even pointing the way and encouraging Graceless that he was very near his destination with the gate being less than a mile up ahead.

But before Graceless began his journey again, he stopped and asked Help a question. The conversation went something like this:

> Graceless: *I am very glad for your help, but I am also curious as to why such an obstacle should be placed in between the City of Destruction and the Small Sheep Gate that leads to everlasting life.*
>
> *Why is this place not mended so that travelers like my poor self might enter the path to life with more security and ease?*
>
> Help: *This miry swamp is such a place as cannot be mended: it is located in a low place where the scum and filth that always attends the true conviction for sin, continually runs and settles.*

Evangelist: And did you understand the meaning of Help's explanation?

Faithless: A little I think, perhaps not fully.

Evangelist: Shall I unfold the mystery of the Swamp of Despair?

Constance: Oh, Father, please do.

Faithless: Yes, please do as I desire to know the meaning of it as well.

Evangelist: When the sinner is awakened to his true lost condition, there arises in his soul many fears and doubts and discouraging apprehensions. These all get together and settle in this place: and this is the reason for the badness of this ground.

It is not the pleasure of the King that this place should remain so bad. His laborers have, by the direction of his Majesty's surveyors, been trying to mend this ground for sixteen hundred years. To my knowledge, this swamp full of fears and doubts has swallowed up at least twenty thousand cart loads, yes, even millions of wholesome instructions, that have at all seasons been brought from everywhere in the King's dominion. Even with material of the highest quality, the very best instructions, wisdom and warnings that can be found anywhere in the Kingdom, the ground remains yet unamended.

It is and will remain as long as men's hearts are governed by fear and unbelief, the Swamp of Despondency, Doubting and Despair.

 22   *Isaiah 35:3-4*

Faithless: Is there no way to cross this swamp in safety?

Evangelist: It is true that there are, by the direction of the Lawgiver, certain good and substantial steps, placed even through the very middle of this swamp.

However, since this low spot is constantly being filled with the filth of unbelief and the muck of fear that spews without warrant or warning, it makes the solid steps hard to see. And, since most travelers are a little dizzy in the head from the effects of their own fallen nature, it remains certain that most, but not all, will be bemired just as you witnessed Graceless was in your dream.

 23   *1 Samuel 12:23 , Proverbs 14:12*

The good news, Faithless, is that the ground is good when you arrive at the gate.

There was a pause in the conversation as everyone gave heed to the warning and perilous conditions that are so often present and caused in the pilgrimage to the Celestial City. Constant attacks and an onslaught of fears and their handmaidens, doubt followed by the ugly sister of despair, were common along the path.

Constance: Can we hear more?

Faithless: Sadly, that is the end of my dream.

Great-Heart and Evangelist agreed this was not the end of the dream since they both knew in their hearts and minds where this dream would finally conclude. There were miles and miles yet to be trodden by Graceless who was about to have his name changed by the King of the country that lay onward and upward, if he continued until he arrived at the Narrow Sheep Gate.

Faithless: And when do you think we shall meet again?

Great-Heart: I am not certain but I do imagine that my brother, Evangelist, who has the King's business to attend to, will return to us the very day that the King of our country beckons you to come and visit us again.

Faithless went to the window and looked up to see where the sun was on its path toward the distant horizon.

Faithless: If I leave now, I will arrive home before the sun goes down.

Fidelity rushed into the kitchen and returned with a small knapsack and a small wooden spoon that was half immersed in a warm goblet of apple crisp.

Fidelity: Please take this to give you some sustenance on your long journey home.

Everyone bade farewell to Faithless. Great-Heart, Fidelity, Evangelist and Constance watched Faithless travel toward the sunset that lit up the shadow of the blackberry bushes laced with three full-grown mulberry trees and one giant oak. They watched and prayed as the figure of Faithless entered the little lane that led back to the City of Destruction where Faithless would have much to contemplate between now and his next dream.

CHAPTER 4

The Dreamer Meets Mr. Worldly Wiseman

It was a little before dusk when Faithless finally made his way into the City of Destruction. The following is what he reported to Great-Heart when next they met.

Faithless: As I was on my way home, situated in the center of the city, I heard a great hub-bub. Curious as to the meaning of this uproar, I headed toward the gathered crowd. At first, I could not see what was causing the uproar, but gathered, from the insults and abuse that some criminal or miscreant had suddenly aroused the ire of the city folk. As I elbowed my way through the crowd I was amazed to see the man who had caused the disturbance.

The crowd was in a fever, heaping insults, mocking and laughing at the poor man who was down on one knee with his hands covering his shamed face.

"What a spineless worm you are." shouted one. "Coward!" shouted another.

In the center of the mocking crowd, with his hands covering his shamed face, was a man I thought I recognized.

The man deflected a large rotten onion that was hurled in his direction. It was then that I saw the face of Pliable, the very man that I had seen in my dream.

It soon became clear to me that the crowd, who had no sympathy for the pilgrimage of Graceless, was incensed by the cowardice of the turncoat Pliable who had showed his backside as he fled at the first sign of difficulty.

Obstinate

And who do you suppose I saw at the center of all this commotion leading the choir of abuse, inciting the crowd with his own un-repeatable insults and name calling?

It was none other than Obstinate, who was happily having his revenge on Pliable, who thought himself the wiser one by ignoring the good advice of the arrogant bully, Obstinate.

I watched as Pliable finally plucked up his courage a little and began blaming his misadventure on Graceless.

The crowd booed at Pliable's cowering defense as they slowly ran out of insults and drifted off to their own homes as the shadows that announced the end of the day crept over the city square.

Within the space of a couple of minutes, there was only Pliable and myself standing in the square looking at each other as the gray shades of night loomed over the City of Destruction. Finally, Pliable shook his head in disbelief and drifted into the back alley that provided an obscured passageway to his home.

I was well aware of the policies that guided the behavior of Pliable, Obstinate and the other city folk. I was not surprised that in the following days scandalous tales ripe with falsehood, innuendo and gossip about Graceless began circulating around the City of Destruction.

 *Matthew 5:12*

Nor was I surprised to discover that the source of all this malicious gossip was non-other than Pliable who became a slandering **Rawgabbit**.*

 1 John 2:19

Pliable, who was for a short season a false pilgrim, spends the rest of his life revealing untruths about the pilgrimage he abandoned at the first sign of trouble in order to try and regain his reputation.

Faithless opened the door to his home and was greeted by his two children and wife who were waiting for him to return with news of his adventure with Great-Heart.

Faithless took a cup of tea and nibbled on a biscuit. He then recited the day's adventures to his wife and two children. He went to bed wondering when the next chapter of his dream would be revealed to him. Faithless wondered if Graceless would finally find himself at the Small Sheep Gate that seemed to hold so much promise and importance.

With this in mind and other mysterious things regarding the dream and the curious words of both Great-Heart and Evangelist echoing in his head, he tried to go to sleep and rose up early the next morning after having spent a dreamless and sleepless night.

Back at King's Cottage, the mood of the two brothers and the two daughters was prayerful and hopeful.

Great-Heart and his brother, Evangelist, spent that evening discussing the King's business and wondering out loud at the circumstance regarding Faithless and his great dream. His vision had arrested their attention but it both had encouraged and dismayed them.

Evangelist: I must leave in the morning at first light.

---

* **Rawgabbit** —Somebody who speaks in strictest confidence about a subject of which they know nothing.
A rawgabbit is the person who pulls you aside and reveals in a careful whisper slander and untruths.

Great-Heart: I know you have urgent business.

Evangelist: Yes indeed, business that will, I am certain, make its way into the next dream of Faithless.

Great-Heart: Yes, I do believe our King has given us both this most miraculous vision as a window into the hearts of two men who, it appears, our Lord means to save from the wrath to come.

Evangelist: True, True. Our King has already informed me, by means of one of his faithful messengers, that I will be needed at the way that leads to Mount Sinai this very week.

Great-Heart: Is it Graceless that needs your aid?

Evangelist: I can only wonder as the message was not ripe with details but only that I should make my way to Mount Sinai as soon as my business here has come to a fruitful end.

Great-Heart: So, Constance will stay here and have happy fellowship with her favorite cousin until you return to us?

Evangelist cocked his head as he considered the plan his brother had put forward.

Evangelist: I imagine that I will be back here just in time to listen to the next episode in the vision of Faithless.

Without any further discussion, this was all Great-Heart needed in way of approval. He clapped his hands together, stood up and pulled Evangelist out of his chair and sent him off to bed with a warm benediction and a brotherly embrace.

Evangelist awoke before the sun came up and made his way to the bedroom where Constance and Fidelity were still asleep. He kissed his daughter on her cheek and whispered his goodbyes.

Great-Heart awoke in time to wish his brother God-Speed.

The days that followed at Great-Heart's cottage passed with peace and tranquility. Fidelity and Constance never tired of each other's company.

Great-Heart delighted in his private times of study, preparing his Bible lessons and sermons for his small congregation, as well as attending to his other pastoral duties that included a bi-weekly service in his home.

He was also glad for the extra time to care for his garden. And, as time permitted, setting his little traps in hopes of relishing another rabbit stew before fall was upon them.

The King's Cottage, as it was known to the eight families that regularly attended the non-conformist home church, were all near neighbors of Great-Heart.

They loved and supported Great-Heart and Fidelity and were happy to be employed in regular prayer for the cares and concerns that seemed to make their way to the King's Cottage on a pretty regular but never over-burdening schedule.

 Philippians 4:6-7

One man, in particular, had become a close friend of Great-Heart. His name was Mr. Merciful, who upon hearing about the vision of Faithless was determined to make it a matter of vigilant and constant prayer.

The King's Cottage seemed to Great-Heart to have a happy rhythm designed by the King himself to cheer his heart, fill his days with labor that had eternity in sight and never ever produce anything even close to a dull moment.

The home of Faithless, on the other hand, was neither happy nor tranquil. The dream had become an obsession he shared with his wife.

At first it seemed to her like a harmless whimsical dream with little importance and she considered it the object of fruitless speculation. It had become for Faithless and his family something of an unwelcome obsession to everyone but Faithless, who was determined to find out its true meaning.

After several days and no further visions, Faint-Hope—for that was the name of the wife of Faithless—was convinced that the night visions she now viewed as nightmares had come to an end. And with the end of the dreams, she was sure that Faithless would return to his trade as the city's metal fabricator and mender of pots and pans.

She was anxious to be done with the dream that had become an obsession, crowding out everything she thought was important to their happiness and welfare. She fancied herself the matriarch of a family seeking prominence among the citizens living in the City of Destruction.

 Luke 17:32

Faint-Hope was disappointed when the following morning Faithless ignored all her pleas to return to his business trade as he prepared to make another trek to the cottage of Great-Heart in search of answers.

Faithless gave his wife a kiss on the forehead and told her he would return before the supper meal, which was usually served piping hot just after sunset.

Faint-Hope held his hand tight, not wanting to let him go, but Faithless could not be persuaded to stay. He was determined to find out what mysteries he might discover in the latest episode of his dream.

Back at the cottage, there was a knock at the door. The knock was quickly answered just before the sun peeked over the little hill that graced the rear of the King's Cottage.

The door opened wide and the two brothers, Great-Heart and Evangelist, stood facing each other, both with a welcoming smile that needed no explanation.

Great-Heart: The prodigal son has returned!

Evangelist laughed at the reference and added…

Evangelist: Prepare the fatted calf and invite all the neighbors.

Fidelity and Constance, who were used to the gentle and harmless banter that was always apparent when the two brothers met, rushed to the front door armed with hugs and kisses. Evangelist finally put an end to the commotion as he raised his arms in surrender.

Evangelist: And what have you two cousins been doing while I was away?

Constance: Oh, the usual **Hugger-Mugger**.*

The two cousins made their way to the kitchen without even being asked in order to prepare a cup of tea and biscuits to celebrate the arrival of Evangelist.

Evangelist: Have you heard from Faithless?

Great-Heart: Not yet, but your arrival signals that we can soon expect him to come knocking on our cottage door.

Evangelist: Indeed.

Great-Heart: What news do you bring?

The two brothers settled into their familiar spots in the living room.

Evangelist: I have just now returned from Mount Sinai.

Great-Heart: Was it as you expected?

Evangelist: Worse than I expected.

Great-Heart: Worse?

---

* **Hugger-Mugger** —A fanciful way to describe secretive or covert behavior.

Evangelist: I will report the news to you in one breath.

   Great-Heart looked expectantly at his brother, patiently waiting for him to reveal what would unravel the mystery of his latest adventure as an ambassador for the King of the country that lies above and beyond.

As if he had just bitten into a sour apple, Evangelist reported...

Evangelist: Mr. Worldly Wiseman!

   Great-Heart winced.

Mr. Worldly Wiseman

Great-Heart: Is that old **Snollygoster*** still lurking about?

Evangelist: Yes, lurking about in search of poor pilgrims like Graceless, sneering, as usual, at the true way as he misdirects burdened pilgrims to the gilded gateway that opens up to Hell itself.

   Great-Heart shook his head and then looked up at his brother and smiled a hopeful smile.

Great-Heart: Was that the King's business that took you to Mount Sinai?

   Before Evangelist could say a word, there was an earnest rap on the door of the King's Cottage, repeated three times with urgency.

Evangelist: I believe the answer to your question has arrived.

---

* **Snollygoster**—A person who has intelligence but no principles.

Love Not the World

The World whispers "come take your prize"

The Lord replies "close your eyes!"

The World mocks "you've much to gain"

The Lord replies "yes, sin and shame"

The World beckons "feast your eyes"

The Lord replies "on lust and lies?"

The World taunts "come be merry"

The Lord replies "I will not tarry.

Soon I will come for my prize

The very ones that closed their eyes

To the world and all its charms

Secured forever in my arms."

CJL

CHAPTER 5
GRACELESS ENCOUNTERS MOUNT SINAI

ust as Evangelist had predicted, the answer to Great-Heart's question and the reason he had been beckoned to the King's Cottage was knocking just outside the door.

Great-Heart went to the door and opened it wide.

Great-Heart: You are up very early.

Great-Heart took the trembling hand of Faithless and ushered him into the living room.

Great-Heart: Why are you trembling?

Faithless stammered and finally asked if he could collect his thoughts and warm himself before he answered.

Great-Heart: I will wager that you have not had your morning meal?

Faithless smiled knowing that he had just received an invitation to what promised to be, judging by the smells, a delicious morning.

Great-Heart: Come and sit with me and my brother while Fidelity and Constance finish preparing breakfast.

All thought of food vanished as Faithless asked with a look of surprise.

Faithless: Evangelist is here? I thought he might be elsewhere.

Great-Heart: You mean elsewhere as in Mount Sinai?

Faithless opened his mouth in disbelief.

Faithless: I saw him in the dream I just awoke from not three hours ago.

Evangelist, upon hearing the conversation between Faithless and Great-Heart, offered his own salutation.

Evangelist: Greetings, Faithless. Yes, I am here having journeyed to this place just a day ago from Mt. Sinai.

Evangelist also noticed the poor man was trembling. Since it was a warm mild morning, he wondered out loud as to the meaning of his distressed condition.

Evangelist: Did you meet some terror on the way from the City of Destruction to the King's Cottage?

Faithless: Of a sort.

Great-Heart: This seems a matter better addressed comfortably seated fortified with a hot cup of tea. Come, Faithless, let's sit together.

Without being beckoned, Fidelity and Constance slipped into the room laden with tea and crumpets, some apple jam and a little pitcher of cream.

The pantry was always overflowing at the King's Cottage. Great-Heart was the pastor of a small assembly made up of a group of neighbors who met in the King's Cottage twice a week. They were humble folk, mostly farmers and their families and farm hands.

While they had little money to contribute to the welfare of their beloved pastor, Great-Heart, they did regularly express their gratitude for the tending of their souls by bringing Great-Heart and Fidelity grain, spices, honey, canned goods, jams, dried meat, pies, vegetables and occasionally a duck or laying hen. These gifts were always well garnished with generous hearts overflowing with God's grace.

Fidelity, whose mother had died when she was in her 18th year, loved cooking. Her legacy lived on in the familiar tasty recipes she had spent a lifetime perfecting. Fidelity would always serve her father a favorite familiar meal with the greeting, "Just like mom made." It would always command a smile and somehow made the humblest meal seem fit for a king.

Constance was delighted to visit the King's Cottage knowing she would spend much of her time in the kitchen with Fidelity imagining what culinary delights they might cook up. This duty was made even more pleasant by the bounty of ingredients that came from the neighbors' pantries which overflowed the cupboards of the King's Cottage.

Faithful looked down at the provisions that had been carefully arranged on the smooth maple tray that was placed in his lap.

Faithless: Thank you so much.

Fidelity gave her father, Great-Heart, a kiss on the cheek.

Constance, who was already halfway back to the kitchen, noticed the gesture and not to be outdone, she returned to the side of her father, Evangelist, and gave him a kiss on both cheeks.

Fidelity took up the challenge and returned to her father, Great-Heart, and evened the score with a large noisy kiss on her father's other cheek.

Everyone in the room was humored by the drama provided by the two cousins who curtsied as they marched out of the room, arm in arm, as if they were conquering heroes returning from some great exploit.

This light mood did much to improve everyone's disposition, except for Faithless, who was obviously troubled by some event that had taken place somewhere between the City of Destruction and the King's Cottage.

After a moment or two of silence, Faithless shared the reason for his current state.

Faithless: As I was making my way up the path and into the fields that led to your cottage, I was approached by a man who was determined to interrupt my journey.

Evangelist: A ruffian or a tramp looking for something to jingle in his pockets?

Faithless: By no means. He was a fair man that you might even describe as elegant in his dress and speech.

Great-Heart interrupted.

Great-Heart: You know this man?

Faithless: I know him by sight and would recognize his smooth words anywhere, but I saw him for the first time just an hour ago.

Both Great-Heart and Evangelist were confused by what seemed like a muddled contradiction.

Great-Heart: I find myself in a bit of a mental jumble. You say you would recognize him by sight but have only seen him an hour ago?

Faithless: Yes, that is true.

Evangelist: Where had you seen him before?

Faithless bowed his head before speaking as if his testimony of the event would seem too incredible to be believed.

Faithless: I saw him first in my dream last night.

Mr. Worldly Wiseman

Both Great-Heart and Evangelist nodded their heads as they pieced the puzzle together, then stiffened and leaned back in their chairs, stunned by this news.

Great-Heart: Faithless, be assured that we have seen many of the details of your dream jump out of your vision and into our lives. Please, dear friend, be assured that we have no doubt that what you are telling us is a true and trustworthy account.

Somewhat reassured, Faithless sat up in his chair and began to unburden his mind.

Faithless: The man's name is Mr. Worldly Wiseman and he seemed to have some knowledge of me even though, as I said, I had never made his acquaintance.

He asked me where I was going and what was my business.

Evangelist: What did you tell him?

Faithless: I told him that I was on my way to the King's Cottage to visit with Great-Heart.

Evangelist: And then what did he say?

Faithless: All his pleasantness disappeared and he began to insult me by saying that others had secretly seen me on the path to the King's Cottage and had reported it to him in order that he might keep me from a life of unwarranted trials and tribulations.

Evangelist: And what did you say?

Faithless: It is what I thought that troubled me the most.

Great-Heart: And what did you think?

Faithless: After listening to his high-sounding words and considering his elevated status and station in life, I thought myself a fool and was

almost determined to return home. Then I remembered my dream.
I had just an hour earlier witnessed the vision of Graceless who also
met Mr. Worldly Wiseman on the path to the Narrow Gate. I saw in
my dream what happened to Graceless when he left the path he was
on and followed the direction and advice of this grand gentleman.
I also saw how Graceless was the worse off for it.

Evangelist nodded as if he knew exactly what Faithless was
talking about.

Great-Heart had not the slightest clue as to what was about to
unfold in the newly turned page of the dream that Faithless was
about to reveal.

Evangelist, on the other hand, did.

At this point, as if overcome by the gravity of the tangled edges of
a dream that was intersecting his life in ways clearly miraculous,
Great-Heart put his hands up in the air as if to stop anything from
going further. Without ceremony he closed his eyes and offered up a
prayer to the King of the Celestial City.

The prayer was short and clear. It was not polished nor was it whisked
upwards with angels' wings or propelled by great sounding words.
The simple prayer seemed to the ears of Faithless to be more like a
desperate son pleading with his father in a time of great need.

Great-Heart: Lord, help us understand what your purpose is in all this
mystery and, dear Lord, I pray you continue to reveal yourself to Faithless.

 James 1:5

The prayer ended as quickly as it began. Faithless had never prayed
before nor had he ever heard his own name mentioned in a prayer.

It might have been disquieting except that it was so simple and
genuine. The effect of the prayer on Faithless warmed his heart and
gave him some comfort that he might one day discover the mysteries

that had made their way into the hearts and minds of the two men he had come to admire, Great-Heart and Evangelist.

Evangelist stood up for a moment to stretch his legs. He then turned to his brother, Great-Heart, and spoke.

Evangelist: I believe the meaning of this will become clear as Faithless recounts the dream that has sped him to this very place.

Evangelist sat down and patiently waited for Faithless to collect his thoughts and share his dream.

Faithless took a quick sip of tea, cleared his throat and began to unfold the dream he had just awakened from that very morning.

Faithless: I saw in my dream that Graceless was walking by himself toward the Small Sheep Gate just as Evangelist had directed him to do. Then I spied someone a good distance away cross over the field and enter the path where Graceless was walking. As I said, the man that met Graceless was Mr. Worldly Wiseman.

He told Graceless that he was a high-born member and greatly esteemed citizen of the town of Carnal Policy, a prominent town.

This town, he assured Graceless, was not very far from the spot where they both now stood as it was within the country ruled by the City of Destruction.

This man, Mr. Worldly Wiseman, obviously had some knowledge of Graceless and knew about the details of his setting forth from the City of Destruction. He said the news was much noised abroad, not only in the town where he dwelt, but it also had begun to be the town-talk in some other places as well.

Mr. Worldly Wiseman, therefore, having some guess of him by beholding his laborious going and by observing his sighs and groans and the like, began to enter into a conversation with Graceless.

This is what I heard:

Mr. Worldly Wiseman: *How, good fellow, is your journey going as I see you are encumbered with a great burden?*

 II Peter 2:1-3

Graceless: *A burdened journey indeed, as ever I think a poor creature had! And since you asked me where I am going, I will tell you, sir, I am going to yonder Small Sheep Gate that lies before me; for there, I am informed, I shall be put into a way to be rid of my heavy burden.*

Mr. Worldly Wiseman: *Have you a wife and children?*

Graceless: *Yes, but I am so laden with this burden that I cannot take that pleasure in them as formerly: methinks I am as if I had no family at all.*

 1 Corinthians 7:29

Mr. Worldly Wiseman: *Will you hearken to me if I give you counsel?*

Graceless: *If it be good counsel, I will, for I am in desperate need of good advice.*

Mr. Worldly Wiseman: *I would advise you, then, that with all speed you get rid of your burden*

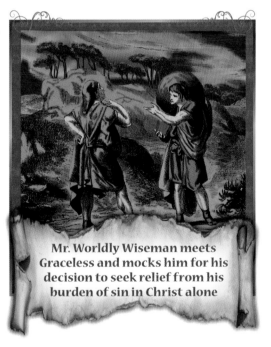

Mr. Worldly Wiseman meets Graceless and mocks him for his decision to seek relief from his burden of sin in Christ alone

for you will never be settled in your mind until then. In short, you cannot enjoy the benefits of the blessings which God has bestowed upon you until this burden you so unnecessarily bear is removed.

Graceless: *That is the very thing I seek. I desire with all my heart to be rid of this heavy burden, but having tried every remedy and method I cannot get it off by myself nor is there any man in our country that can take it off my shoulders; I am going to the Narrow Sheep Gate, as I told you, that I may be rid of my burden.*

Mr. Worldly Wiseman scowled as he said in a loud voice that echoed across the little meadow:

Mr. Worldly Wiseman: *Who told you to go this way to be rid of your burden?*

Graceless: *A man that appeared to me to be a very great and honorable person. His name was Evangelist.*

Mr. Worldly Wiseman: *I would scold him to his face for his counsel!*

There is not a more dangerous and troublesome way in the world than the way he directed you.

You could not have embarked on a more dangerous and desperate journey. I see that the muck and dirt of the Swamp of Despair is evidence that you have already met with difficulty. If you continue the way you are now going, even more sorrows and tribulations will overcome you.

What awaits you is wearisomeness, painfulness, hunger, perils, nakedness, sword, lions, dragons, darkness and in a word, death.

 II Corinthians 11:25-27

Listen to me, I am older than you.

 I Timothy 4:12

Why should you so carelessly cast away yourself by giving heed to a stranger?

Faithless paused to catch his breath and to allow Evangelist to offer a rebuttal, but Evangelist was only interested in hearing the rest of the dream.

Graceless: *Why sir, this burden on my back is more terrible to me than are all these things which you have mentioned. No, I think I care not what I meet with in the way I am going if by so doing I can be delivered from my burden.*

Faithless: Mr. Worldly Wiseman took a step back and looked at poor Graceless as he put his index finger to the corner of his mouth as if inspecting a horse he was about to purchase. And then he said the following:

Mr. Worldly Wiseman: *How did you come to have this burden in the first place?*

Faithless: Graceless pulled the Great Book out of his bosom and lifted it up for Mr. Worldly Wiseman to see.

Graceless: *By reading this book that I now hold in my hand.*

Mr. Worldly Wiseman: *I thought so! It has happened to you as to other weak-minded men. Don't you know that meddling with things too high for you will cause you to suddenly fall into the very condition you seek so earnestly to cure?*

 *I Corinthians 1:27*

And be assured that this condition...

Faithless stopped mid-sentence as he remembered his dream.

Evangelist: Go on good fellow, please continue unfolding your dream.

Faithless: It was at this place in my dream that I saw Mr. Worldly Wiseman poke at Graceless' burden. First, he poked and then he pushed at it. Then he grabbed ahold of it with both hands and shook it violently. It caused Graceless to cry out for a moment as he tumbled backward. Finally, somewhat recovered but unable at the moment to rise up, he steadied himself on one knee. While Graceless was in this posture, Mr. Worldly Wiseman gave the burden a swift kick as if it were a child's play-ball. But for all his efforts he could not loosen the burden from the back of Graceless.

 Hebrews 10:38

This frustrated Mr. Worldly Wiseman who then railed against Graceless for a moment before he regained his civil composure and spoke once again.

> **Mr. Worldly Wiseman**: *Be assured that this state of confusion and consternation you have put yourself into is all caused by reading the book you cling to. You do not understand that the condition you now find yourself in is a malady that is against nature and your own self-pride and manliness.*
>
> *You are not the first fool to run headlong into desperate adventures in order to obtain you know not what.*
>
> *I have been able to separate many poor fools from their burdens with good counsel and a swift kick to the backside. Others, like yourself, who have boiled their brains in matters too deep for the unlearned, simpering mind to understand require more desperate measures in order to find relief.*

 Romans 7:7

> *Reading this Book without the counsel of good, wise men who are skilled at moderating its effect on the soul is a dangerous thing to do, as is evidenced by the sorry sight that now stands before me.*
>
> *Since you have read this Book without the instruction or counsel of wise men and have mistaken its meaning, taking it personally and literally, the remedy available to you is by reason of your severe condition, strict and structured.*

 I John 2:27-28, II Peter 1:16

In a word, you have no idea what you really want as you are in a fever caused by the careful and deliberate reading of the Book.

Graceless: *I know what I want and what I would obtain; it is ease from my heavy burden.*

Mr. Worldly Wiseman: *Yet you would be so foolish as to seek ease from your burden in the way that leads to the Narrow Gate. A true remedy would be heralded by a wide gate, a more gracious route that invites all men to enter it for safety and ease.*

 Matthew 7:13-14

Mr. Worldly Wiseman then pointed up the path and in the direction of the Small Sheep Gate.

Mr. Worldly Wiseman: *A way with so many dangers can certainly not be the way the Creator desires men to tread.*

If you were not in such a fever of mind you would be patient and listen to me as I could direct you to the place that would take off your burden as you so desire, without the dangers that attend you in the way you are now heedlessly going. I can assure you that the remedy you seek is at hand.

Besides, instead of all the danger that will meet you if you continue on the path you are now on, you will instead be greeted

Mr. Worldly Wiseman points Graceless to the Village of Morality *with relief from your burden, rewarded with safety, friendship, and contentment.*

Evangelist interrupted the telling of the dream.

Evangelist: I am most curious how Graceless responded to all the false promises of Mr. Worldy Wiseman.

Faithless: At first, Graceless seemed determined to stay on his present course but slowly I could see him weakening as his desire to get rid of the burden grew in importance.

Evangelist: Did he speak at all about eternity and escaping the wrath to come?

Faithless: No. His only concern was the burden on his back and how he might have it removed.

The next thing I saw in my dream was Graceless pleading with Mr. Worldly Wiseman. I remember the conversation went as follows:

Graceless: *Sir, I pray, open this secret to me.*

Mr. Worldly Wiseman: *Why, in yonder village named Morality there dwells a gentleman whose name is Mr. Legality, a very judicious man, and a man of a very good reputation. He has the skill to help men off with such burdens as yours.*

I have heard and believe it is a true statement that he has done a great deal of good this way; yes, and besides, he also has the skill to cure those poor creatures that are somewhat crazed in their wits with their burdens.

 *Galatians 6:5*

Faithless: Graceless was amazed by the news there was a pleasant path free from dangers and that a short journey might provide the relief he so desperately sought.

Mr. Worldly Wiseman:
I would recommend that you go to Mr. Legality immediately and seek his help. His house is not quite a mile from this place; if he should not be at home, he has a fine young man for a son, whose name is Civility, that can relieve you of your burden as well as the old gentleman himself.

Faithless: Mr. Worldly Wiseman continued to press Graceless as he kept pointing and poking at his burden, impatiently asking him why he would bear it any longer since relief was such a short distance away.

Mr. Worldly Wiseman seemed to sense some hesitation in the mind of Graceless and added one more detail to his appeal, a detail that was meant, I am sure, to entice Graceless to follow his advice.

Mr. Legality attempts to remove the burden of sin by teaching the outward observance of the laws of God and self-righteous living

Mr. Worldly Wiseman: *And if you are so inclined not to return to your former home in the City of Destruction, you can send for your wife and children who can join you in this charming village where there are fine houses now standing empty, houses you could obtain for a small price. You would find your neighbors to be honest, respectable and fashionable.*

So, besides relieving yourself of this great burden that is causing such a fever in your mind and having an ill effect on your reason, you can be relieved of it and gain in the exchange

a good living in a place that is, by design, meant to make you feel happy and secure.

Graceless was somewhat awestruck by the invitation and tempted beyond any reason to dwell in the gilded cage that would put him in honest company, burden-less and happily content living in harmony once again with his wife and children.

12 *Luke 9:62*

Graceless: *Sir, please point me in the direction that leads to the way to this honest man's house.*

Mr. Worldly Wiseman: *Do you see yonder high hill?*

Graceless: *Yes, very well indeed.*

Graceless terrorized by the demands of the law and is overcome by the truth that he is incapable of keeping the perfect law of God

Mr. Worldly Wiseman: *Go near. Up and over that hill, the first house you come to will be his.*

Faithless: So Graceless offered his hand to Mr. Worldy Wiseman hoping to be lifted up so he could continue his journey. As hard as he tried, Mr. Worldy Wiseman was unable to lift Graceless up and so he started back the way he had first arrived.

Graceless struggled for several minutes and

was finally able to right himself. Standing up he circled around so he was facing the direction that was pointed out by Mr. Worldly Wiseman. I saw Graceless turn out of the way that leads to the Narrow Gate in order to go to Mr. Legality's house for help.

I saw that when he was just halfway up the hill that leads to the town of Morality, he suddenly stopped. The mountain loomed over the head of Graceless and seemed much higher than it had appeared from a distance. Not being steady on his feet, he began to fear he would fall into a cavern as the pathway narrowed. All of a sudden, Graceless was in fear for his life. He was afraid to venture any further. He thought of turning back but just then the hill began to shake as if it had fallen on his head and he was paralyzed with fear of either going forward or back the way he came.

Just at that moment, it began to thunder. Great bolts of lightning began to fall all around Graceless and his burden seemed heavier and heavier. He cried out as he was afraid that he should be burnt up or swallowed up.

 Exodus 19:16, Hebrews 12:21

Graceless was in this condition for what seemed like the space of half an hour.

In my dream, I heard the sorrowful lament of Graceless through the thundering and lightning. I could see him trembling as he heaped insults upon himself for ever listening to the advice given by Mr. Worldly Wiseman.

Evangelist: And did you see me come to him when he was in this terrible condition?

Faithless: Oh yes, and I was happy to see you arrive. I feared my dream would end with Graceless' sudden destruction.

Yes, I witnessed in my dream that Graceless began to blush as you drew nearer and nearer.

I saw the manner in which you greeted Graceless. It was a severe and dreadful look that seemed to remove his fear of perishing, replacing it with a sorrow and shame at what he had done.

Yes, I heard what you asked Graceless and listened carefully to your counsel. I saw how it silenced Graceless and put him to shame. I heard you ask...

> **Evangelist**: Are you not the same man that I found crying outside the walls of the City of Destruction?
>
>  *Galatians 3:1*

> **Graceless**: Yes, I am that man.

> **Evangelist**: Then what are you doing here?

> **Graceless**: I was persuaded to turn aside from the true way by Mr. Worldly Wiseman.

> **Evangelist**: I want you to stand still for just a moment so that I might show you the Word of God.

Faithful: I saw Graceless trembling and crying as he listened to your words of warning.

 *Hebrews 12:25*

I heard the words of the Lord of the Great Book. I learned from my dream that the 'just shall live by faith;' but if any man draws back, that the Lord would have no pleasure in him.

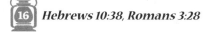 *Hebrews 10:38, Romans 3:28*

Then I saw Graceless fall down at your feet as if he were dead. I heard his remorseful cries of 'Woe is me,' and I saw how you caught him by his right hand and lifted him up, giving him strength once again as you spoke the words contained in the King's Book.

You read to him that "All manner of sin and blasphemies shall be forgiven unto men."

 Matthew 12:31

"Be not faithless, but believing."

 John 20:27

I saw Graceless a little revived, standing up and trembling.

At this point, Faithless stopped rehearsing his dream. He asked Evangelist a question that had to do with his own journey that very morning as he made his trek to the King's Cottage to meet with Great-Heart and Evangelist.

Faithless: Who is this man I met on the way to your cottage this morning, the man in my dream? I know his name is Mr. Worldly Wiseman, but who is he?

Evangelist: The man you met this morning and the man in your dream is rightly named Mr. Worldly Wiseman. It is partly because he loves only the doctrine of this world (therefore he always goes to the town of Morality to church), and partly because he loves only those doctrines that save him from ever considering the Cross of Christ or the precious cleansing blood that flowed from His sacrifice. And because he is a carnal man, filled with the lies of this world and such an arrogant man he thinks it is his job to pervert the true Gospel of Salvation and by so doing has brought a great curse upon himself that he does not yet see or experience.

 1 John 4:5, Galatians 6:12,
I Corinthians 1:18,
Galatians 1:8

Evangelist rescues Graceless

Now let us return to your dream. What did you see or hear next?

Faithless recovered himself and said:

Faithless: I heard the instructions you gave to Graceless.

Evangelist: Do you remember what I told him?

Faithless: As best I can remember, you told Graceless the following:

> **Evangelist:** *There were three things in Mr. Worldly Wiseman's counsel that you must utterly abhor.*
>
> **1.** *He turned you out of the way.*
>
> **2.** *He labored to render the cross odious to you.*
>
> **3.** *And he put your feet in the way that leads to the administration of death.*

Evangelist scolds Graceless for seeking a false path while ignoring the true blood bought way based on the meritorious work of Christ alone

Faithless: Could you unfold those three lessons so that I might fully understand what they mean?

Evangelist looked at his brother as if throwing him a ball. Great-Heart was quick to answer the call.

Great-Heart: This is the lesson my brother was trying to teach Graceless. You will find yourself greatly improved by listening to it and taking it into your own heart.

First, you must abhor Mr. Worldly Wiseman turning Graceless out of the way; yea, and his consenting to it, because this is to reject the counsel of God for the sake of the counsel of the world.

The Lord says, strive to enter in at the strait gate, the gate to which I send you; for strait is the gate that leadeth unto life, and few there be that find it.

 Luke 13:24, Matthew 7:13-14

From this Little Sheep Gate, and from the way thereto, this wicked man has turned Graceless, bringing him almost to destruction. You must hate his turning Graceless out of the way.

Secondly, Graceless must abhor Mr. Worldly Wiseman laboring to render the Cross odious unto him; for Graceless is to prefer the Cross before the treasures of Egypt.

 Hebrews 11:25-26

Besides, the King of Glory has told all of us including you, Faithless, that He who will save his life shall lose it. And he that comes after Him, and hates not his father, and mother, and wife, and children, and brethren, and sisters, yea, and his own life also, he cannot be His disciple.

 Mark 8:38, John 12:25, Matthew 10:39, Luke 14:26

For a man such as Mr. Worldly Wiseman to labor to persuade anyone there is any other way to live except through faith in the Lord Jesus Christ, he cannot himself ever obtain eternal life and should not be leading others to meet his horrible destiny. His doctrine is to be abhorred.

Thirdly, Graceless must hate the setting of his feet in the way that leadeth to the administration of death. And you must consider to whom he sent Graceless and how unable either Mr. Legality or Civility are to deliver anyone from their burdens.

The person, Mr. Legality, to whom Mr. Worldly Wiseman sent Graceless to find ease from his burden, is the son of the bond-woman who is still in bondage along with all her children.

 Galatians 4:21-27

Mount Sinai, which Graceless feared would fall on his head and send him into everlasting doom, was testimony that Graceless had already received enough of God's truth into his heart to know that no man can ever be saved by good living or the keeping of the law. Now, if Mr. Legality and Civility are in bondage, how can anyone expect them to set anyone else free?

 John 8:36

This Mr. Legality, therefore, is not able to set Graceless or anyone else free from their burden. No man has ever gotten rid of his burden by him; no, nor ever will.

 Galatians 3:10

You cannot be justified by the works of the law, or by the deeds of the law. No one can be rid of his burden by means of keeping the law. Therefore, Mr. Worldly Wiseman is an alien and Mr. Legality is a cheat; and as for his son Civility, notwithstanding his simpering looks, he is but a hypocrite and cannot help Graceless or anyone else.

Believe me, there is nothing in all this noise that you have heard of these sottish men but what is a design to beguile and cheat Graceless out of salvation by turning him from the way in which Evangelist, my brother, had set him.

Faithless: I am grateful to you, Evangelist, for rehearsing all these lessons and to you Great-Heart for helping me understand the meaning of them as the sound of the thunder and fierceness of the lightning made it difficult for me to comprehend.

I do remember one thing most vividly.

Great-Heart: And what was that?

Faithless turned to Evangelist and asked him to recount what happened next.

Evangelist was deep in thought as he considered the strange circumstances he now found himself in.

Evangelist: I suppose, Faithless, that you are remembering that I called aloud to the heavens for confirmation of what I had said to Graceless in order that he might know the truth of it.

Faithless: Yes, after your words were spoken, fire came out of the mountain. I then saw poor Graceless fall to his knees once more in fear and trembling, looking for nothing but death to follow and cursing the moment he heeded the deadly instructions of Mr. Worldly Wiseman. And then a voice came down from the mountain.

Evangelist: Do you remember what the voice said?

Faithless: Yes, it boomed about works and law and such.

Evangelist shook his head in agreement as he quoted the very words that Graceless and Faithless had heard.

> **Evangelist**: *As many as are under the works of the law, are under the curse; for it is written, cursed is every one that continueth not in all things which are written in the book of the law to do them.*

Evangelist: Do you remember what happened next?

Faithless: Yes, Graceless looked for nothing but death and began to cry out lamentably; again, cursing the time in which he met with Mr. Worldly Wiseman and calling himself a thousand fools for hearkening to his counsel. He also was greatly ashamed to think that this gentleman's arguments, flowing only from the flesh, should have prevailed so persuasively so as to cause him to forsake the right way.

 *Proverbs 14:12*

Then there was a moment of silence as the thundering and lightning ceased.

Graceless was again lifted up. When he arose, he asked again and again if there was any hope for him. I remember the conversation between you and Graceless:

Graceless: *Can I now go back to the Small Sheep Gate?*

Will I be abandoned by the King of the Country for my error?

Can my sins that are many yet be forgiven?

Evangelist: *Your sin is very great, for you have committed two evils: you have forsaken the way that is good, to tread in forbidden paths. Yet will the man at the gate receive you, for he has good-will for men;*

 John 6:37

Take heed to not turn aside again, or else you may perish from the way, when his wrath is kindled but a little.

 Psalm 2:12

At this point, Faithless broke down in tears as he placed his head in his hands and buried his head between his knees.

Evangelist: Why are you sorrowful? Tell me, sir, what has distressed you?

Faithless: Mr. Worldly Wiseman did all he could to persuade me to return back to my home and to leave the matters that were troubling me alone. He told me that all my alarming visions would soon disappear as suddenly as they first arose. He told me my dream was a silly fantasy not fit to be told to anyone but old women and small children who were as witless and empty-headed as I was.

Evangelist: That is not surprising, is it?

After all, it is the nature of Mr. Worldly Wiseman to defeat any stirring of the Spirit that might convince a sinner to flee the wrath to come and find refuge in the King's Son alone.

 *I Thessalonians 5:19*

Faithless: Yes, this all must be true. I told you that I ignored his counsel and that is not the whole truth.

I told Mr. Worldly Wiseman I would heed his advice and return to my home and lay the matter to rest. But as I walked back to the City of Destruction I began to consider Graceless and what almost became of him when he heeded the advice of Mr. Worldly Wiseman.

I turned around and looked, like a coward, to make sure that Mr. Worldly Wiseman was well out of sight and then like a sneak thief I made my way here to your door.

Evangelist rose and went over to where Faithless was sitting and put his hand on his shoulder.

Evangelist: Mr. Worldly Wiseman is the son of Fear and his mother is from the famous family that bears the name of Shame. It is his character and his stock and trade to discourage and defeat those that would be pilgrims on the King's Highway.

It is true that you lacked courage, as you also lack understanding. I am not suggesting that you are without offense against the King, but only that you need to keep reading His Word and asking Him to reveal Himself to you. It is only then that courage and understanding will follow, as certain as day follows night.

And besides, it took courage to own up to your faltering moments. You have repented of it without any assistance from me, as is clearly evidenced by the fact that you are here. And my dear friend, this is exactly where you are supposed to be at this moment in your own pilgrimage.

Faithless: Am I on a pilgrimage?

Great-Heart and Evangelist laughed a little as they sensed it was time for rest and refreshment.

Faithless: Shall I tell you the rest of the dream?

Great-Heart: I cannot wait to hear the rest of your dream.

Just then both Constance and Fidelity came into the room, curtsied as they announced that breakfast was now being served.

CHAPTER 6
GRACELESS ENTERS IN THROUGH THE NARROW GATE

As the last crumbs were rescued from the wash basin, the conversation once again turned to the dream.

But, it was not before everyone complimented Fidelity and Constance for a delicious meal.

Great-Heart launched the conversation with a question addressed to Faithless.

Great-Heart: Did Grace-less address himself to go back to the path that leads to the Small Sheep Gate?

Evangelist comforts Graceless and sends him back to the path that leads to the Narrow Gate, which is Christ alone

Faithless: Oh yes, I witnessed your brother kiss him on the forehead, give him a manly embrace and wish him God's speed.

Graceless went from that place like a man fleeing a burning barn. He did not speak to anyone on the way and if someone asked him a question, he ignored them.

He went like one that was both deaf and dumb, all the while treading on forbidden ground. He acted like he could by no means think himself safe until he was back, once again, on the path that he had left to follow Mr. Worldly Wiseman's counsel. So, in a short amount of time, Graceless got up to the Small Gate.

Evangelist: Did you see the gate?

 Proverbs 4:25-27

Faithless: Yes, in my dream I saw the gate that appeared to be more like a door, and over the door there was a sign.

Great-Heart: What did the sign say?

Faithless: It said "Knock, and it shall be opened unto you."

 Matthew 7:7

Graceless knocks on the door to the Narrow Way

Evangelist: Did Graceless heed the invitation to knock?

Faithless: Oh yes, he knocked and knocked and when the door was not opened immediately, he began to beg and plead for it to be opened.

Evangelist: Do you remember what he said?

Faithless: In my dream I heard Graceless say this.

Graceless: *May I now enter here?*

Will you open the door to a sorry sinner?

Graceless pleads to enter through the door

I am but an undeserving rebel.

If you open I shall not fail to sing the Praises of the King and His Son with lasting praise on high!

Faithless: At last there came a man well on in years to the gate. His name was Goodwill.

Goodwill: *Who is it that is asking to enter?*

Where did you come from and what would you have me do?

Graceless: *I am a poor burdened sinner.*

I come from the City of Destruction but I am going to Mount Zion that so I may be delivered from the wrath to come. I would therefore, sir, since I am informed that by this gate is the way thither, know if you are willing to let me in?

Goodwill invites Graceless to enter the Narrow Way

Goodwill: *I am willing with all my heart.*

And with that Goodwill opened the gate.

Faithless: Just as Graceless was stepping in, Goodwill gave him a pull that put Graceless off his feet. Goodwill then slammed the door shut and gently raised up poor Graceless who was miffed by the sudden circumstances that left him on the floor on the other side of the Small Sheep Gate.

Satan makes one final attempt to prevent Graceless from coming to Christ

Graceless: *Why did you pull me in with such force, I would have most willingly entered without prodding?*

Faithless: At that Goodwill laughed leaving Graceless wondering what was so funny and what had just happened.
Goodwill then lifted Graceless up from off the floor and bade him look out the window and to the left.

Great-Heart: What did Graceless see?

Faithless: A little distance from this gate there is erected a strong castle, of which Beelzebub is the captain. From there both he and they that are with him shoot arrows at those who come up to the Small Sheep Gate, if haply they might kill or mortally wound a poor pilgrim before he can enter in.

 Ephesians 6:16, Mark 4:15

Great-Heart: And then what did Graceless say?

Faithless: As best I can remember in my dream this is what happened:

Graceless: *I rejoice and tremble that you have rescued me from the darts and arrows of the enemy.*

Goodwill: *Tell me, my friend, who it was that directed you to the King's Door to the Celestial City?*

Graceless: *I was enlivened to the prospect of coming to this spot by the Great Book I carry in my bosom. After reading the book, the King of the country I seek to enter sent Evangelist to help me understand the promises our great King has made to poor sinners like myself.*

Evangelist pointed me to this place and told me to come and knock and the door would be opened and I would be told what to do next. So, here I am as you can see, full of joy unspeakable for the way of deliverance that has been opened up to me.

Goodwill: *An open door is set before you, and no man can shut it.*

Graceless: *Now I begin to reap the benefits of my hazards.*

Goodwill: *But how is it that you came alone?*

Graceless: *Because none of my neighbors saw their danger as I saw mine.*

Goodwill: *Did any of them know of your coming?*

Graceless: *Yes, my wife and children saw me at the first and called after me to turn again. Also, some of my neighbors stood crying, calling after me to return, but I put my fingers in my ears and so came on my way.*

Goodwill: *But did none of them follow you, to persuade you to go back?*

Graceless: *Yes, both Obstinate and Pliable.When they saw they could not prevail, Obstinate went railing back but Pliable came with me a little way.*

Goodwill: *But why did he not come through?*

Graceless: *We both indeed came together until we stumbled into the Swamp of Despair, into the which we also suddenly fell. And then my neighbor, Pliable, was discouraged and would not venture farther. Wherefore, getting out again on the side next to his own house, he told me I should possess the brave country by myself. So, he went his way, and I went mine.*

 Mark 4:16-17

Pliable went after Obstinate, and I came to this gate.

Goodwill: *Alas, poor man; is the celestial glory of so little esteem with them that he counted it not worth running the hazard of a few difficulties to obtain it?*

 Luke 14:28

Graceless: *Truly, I have said the truth of Pliable; and I should also say the truth of myself. I am no better than him. It is true, he went back to his own house, but I also turned aside to go in the way of death, being persuaded thereto by the carnal arguments of one Mr. Worldly Wiseman.*

Goodwill: *Oh, did he light upon you?*

I am very familiar with his wicked counsel and venture to say that he would have had you seek for ease at the hands of Mr. Legality!

They are both of them cheats.

But did you take his counsel?

Graceless: *Yes, as far as I dared. I went to find out Mr. Legality, until I feared that the mountain that stands by his house would have fallen upon my head; and there I was forced to stop.*

Goodwill: *That mountain has been the death of many and will be the death of many more. It is well you escaped it or you would have been dashed to pieces.*

Graceless: *What you say sir is true; I do not know what would have become of me there had not Evangelist rescued me as I was paralyzed in the middle of my trial. It was God's mercy that he came to me again because if he had not, I would never have found my way to this place.*

But now I am here, such a one as I am, more fit indeed for death by that mountain, than to be standing here talking with my Lord. And let me say with all sincerity what a mighty favor it is, of no small consequence, that I am admitted entrance here!

 Ephesians 2:8-9

Goodwill: *We have no objections against anyone, notwith-standing all they have done before they come here to the Gate that leads to the Celestial City; it does not matter how notorious a former rebel was, because none who enter here are ever cast out.*

 John 6:37

And therefore, good Christian, come with me and let us talk together as we walk the King's path a little way, and I will teach you about the way you must go.

Faithless: I then saw in my dream Goodwill addressed Graceless with a new name, calling him *Christian*.

Evangelist: And how did my new brother respond to that fair greeting?

Faithless paused for a minute considering how quickly Graceless had been given a new name and how news of it had so cheered the heart of Evangelist that he would call him his brother.

Faithless: Graceless was somewhat taken back at first because he thought perhaps Goodwill, by virtue of his great age, had forgotten his name.

Evangelist: I suppose that Goodwill, having been employed in the business of welcoming poor sinners into the Strait Way that opens up the path to Eternal life for over sixteen hundred years, was prepared to give Christian an answer.

Faithless: Yes, indeed he was. Goodwill told Christian that all those who enter in through the Small Sheep Gate are by virtue of the gracious sacrifice of the King's only begotten Son now adopted by the King and are from that day forth members of HIS family.

He further told him that his new name, Christian, was given in order to identify him with the Appointed One that God the Father sent from Heaven to make the Strait Way he was now standing on; a way prepared for those who may travel it with the assurance that despite all the trials ahead, they would be welcomed into the Celestial City.

In my dream I heard Christian ask Goodwill a question that I do not fully understand.

Evangelist: Please Faithless, ask the question.

Faithless paused for a minute to collect his thoughts in order to express his question in a way that was designed to search out the answer without too much confusion.

Faithless: How can such a certain assurance be given to Christian since the Strait Way is beset by so many dangers, trials and tribulations? It seems to me that by all reasonable calculations, traveling this path would certainly result in the destruction and desertion of some who set upon it.

Evangelist: I understand your question, and by all the reasoning of man to venture forth on such a perilous adventure would certainly seem reckless with no guarantee of success.

Evangelist paused for a moment searching for an illustration of the truth he wanted Faithless to apprehend. After a moment of contemplation Evangelist continued.

Evangelist: Faithless, may I ask you a question?

Faithless: Certainly.

Evangelist: Would you calculate by human wisdom—that is to say the common wisdom of this world—the following question? If ten men are cast overboard into a raging sea at midnight, what are the chances of even one surviving?

Faithless: It is not uncommon to hear of such miracles and certainly if one survived it would be considered good fortune but not something unreasonable.

Evangelist: So, we might call one in ten surviving the ordeal of being cast overboard in a howling sea a good result but nothing too out of the ordinary?

Faithless: Yes, I suppose that is a fair account.

Evangelist: But if all ten survived how would it be seen and understood?

Faithless: I suppose It would be considered a most fortunate and very unusual circumstance!

Evangelist: And what if instead of ten men a thousand who could not swim were thrown into the tempest tossed sea?

How many do you suppose would perish and how many might be saved?

Faithless thought about it and then finally answered.

Faithless: It would be a miracle if even one of them survived.

Evangelist: Now, if you can, imagine ten thousand men, women and small children cast into a raging, frigid sea with no visible means to give them any hope of survival. And there is nothing to hang on to in order to keep afloat.To reduce the odds of success even more, let us add that none of them know how to swim, and they are miles away from shore. How many would survive?

Faithless: I fear they would all be lost, every last one of them.

Evangelist: So, what if the frigid water, the inability to swim, nothing visible to keep them afloat, the crashing waves, the dangerous sea creatures and all the demonic forces of Hell determined to kill all these castaways failed? And what if when the sea calmed it was clear that all of them were safely on solid ground without even one soul lost at sea.

Faithless was silent as he considered the truth that Evangelist was trying to demonstrate. There was no reason for Faithless to answer since obviously no amount of human reasoning could account for such a miracle.

Evangelist: The trials and tribulations that are likely to befall all those who enter the path that leads to the Celestial City are too many and too dangerous to calculate. By all human reasoning only one in a thousand, ten thousand, nay, ten thousands, who began the journey would haveany chance of safely arriving at the gates of the Celestial City.

It would be in the words of Obstinate, a fool's adventure that is destined to end badly. There are just too many bad things that can and will happen to make any human guarantee of success a fool's pipe dream.

Remember the words of Pliable, "If the journey begins with such trials such as the Swamp of Despair, what will the end be like?"

The answer is *worse and worse!*

It would be a fruitless and terrifying adventure that was not worth the risk by all human calculations. Better to stay in the City of Destruction, and reap the rewards of this life than to set off on such a perilous journey that offers by human reckoning such a slim chance of success.

Faithless was speechless and silent, waiting for Evangelist to give the solution to a human calculation that seemed bleak and hopeless.

Evangelist: Now let's consider all those who come in through the Door, which is the King's Son. That is, consider all those who put their faith and trust in Him alone, and rely on Him alone to pay the sin debt and who will be presented faultless before the King of Heaven.

 John 10:1

How is this possible?

The answer is that all such redeemed sinners are sealed eternally with a promise that cannot be broken. This promise is given to all those who enter through the Narrow Gate. It is a promise that is unconditional and does not depend upon the Pilgrim but only upon the King of the Celestial City, His Spirit and His Son.

 Romans 8:38-39, Ephesians 1:13

Faithless: The promise, then, is that the way to the Celestial City will be safe and secure and given at the end of their journey, eternal life.

Evangelist: No, indeed not.

Faithless cocked his head and asked Evangelist to repeat the answer, fearing he had not heard it correctly. Evangelist, sensing his muddle, gave Faithless a few moments to consider the apparent contradiction. Finally Evangelist looked Faithless in the eyes and gently unfolded the matter that was causing him such consternation.

Evangelist: The great promise is that all who enter the path through the Small Sheep Gate, which is a picture of the King's Son, Jesus the

Christ, have already been granted eternal life.

 Ephesians 2:10

They do not gain eternal life by virtue of their pilgrimage, although the rewards awaiting Christian and all true pilgrims who travel the path in a manner prescribed in the Great Book will receive a reward that is well worth whatever small sacrifice must be borne in the short pilgrimage that lies before them.

Faithless pondered the answer and it was clear he was still confused.

Evangelist: Graceless did nothing to deserve the grace and mercy that was granted to him as is evidenced by his new name, Christian. It was a free gift given by God the Father to all those who have trusted in the finished work of the cross and blood sacrifice of His only begotten Son, accomplished on Mt. Zion over 1600 years ago.

 Ephesians 2:8-9

Faithless: So, all who enter in through the Small Sheep Gate will at the end of their successful journey be given Eternal Life?

Evangelist: Certainly NOT!

Faithless was stunned by the answer and could no longer make any sense out of what he thought he had just heard Evangelist say just moments ago.

Evangelist waited for the contradiction to settle firmly in the befuddled mind of Faithless. He knew from experience that misunderstanding this simple

Goodwill instructs Graceless, now called Christian, to follow the straight and Narrow Way

truth was the shipwreck of many a pilgrim who entered the path thinking they would gain entry to the Celestial City by their own merits, holiness, obedience, faithfulness and righteousness.

Faithless turned this all around in his mind. Evangelist could see written on the face of Faithless all the signs of confusion and bewilderment.

Finally, after what seemed like an hour, Evangelist took hold of Faithless by both hands and asked him to look straight into his piercing blue eyes.

Evangelist: Faithless, my dear friend, all who enter in by way of the Door, that is to say Christ, have been given, the moment they first set one foot on the path that leads to the Celestial City, ETERNAL LIFE!

 John 10:7, John 10:10

It is not waiting for them at the end of the journey as if to be given only to those who have performed well without failing or faltering along the way.

My new brother, Christian, who was formally Graceless, the son of Fit-For-Wrath, has been granted Eternal Life. It cannot be lost, stolen, or taken away by any force on earth or in the heaven above, neither by angels or demons, life or death, faithlessness or fear, or any other thing.

 Romans 8:38-39

It is guaranteed by the Great King of the Celestial City, God the Father Himself, Who can neither lie or ever be defeated in the administration of His sovereign will and purpose. In other words, the ONE who makes the promise would deny His own nature if the promise was ever broken. Besides He and He alone has the power to warrant that the promise be kept and there is no one in heaven or earth that can contest His bountiful, gracious and certain promise.

 Isaiah 46:10

Faithless was speechless as he considered the words of Evangelist.

Evangelist: I want you to ponder what I have told you, Faithless. Now please continue to tell us what happened next in your dream.

Faithless, a little shaken and with a voice that revealed a small quiver, continued to unfold his dream as he recalled it.

Faithless: Goodwill produced a parchment and pointed to the name, Graceless, that had been crossed out and replaced with the name, Fit-For-Glory.

I heard Goodwill say this:

Goodwill: *So, you are now Christian Fit-For-Glory!*

Evangelist: And how did Christian respond to this news?

Faithless: Christian made a puddle in the path as his tears streamed down his face. I saw in my dream that Goodwill comforted and encouraged Christian with words I could not hear as he embraced Christian, who was joyfully sobbing, for the space of what seemed half an hour.

Then finally Goodwill took him by the hand and led him down the path a little way and stopped. In my dream I heard Goodwill say this:

Goodwill: *Christian, now look down the narrow way and tell me what you see.*

Faithless: Christian's eyes were still blurry with tears but he finally did clear the mist from his vision and reported what he saw.

Christian: *I see the Patriarchs and the Prophets. I see Christ and His apostles.*

Goodwill: *Now tell me what else you see.*

Christian: *I see that the Way is both Straight and Narrow.*

Goodwill: *Yes, and that is the way you must go!*

Christian: *Are there no turnings or windings by which a stranger may lose his way?*

Goodwill: *Yes, there are many bypaths and highways, large and small, that come across the King's Highway, and they are always crooked and wide. But you, Christian, can distinguish the right from the wrong: the right way is always the straight and narrow way.*

 *Matthew 7:14*

Faithless: In my dream I heard Christian ask Goodwill if he could not help him off with his burden that was upon his back. For as yet he had not gotten rid of it; nor could he get it off without help. I heard Goodwill tell him this:

Goodwill: *As to your burden, be content to bear it until you come to the place of deliverance, for there it will fall from your back of itself.*

Faithless paused and then asked Evangelist a question.

Faithless: Sir, I thought that Graceless, once safely inside the path that leads to the Celestial City, and having entered the Small Sheep Gate would have immediately been relieved of the burden on his back?

Evangelist: Do you remember what the burden is?

Faithless thought for a moment and then reported.

Faithless: I remember you said it was the sense of his own sin.

Evangelist: That is right, Faithless. I am glad you remembered. Let me see if I can explain it in a simple way that will give you some comfort.

Graceless has entered in at the Way that leads to life, and he has entered in through the Door that is Christ Himself. He is now a Christian who is in Christ, his sins have ALL been forgiven.

Faithless interrupted.

Faithless: And yet he still has his burden?

Evangelist: He still retains a sense of his own sin and unworthiness. Christian has had his sins all forgiven based on the finished work of Jesus Christ who has paid his debt of sin on the cross in full. He is no longer a debtor to sin. He has been eternally and forever cleansed of all unrighteousness and been given a righteousness that is not his own in exchange for his non-meritorious faith in the finished and complete work of the King's Son on the Cross.

Faithless: What is non-meritorious faith?

 John 17:1-3

Evangelist: It is faith that is not a work. No works except the work of the King's only begotten Son are accepted in the courtroom of Heaven. None of your own work, now or in the future, can merit the forgiveness of God.

 Ephesians 2:8-9, John 6:28-29

Faithless: What about good men who are righteous?

Evangelist: It is true that we can observe good men who have a righteousness of their own, but it is a relative righteousness that does not meet God's standards of perfect righteousness.

Faithless: So, if you had perfect righteousness God would not judge you?

Evangelist: That's right, if you have never ever committed a sin, in thought or in deed, then your righteousness is acceptable to God. But even one sin, no matter how small we may think it is, disqualifies us and marks us as sinners. No one except the Son of God has lived a sinless—completely sinless—righteous life in both thought and deed.

 James 2:10, 1 John 1:8

We, on the other hand, are ALL sinners fit for wrath.

 Romans 3:23

Do you understand?

Faithless: I think so, but I am still not sure why Christian still carries the burden of sin if his sins have been forgiven and are no longer counted against him.

At this point Great-Heart intervened.

Great Heart: Faithless, let me see if I can answer your question.

Almost twenty years ago I had a neighbor who was a **Killbuck** * and ill-tempered to boot. He was as unkind as anyone I ever knew. He was brutish to his wife and children and cruel to his poor dog who was always addressed in a surly manner as "bad dog" and other pejoratives that should not be uttered in good company.

There was hardly a day that passed that I did not hear the whimpering and yelps from the poor beast. For three long years we heard the complaints and abuse heaped upon the poor dumb animal that had started from the time he was just a pup up until he was three years old.

Faithless: What happened when the dog was three years old?

Great-Heart: My neighbor owed money to many creditors and even some of his neighbors and instead of diligently working to pay them back, he disappeared in the middle of the night along

---

* **Killbuck**—A fierce looking fellow.

with his wife and three children, their horse and wagon and all he counted as valuable.

Except one valuable.

Faithless: He left the dog?

Great-Heart: He left the dog tied up to a large cobble stone with no food or water. When I finally discovered the poor animal, he was half dead from starvation and neglect.

I rescued the animal and carefully and gently nursed him back to health.

I brought the poor beast inside my home and made a place for him in front of the fireplace in winter and in the kitchen by an open window in the summer.

After a couple of months of care the dog was as healthy as could ever be expected. He was getting two meals a day and lots of love, attention and exercise as he was my constant companion whenever I ventured outside.

He was constant but he was not happy, as I will explain.

Faithless: I am not sure I understand what this has to do with Christian and his burden.

Great-Heart: Let me see if I can help you understand.

We renamed the dog *Ardent* since it was clear from the beginning that it was his nature to please us. Ardent had been unconditionally welcomed into my family. We all ignored his bad habits as we spent endless hours teaching him how to act in the home.

My wife and I allowed the dog into the house whenever he wished to venture in and that, at first, always resulted in one calamity or another. We determined we would under no circumstances ever hit Ardent, but rather hold his head firmly but gently, and speak to him like one would speak to a small child.

At first it seemed to have no effect but gradually Ardent began to pay attention because he was eager to please. If only he could understand what it was that pleased us. This was a job we took on with patience and resolve. So, as I said, we never once hit the dog with our hands or with a whip or chased him with a broom.

Ardent had a new master and mistress that loved him and would never beat or neglect him. His situation had completely changed.

And when did it change?

It changed the moment I cut Ardent loose from the rope that was half strangling him. He was from that moment on under new administration.

Just like Graceless is now Fit-For-Glory, my adopted dog, Ardent, went from beaten and neglected to become the best friend we ever had that was not a person.

Ardent was given every luxury, and a warm place to stay and con-stant care. Ardent was treated far better than any dog in the coun-try. It was not done out of obligation or because he was such a good dog, although in time he became a model dog with good manners and a wonderful temperament. But to be clear, it was in our gracious nature to love and care for this poor mistreated and abused animal. Ardent could offer nothing in return for our love and care.

Now to illustrate the connection between Ardent and Christian with his burden of sin:

For the first year after we adopted Ardent, without any reason or warrant for doing so, the dog would wince and cower when you raised your hand to him. If you were offering him a treat he would yelp, cower and retreat. If you reached your hand out to pet him gently he would run away whimpering as if he had been beaten by a hickory stick. The scars from his beating were still fresh in his mind long after they had healed up on his body.

Why do you suppose it took Ardent a year before he could finally welcome an outstretched hand offered in love and friendship?

Faithless: I think I understand. Christian has a new master that loves and cares for him and means him nothing but good, but his memories of his old master, his sense of unworthiness and his sin keep him in a bondage with a burden that was all of his own imagination since it has now been washed clean by the blood of Jesus.

Great-Heart was suddenly filled with joy and hope as he listened to Faithless unravel the mystery of the grace of God with little help from him or his brother.

Great-Heart: Christian has saving faith but it is small and needs to grow and flourish. What he has accepted as real in his mind is still working itself out in his heart.

Faithless: Is this the case with all who come into the Way through the gate?

Great-Heart: No, it is not. Some Christians lose their burden instantly as it rolls off the first steps of the path that leads through the Small Sheep Gate. Others struggle with the burden for months, and sometimes for years. And yes, there are even some who only lose their burden when they cross the river that separates us in this life from the life that is to come.

Faithless: And Ardent?

Great-Heart: After a year of patient and gentle care, Ardent began to trust us as he stopped thinking the worst whenever a hand was offered. After a couple years the dog that winced when a hand was put forth would come and find us and nuzzle and lick our hand in hopes that we would pet him or give him a treat.

Just like Ardent needed a little time, so Christian now needs a little space of time in order that his love and gratitude grow larger than his fear and tiny faith. It will happen just like God's Goodwill toward sinners predicted. In a little while the burden will fall off on its own and be seen no more.

But in the meantime, there is another lesson to be learned.

Graceless was turned out of the way by Mr. Worldly Wiseman because he had more concern for his current condition of guilt and shame than he did for his concern about his eternal condition.

There is no question that coming to Christ offers peace for the soul in this lifetime, but this lifetime is just a breath compared to the eternal state. One day Christian may see this error and be grieved by it, but for now we are happy that it drove him to the path that leads to life eternal.

 *John 10:27-30*

   Evangelist, who had been listening carefully and nodding in agreement at his big brother's illustration, finally offered a comment.

Evangelist: There is one very big difference between the bad and beaten-down dog that was adopted into the family of my brother and became Ardent the good dog, and Graceless who became a Christian.

Can you tell me what it is, Faithless?

Faithless: Ardent is a dog and Christian is a man!

Evangelist and Great-Heart both laughed and smiled at the simple, obvious answer offered by Faithless.

Great-Heart spoke up and provided the answer that Evangelist was seeking.

Great-Heart: I think what my brother is trying to say is that Ardent's circumstances changed for the better but his nature as a dog never changed. Ardent was the bad, mistreated dog that fell into good hands and became a good dog, who retained his nature as a dog.

Graceless, on the other hand, has experienced something super-natural when he put his faith and trust in the King's Son. He not only changed masters and his citizenship because he is no longer an earth dweller bound to the destiny of the City of Destruction, he himself was changed.

 II Corinthians 5:17, Romans 6:11-13

Faithless: Changed?

Great-Heart: Yes, Faithless, Christian not only had his named changed but his nature was changed because his spirit, once dead to righteousness and in bondage to sin, was quickened and made alive. This was accomplished by the supernatural power of the Holy Spirit of God who promises to indwell all those who put their faith and trust in His Son and His finished Cross-work.

 I John 4:13

This is all illustrated for us in the King's Great Book.

CHAPTER 7

CHRISTIAN AT THE HOUSE OF THE INTERPRETER

After a hearty breakfast, Great-Heart invited Faithless and Evangelist to step outside and take a short walk to visit one of his favorite places on the grounds of the King's Cottage.

As the three headed out the kitchen door, Evangelist ventured a guess as to where his brother was taking them.

Evangelist: Lookout Mountain?

Great-Heart: Yes, indeed.

Faithless stopped in his tracks.

Faithless: We are going up a mountain?

Faithless was somewhat alarmed since the only mountain he could see was a two-day's journey away.

Great-Heart and Evangelist laughed.

Evangelist: My brother named it Lookout Mountain as a wee lad when every molehill looked like a mountain.

See up ahead about a hundred yards the little hill with the Maple tree and the long hand-hewn bench?

Faithless: Oh yes, I see it now.

Evangelist: I see you have added a place to sit. Remember how mother used to chide you for coming back from your little adventures on Lookout Mountain with the bottom of your britches soaked and grass-stained?

Great-Heart: I remember it well. Mother would plant me in front of the fireplace or stove until I dried out and then she would lead me out to the back porch and take a broom to my britches to clean off all the dried mud. It was the closest thing to a whipping I ever got in those wonderful days.

Evangelist: I think I remember singing a little ditty as she walloped your hindquarters.

Great-Heart: Walloping is a little exaggeration, my dear little brother, it was only a friendly rebuke that always ended in the two of us laughing, as I recall.

Evangelist: Oh yes, I remember it well. I do not want to give Faithless the wrong opinion of our mother, who was by all accounts, a joyful, even-tempered woman full of good humor, wit and lots of fun.

Faithless listened to the brothers banter out of one ear as he listened to the wind whip up a chorus of whistling and thumps that suddenly appeared out of nowhere.

Faithless did not need to squint as he had already noticed the wooden bench silhouetted against the warm, amber rays of the rising sun.

The three arrived and all found a place to sit on the damp, oak-hewn bench that was crawling with little insects that were about their own morning duties.

The view was pleasant enough and after a few silent moments, Great-Heart stood up and opened a wooden box that was sitting next to the Maple tree. He carefully unwrapped a spyglass, held it out as if to admire it and addressed it as 'Old Faithful.'

Great-Heart handed Old Faithful to Evangelist who bowed his head and prayed silently. He then put the spyglass up to his right eye, squinted and smiled.

Evangelist: I see the glimmer and glory of it!

Evangelist handed Old Faithful back to Great-Heart who polished the lenses and bowed his head for a silent moment of prayer. He then put it up to his right eye and smiled a broad smile.

Evangelist: You can almost see the Gates of Pearl.

Great-Heart: Almost? I see them clearly as if I was standing next to them.

Evangelist: Soon!

Great-Heart: Very soon, indeed.

Faithless was intrigued as his curiosity rose.

All he could see across the valley below was a mountain, a meadow and mist, lots of mist.

Great-Heart handed the spyglass to Faithless.

Great-Heart: Look in the direction of the narrow meadow to the right of the dark mountain and tell me what you see.

Faithless dutifully did as he was told as he pressed and screwed up his face in order to see what Evangelist and Great-Heart had reported. But as hard as he tried, he could see nothing through the narrow pass but a mist and a fog.

Faithless: I cannot see anything but fog.

Evangelist: Perhaps one day soon you will.

Faithless sheepishly handed Great-Heart the spyglass.

Great-Heart: Faithless, I was hoping you could tell us the rest of your dream.

The two brothers nodded their consent and Faithless began to report his dream.

Faithless: In my dream, I saw Graceless, I mean to say Christian, dust himself off and with a face like flint, address himself to his journey.

I saw Goodwill walk with him some distance. I heard him tell Christian to continue on the way until he came to the Great House. And once there he should knock until the door was opened to him.

I heard Christian ask:

Christian: *Whose house is it?*

Goodwill: *It is the House of the Interpreter who will grant entry with joy and show you excellent things. Now I must take my leave as I have other poor sinners to attend to. I bid you God-Speed.*

I saw Goodwill grab Christian around the neck and pull him tight with a manly embrace, whispering something in his ear that I could not hear. But whatever it was, it made Christian beam as he embraced the old man, Goodwill, with tears of joy in his eyes.

Christian went on for some time until he came to the House of the Interpreter where he knocked over and over. At last, someone came to the door.

Servant of the house: *Who is there?*

Christian: *Sir, I am a Pilgrim bound for the Celestial City. I was asked by Goodwill to seek out the good man of this house and to call here for my instruction into things most profitable. I would most humbly ask if I might speak with the master of the house.*

 I Corinthians 2:14, John 16:13

Faithless: The servant who answered the door then called for the master of the house, who, after a little time, came to meet Christian.

> Interpreter: *How might I be of service to you?*

> Christian: *Sir, I am a man who has come from the City of Destruction. I am going to Mount Zion and I was told by Goodwill, who stands at the gate at the head of this way, that if I called here, you would show me excellent things that would be helpful to me on my journey.*

> Interpreter: *Come in, I will show you many things that will be profitable to you.*

Faithless: He commanded his servant to light the candle and then asked Christian to follow him.

The Interpreter led Christian into a private room and asked his servant to open a door that was located just inside. Once the door was open, Christian saw the picture of a very grave person framed and hanging on the wall. This is what he said:

> Christian: *The eyes of the man were lifted up to heaven. He had the best of books in his hand, the law of truth was written upon his lips, and the world was behind his back. He stood as if he pleaded with men. Finally, I noticed a crown of gold hung over his head.*

> *What does this mean?*

> Interpreter: *The man in the picture was one in a thousand:*

> *You noticed his eyes, they are lifted up to heaven.*

> *You noticed the book he held in his hand, it is the best of books.*

> *You noticed the law of truth written on his lips. It is to show you, Christian, that his work is to know and unfold dark things to sinners.*

You noticed him standing as if he is pleading with men; this is his vocation.

You noticed the world behind him; this man despises the practices and policies of the present world.

And finally, you noticed the crown that hangs over but not on top of his head. This is to show you, Christian, that slighting and despising the things of this present world, because you love your Master's service, will one day result in both glory and reward.

 1 Corinthians 4:15, Galatians 4:19, I John 1:7

Now, I have shown you this picture first, because the man in this picture is the only man whom the Lord of the place where you are going has authorized to be your guide. In all the difficult places you may meet in the way, take good heed to what I have shown you. Bear well in your mind what you have seen, just in case in your journey you meet with some who pretend to lead you right, but their way goes down to death.

Faithless: Then the Interpreter took Christian by the hand and led him into a very large parlor that was full of dust because it had never been swept. After Christian had reviewed the room for a little while, the Interpreter called for one of his servants to come and sweep the room.

Now, when he began to sweep, the dust began

The Interpreter teaches Christian the futility of keeping the law as compared to the efficacy of the Gospel to cleanse the heart

to fly all about filling up the room with such a cloud of dirt and dust that Christian could hardly breathe. He would have choked to death if the Interpreter had not called a damsel who was standing by with a large pitcher of water. 'Bring in the water, and sprinkle the room,' the Interpreter commanded. When this was done, the room was swept and cleansed and the smothering dust disappeared. The room then looked clean as the floor once covered with dirt and dust sparkled and shone.

Christian: *What does this mean?*

Interpreter: *This parlor is the heart of a man that was never sanctified by the sweet grace of the Gospel. The dust is his original sin and inward corruptions that have defiled the whole man. The one who began to sweep the room is the law; the damsel who brought water that was sprinkled is the Gospel.*

Now you saw that as soon as the LAW began to sweep, the dust did fly about the room. No matter how much the LAW swept, it could not clean the room. Instead of cleaning the room, which is the human heart, it almost choked you to death.

This is to show you that the law, instead of cleansing the heart (by its working) from sin, doth revive sin and give it strength and power and increase the influence of sin that causes death.

 Romans 7:9, 1 Corinthians 15:56, Romans 5:20

Christian observes the effect of the sweet unmerited Grace of the Gospel of Jesus Christ

Then you saw the damsel sprinkle the room with water, which cleansed the room and made it truly clean. This is to show you, that when the Gospel comes into your heart, it has sweet and precious influences.

Just as you saw the damsel clear the dust by sprinkling the floor with water, so is sin vanquished and subdued, and the soul made clean, through faith in the only One who could perfectly keep the law and count it as righteousness to all who receive it by faith.

 Ephesians 5:27

As a result of this supernatural cleansing, the King of Glory may now inhabit the cleansed room that is the heart of every true believer.

 John 15:3, Ephesians 5:26, Acts 15:9, Romans 16:25-26

Faithless: I also saw in my dream that the Interpreter took Christian by the hand and led him into a little room where he found two little children sitting, each one in his own chair.

The name of the eldest boy was Passion and the name of the other boy was named Patience.

Passion seemed to be very discontent, but Patience was very quiet.

Christian: *Why is Passion so discontent?*

Interpreter: *The governor of these two children would have them wait for his best things that will be arriving the beginning of the next year, but Passion wants it all now; Patience is willing to wait.*

Faithless: Then I saw in my dream that a servant entered the room and stood in front of Passion. The servant had brought with him a bag of treasures and poured it down at Passion's feet. Passion began rummaging through the treasure, rejoicing as he mocked Patience, scornfully, for not demanding his treasure now.

 Psalm 46:10, Isaiah 40:31

But after a little while, I saw all the treasure turn to trash and Passion was left in the end with nothing but rags.

Christian: *Please explain this matter more fully to me.*

Interpreter: *These two lads are figures: Passion is a figure of the men of this world, and Patience is a figure of the men of the world which is to come. As you saw, Passion wants to have it all now, this year, that is to say, in this world; so are the men of this world. They must have all their good things now. They cannot wait until the next year, that is, until the next world for their portion of good.*

The men of this world live by the proverb, 'A bird in the hand is worth two in the bush.' This proverb has more authority with them than all the divine testimonies of the abundant glories of the world to come.

But as you saw that Passion quickly wasted it all away and had, in the end, nothing but rags, so will it be with all such men at the end of this world.

Christian encouraged to patiently wait for the future promises of God

Christian: *Now I see that Patience is the wisest. And that for two reasons:*

1. *Because Patience waits for the best things.*

2. *And also because he will have the good things when Passion has nothing but rags.*

Interpreter: *Yes, what you say is true and I will add another:*

> **3.** *The glory of the next world will never wear out, but the treasure that was desired by Passion is suddenly gone.*

Passion now has no reason to laugh at Patience because he had his good things first. Patience will have the last laugh with things that last forever. Passion had his first things first but they did not last nor could they. Passion wisely chose the best things that last and will never be corrupted or fade away.

The first must give place to the last because the last must prevail as it is eternal. The last gives place to nothing, for there is nothing that comes after it.

As it was said of Dives, the rich man, in your lifetime you received your good things, and likewise Lazarus evil things; but now he is comforted, and you are tormented.

 Luke 16:25

Christian: *Then I perceive it is best not to covet the things that are now, but to wait for things to come.*

Interpreter: *You speak the truth: for the things that are seen are temporal, but the things that are not seen are eternal.*

 2 Corinthians 4:18

But this is not an easy thing to do as our fleshly appetites are such near neighbors one to another; and again, because things to come and our carnal sense of what is now before our eyes and senses are strangers one to another.

Faithless: Then I saw in my dream that the Interpreter took Christian by the hand and led him into a place where there was a great fireplace. Next to the fireplace stood a man with a great barrel filled with water and a pitcher in his hand. Christian saw the man dip his pitcher into the water and then throw the water onto the fire in order to quench it, but it did not extinguish the flame.

Christian learns how the Grace of God is maintained in the soul despite all the attempts of the enemy to extinguish it

Contrariwise, the more water the man heaped upon the flame, the brighter and hotter the fire became.

 2 Corinthians 12:9

Christian: *What means this?*

Interpreter: *This fire is the work of grace that is wrought in the heart of every true believer. The one who i s pouring the water upon it, to extinguish and put it out, is the devil: but as you can see the fire is burning higher and hotter.*

Christian: *How is this possible?*

Interpreter: *Let me show you.*

Faithless: Then I saw Interpreter take Christian behind the wall where the fireplace stood.

Interpreter: *So you see the reason?*

Christian: *I see a strong and able man with a vessel in his hand secretly pouring the contents into the fire.*

What is in the vessel?

Interpreter: *The vessel is filled with oil that never runs out.*

Christian: *What does this mean?*

Interpreter: *This is a picture of Christ, Who continually, with the oil of His grace, maintains the work already begun in the heart. By this means the plans of the devil are defeated and the souls of the Saints are graciously preserved.*

Christian: *It fills me with joy to know that despite all the evil plans and schemes the devil could employ to try and defeat me, because I have put my trust in Christ, they will all fail.*

 Ephesians 6:16

Christ himself maintains the work He has begun in the hearts of those who trust Him

Interpreter: *That is a wonderful promise.What else have you learned?*

Christian: *I see in this scene that God is ABLE to keep us despite all the schemes of His enemies and our own weakness and frailty.*

 John 10:29, Jude 1:24-25

Interpreter: *Yes, that is true and I will add one more thing. He is not only able to keep His children from falling, but is **willing** to do so and confirms it with an unbreakable promise that He will complete that work without any other conditions.*

Christian: *With no conditions?*

Interpreter: *If you have entered into the Straight Narrow Gate, which is a picture of Christ, and put your faith in Him alone, both believing in your heart and confessing with your mouth that He is your God and Savior, then there are no other conditions that can be added, and no condemnation can ever be brought against you.*

Faithless: The next thing I saw in my dream is that Interpreter took Christian by the hand and led him into a pleasant place where a stately palace was built. Beautiful to behold, the sight of it greatly delighted Christian. He also saw upon the top wall of the palace, people, all clothed in gold, who were walking.

Christian stopped, fixated as he looked at the palace with the saints clothed in gold and glory all about. He nodded his head signifying that he understood that he was casting his eyes upon the Celestial City.

Christian: *Thank you for showing me all these scenes meant to inform and comfort me on my pilgrimage. I think it is time for me to continue my journey.*

Interpreter: *Please stay a little longer, dear Christian, as I have more things to show you that will improve your pilgrimage.*

Faithless: Then Interpreter took him and led him up towards the door of the palace. Behold, at the door stood a great company of men who desired to go into the palace but were afraid to enter.

There was a man seated a little distance away from the door, at a small table, with a book and an inkhorn. Christian watched the man write down the names of those who would enter the palace. Christian also saw that in the doorway stood many men in armor guarding the door, determined not to let anyone enter in. And if anyone tried, they were resolved to do as much damage and inflict as much pain as they could.

Christian was somewhat amazed. At last, when it looked like every man was staying as far away from the armed guards as they could,

Christian saw a very stout man come up to the man that sat at the desk. He said, "Set down my name, sir," and when he had done so he saw the man draw his sword, put a helmet on his head, and rush towards the door upon the armed men who laid upon him with deadly force. The man, not at all discouraged, fell to cutting and hacking most fiercely. So, after he had received and given many wounds to those who attempted to keep him out, he cut his way through them all and pressed forward into the palace.

Strive to enter the Straight Gate

Matthew 11:12, Acts 14:22

Then I heard a kind and pleasant voice say:

"Come in, come in.
Eternal glory thou shalt win."

So, he went in and was clothed with glorious garments.

Christian: *I think I know what this means.*

Faithless: Then Interpreter took Christian by the hand again and led him into a very dark room where there sat a man in an iron cage.

Faithless: Now the man seemed very sad; he sat with his eyes looking down to the ground, his hands folded together, and he sighed as if his heart was broken.

Christian ponders the dreadful plight of the Man in the Iron Cage

Christian: *What does this mean?*

Interpreter: *Ask the man what it means.*

Christian: *Who are you?*

The Man: *I am not what I once was.*

Christian: *What were you once?*

The Man: *I was once a fair and flourishing professor, both in mine own eyes and also in the eyes of others. I was once, as I thought, headed for the Celestial City and even had joy at the thought that I should arrive there one day.*

 13 *Luke 8:13*

Christian: *Well, what are you now?*

The Man: *I am now a man of despair and am shut up in it, as in this iron cage. And I cannot get out!*

Christian: *But how did you come to be in this condition?*

The Man: *I stopped being watchful and sober and I laid the reins upon the neck of my lusts. I sinned against the light*

The Man in the Iron Cage no longer believes the promises of God and is filled with regret and despair

of the Word and the goodness of God; I have grieved the Spirit, and He is gone; I tempted the devil, and he is come to me; I have provoked God to anger, and He has left me. I have so hardened my heart, that I cannot repent.

 ***Romans 1:18***

Christian turned to Interpreter:

Christian: *Is there no hope for such a man as this?*

Interpreter: *Ask him.*

Christian: *Is there no hope for you? Must you stay **Carked*** in this iron cage of despair?*

The Man: *I have no hope, none at all.*

Christian: *Why? The Son of the Blessed One is very pitiful.*

The Man: *I have crucified Him to myself afresh. I have despised His person andI have despised His righteousness; I have counted His blood an unholy thing; I have done all this despite the spirit of grace. I have shut myself out of all the promises and there now remains to me nothing but threatenings, dreadful threatenings, faithful threatenings of certain judgment and fiery indignation which shall devour me as an adversary.*

 Hebrews 6:6, Luke 19:14, Hebrews 10:29

Christian: *How did you bring yourself into this condition?*

The Man: *I ran after the lusts, pleasures, and profits of this world; I was enticed by the promised enjoyment that all these worldly delights offer. Now every one of those delights pierces me and gnaw at me like a burning worm.*

---

* Carked—Fretfully anxious.

Christian: *But can't you now repent and turn away from all these worldly enticements?*

The Man: *God has denied me repentance. His word gives me no encouragement to believe. The Lord Himself has shut me up in this iron cage, nor can all the men in the world let me out. Oh, eternity! eternity! How shall I grapple with the misery that I must meet with in eternity?*

Then Interpreter turned to Christian:

Interpreter: *Let this man's misery be remembered by you as a caution.*

Christian: *Well, this is fearful! God help me to watch and to be sober, and to pray that I may shun the cause of this man's misery. Sir, is it not time for me to go on my way now?*

Interpreter: *Tarry until I shall show you one more thing and then you may go on your way.*

Faithless: So, he took Christian by the hand again and led him into a chamber where there was a man rising out of bed. As the man put on his clothes, he shook and trembled.
Christian: *Why doth this man tremble?*

Faithless: Interpreter then asked the man to tell Christian the reason for his fear and trembling.

The Dreamer: *This night, as I was in my sleep, I dreamed, and behold the heavens grew exceeding black; also, in my dream, there was thundering and lightning that caused me to fear and tremble.*

So, I looked up in my dream and saw the clouds form at an unusual rate. Then I heard a great sound of a trumpet and saw a man sitting upon a cloud, attended with thousands of heavenly hosts. They were all clothed in flaming fire and the heavens resembled a burning flame.

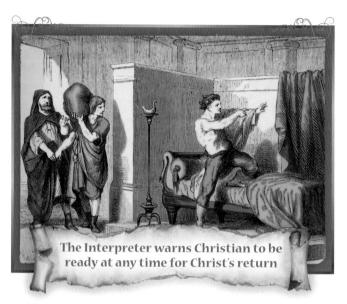

The Interpreter warns Christian to be ready at any time for Christ's return

Then I heard a voice saying, 'arise, ye dead, and come to judgment.' And with that the rocks split, the graves opened, and the dead who were therein came forth. Some of them were exceeding glad and looked upward and some sought to hide under the mountains.

Then I saw the man who sat upon the cloud open the book as He commanded the world to draw near.

Then I saw a fierce flame that came forth to separate the man in the cloud from the world He had come to judge.

 1 Corinthians 15, Jude 1:14, John 5: 28-29, 2 Thessalonians 1:8-10, Revelation 20:11-14, Isaiah 26:21, Micah 7:16-17, Psalms 5:4, 50:1-3, Malachi 3:2-3, Daniel 7:9-10

I heard it proclaimed to all in attendance, "Gather together the tares, the chaff, and stubble, and cast them into the burning lake."

 Matthew 3:12, 18:30, 24:30, Malachi 4:1

And with that the bottomless pit opened, just where I stood; out of the mouth of it came smoke, and coals of fire, along with hideous noises.

The man on the clouds said, "Gather my wheat into the garner."

 18 *Luke 3:17*

And with that, I saw many who were caught up and carried away into the clouds, but I was left behind.

 19 *1 Thessalonians 4:16-17*

I also sought to hide, but I could not, for the man who sat upon the cloud kept His eye on me; my sins also came into my mind, and my conscience did accuse me on every side.

 20 *Romans 2:14-15, II Corinthians 3:10*

It was just then that I awakened from my sleep.

Christian: *But what was it that made you so afraid of this sight?*

The Dreamer: *Why, I thought that the day of judgment was come and that I was not ready for it. But what frightened me most was that the angels gathered up several and left me behind. And, the pit of Hell opened her mouth right where I stood. My conscience also accused me. I thought the Judge had His eye upon me and His countenance was most frightful.*

Interpreter: *Christian, have you considered all these things?*

Christian: *Yes, and they put me in hope and fear.*

Interpreter: *Well then, keep all these things in your mind, as a goad in your sides, to prick you forward in the way you must go.*

Faithless: Then I saw Christian begin to gird up his loins and to address himself to his journey.

Interpreter: *The Comforter be always with you, good Christian, to guide you in the way that leads to the city.*

Christian: *Here the Interpreter has shown me things rare and profitable; things pleasant and dreadful, things to make me stable in what I have begun to take in hand. I am grateful that you have shown me all these things. I have been both encouraged and warned and now I cannot leave without saying, thank you, O good Interpreter, I will not forget what you have shown me.*

The Interpreter directs Christian

CHAPTER 8

The Mystery of the Man in the Iron Cage

Great-Heart and Evangelist listened in silence as Faithless rehearsed all the things that Christian learned and observed at the House of the Interpreter. The things he was recounting were holy things that pertained to the Holy Spirit of God—the very Spirit that now indwells Christian.

Great-Heart: Is there anything that you witnessed at the House of Interpreter that troubled you, something you did not understand?

Faithless: I wouldn't be honest if I said that I fully understood all of it, except in some small way I did grasp the general meaning.

But, there is one vision in the dream that confuses me.

Great-Heart: What part of the dream has you bewildered?

Faithless: The Man in the Iron Cage.

Evangelist: What in particular troubles you?

Faithless: The Man was not locked in the Iron Cage and he could have escaped at any time and yet he would not even so much as push the door open in order to be free.

This puzzles me greatly.

Great-Heart: Do you know what hidden force kept The Man inside the Iron Cage even though he was not shackled and the door to the cage was not locked?

 Romans 5:6

Faithless: The Man himself said that the Lord had locked him in that cage!

Great-Heart: Yes, that is what he said.

Faithless: Is it true that the King or His Son put The Man in the Iron Cage?

Great-Heart: What do you think?

Faithless: It does not seem to me that the King or His Son would take any pleasure in torturing the poor man and so I must answer no.

Great-Heart: You have answered well.

 John 3:16-17

Faithless: So, if neither the King nor His beloved Son imprisoned him, then what keeps him locked up and in such a terrible condition?

Great-Heart: I have one more question for you, Faithless, before I answer.

Do you think The Man entered the path through the Small Sheep Gate?

Faithless: Is there any other way he might have found himself on the path, professing himself to be a true pilgrim as he says?

Great-Heart: There are scores of ways in which The Man could have entered the path without entering in through the Small Sheep Gate.

Faithless: Do tell.

Great-Heart: There are a hundred bypaths and highways that intersect the Strait Way and there are many who come to be on the True Way without ever entering in through the Only Way that promises them safety and security.

Some travel on the Way for a while and then venture off onto a bypath and are never seen again.

Some meet true Pilgrims on the King's Highway and are persuaded to repent and turn back so they might enter in through the One Way that all who hope to be received into the Celestial City must enter.

And some, sadly, finish their journey having never entered in through the Only Way provided by the King of the True Way. They expect to find themselves welcomed into the Celestial City only to be denied entrance and cast away. Instead of the Celestial City, they find them in another place, a place that burns with fire day and night, a place where all hope is gone for eternity. A place of everlasting torment!

Faithless shuttered at the news of this.

Great-Heart continued.

Great-Heart: The first clue as to the nature of The Man is the name of The Man in the Iron Cage.

The Man in the Iron Cage bears the name MAN. He is the son of the first Adam by birth and practice, as he himself has admitted. His name, MAN, and his nature agree with each other. In a word, he has entered the path through another way and all other ways lead to death. His nature has not been supernaturally changed, he remains under the curse of the first Man, Adam.

The second thing you must notice about The Man in the Iron Cage is how he slanders the King.

Faithless: How so?

Great-Heart: Did he not say there was No Hope?

Did he not confess there were No Promises for such a person as himself?

Did he not say God had denied him Repentance?

Did he not say he could not be delivered from his lust and the seeking of the pleasures and profits of this world?

And who did he blame for this terrible condition?

 James 1:13-14

Faithless: Yes, I see. In my dream, I heard The Man in the Iron Cage proclaim all these things and many more things that seemed grievous to me. He said he could not alter his condition in any way because God had forbidden it.

Great-Heart reached into his coat and pulled out the King's Great Book. Opening the book, he began to read all the promises that God had made to sinners who had no strength and no hope of their own. After reading a dozen or so passages, he turned to Faithless and spoke.

Great-Heart: The thing you must know about The Man in the Iron Cage is that he is repeating the lies of the Evil Slanderer, Satan, who comes only to steal, kill and destroy.

The Man says there is no hope for men such as himself.

God's Word says there is.

 Romans 7:24-25

The Man says his sins are greater than God's Grace.

God says that His Grace is greater than all our sins.

 Romans 5:20

The Man says the good promises of God offered freely to sinners do not include him.

God says that anyone who puts their trust in the finished work of the Cross may come to Him with true faith and find forgiveness and eternal life.

Finally, Faithless, there are three things I want you to notice about The Man in the Iron Cage.

1. He is not willing to leave off with his lusts and worldly pleasures and blames it on the LORD by saying that God has taken away his ability to repent.

   The truth is that he will not repent because he does not have saving faith and never did. He only had a profession of faith but never had his heart changed because he did not enter in through the Way and the Life.

2. He uses the Word of God in a way that is deceitful as he picks and chooses verses to bolster his bad opinion, knowing full well that it is his own opinion that he is elevating, not the whole counsel of the Word of God.

3. He hates God and slanders the Lord's sure and fast promises.

So, I will inquire again. Do you know what hidden malevolent force kept The Man inside the Iron Cage even though he was not shackled and the door to the cage was not locked?

Faithless: I am certain it was not the LORD!

But I do not know what unseen force had such power to keep The Man in the Iron Cage.

Evangelist, who had been carefully listening to the conversation between Faithless and Great-Heart finally spoke up.

Evangelist: Shall I tell him?

Great Heart: Yes, brother, by all means!

Evangelist: The answer to what invisible force holds The Man in the Iron Cage can be summed up in one word.

Faithless: And what word is that?

Evangelist: UNBELIEF!

 Mark 9:23

Faithless pondered the answer as Great-Heart wrapped up the spyglass and carefully put it back in the wooden box that lay next to the large Maple tree that stood atop Lookout Mountain.

Faithless: Thank you for your instruction and now I must bid both of you good-bye. I am anxious to get back home in order not to **Kiss the Hare's Foot*** and to be with my family.

Great-Heart: Please, Faithless, stay just long enough for Fidelity and Constance to pack you a lunch since it is almost midday.

With lunch packed and a wicker basket in hand, Faithless headed back to the City of Destruction, thinking all the while of the dream and its meaning.

---

* **Kiss the Hare's Foot**—To be so late as to miss dinner; to eat left-over scraps.

CHAPTER 9
CHRISTIAN LOSES HIS BURDEN

Halfway home, Faithless spotted a shady, cool place under the bow of a large Oak tree. It seemed the perfect place to stop and rest for a moment while he ate the lunch that Fidelity and Constance had put together with such care.

As Faithless sat in that warm, shady spot, he began to feel drowsy and it was not long before he fell asleep. While he was asleep, he was visited with another dream.

Upon awakening from his dream, he stood up and began to make his way back as swiftly as he could to the King's Cottage. Before he was halfway there, he met Evangelist who had just left his brother's home.

> **Evangelist**: Faithless, I am surprised to find you here as I thought you would have been home by now.

> **Faithless**: I would have been except I decided to eat the delicacies prepared by Fidelity and Constance while sitting under yonder large Oak that overlooks the City of Destruction. Feeling sleepy I purposed to take a short nap, but while I slept I was visited with another dream.

> **Evangelist**: So, our meeting is no accident.

> **Faithless**: I suppose it was not.

Evangelist: I have been summoned by the King to meet a man named Without-Strength in the open field that is just before us.

Evangelist pointed to the wide-open field that lay just outside the City of Destruction.

Faithless: I must not keep you from your appointment.

Evangelist: It seems I have two appointments, and I am sure one will follow the other with an orderly ease, if I am not mistaken. Under the Oak tree where you had your dream, there looks like a cool shady spot from which I can see the gate that leads to the open field. Because as I am fast on my feet, I believe I can meet him before he gets to the center of the open field, once I spy him going out of the City of Destruction.

Faithless: May I tell you my dream?

Evangelist: Of course, that is why we have met, is it not?

Faithless: This is most fortunate as the dream is fresh in my memory and I was just on my way back to the King's Cottage in hopes that you or your brother could help me understand its meaning.

Evangelist: Come along then Faithless, keep me company under the oak tree that lies just ahead and tell me your dream.

Faithless began walking briskly toward the Oak tree where he began to relate his most recent dream.

Faithless: Now I saw in my dream that the highway upon which Christian was to go, after he left the House of the Interpreter, was fenced on either side with a wall, and that was called Salvation.

 Isaiah 26:1

Up this way burdened Christian ran, but not without great difficulty because of the burden on his back.

Christian is delivered from his burden as he now clearly sees the work done on his behalf at the Cross

Christian ran until he came to a place somewhat ascending. Upon that place stood a rugged, wooden cross and a little below the cross, at the bottom of the hill, was a sepulcher.

Evangelist: I am glad to hear it!

Faithless: So, I saw in my dream, that just as Christian came up to the cross, his burden came loose from his shoulders and fell off his back, tumbled into the mouth of the sepulcher where it fell in, and I saw it no more.

 Psalm 103:12

Evangelist: I suppose that Christian was glad to be rid of that great burden and feeling light on his feet.

Faithless: Yes, and with a merry heart he sang out:

He has given me rest by His sorrow, and by His death, He has given me life.

Then Christian stood still there for a little while to look and wonder; it was very surprising to him that the sight of the cross should ease him of his burden.

He looked and looked again until the fountains sent the waters down his cheeks.

 Zechariah 12:10

Now as I watched Christian standing and looking and weeping, three Shining Ones came to him and saluted him.

Evangelist: And what did they say to Christian?

Faithless: The one said, "Peace be to you, your sins have been forgiven you."

 Mark 2:5

The second Shining One stripped him of his rags and clothed him with a change of raiment.

 Zechariah 3:4

The third Shining Ones set an indelible mark on his forehead.

 Ephesians 1:13

Evangelist: Is that all?

Faithless: No. That same

Behold, Three Shining Ones came to him

Shining One also gave him a scroll with a seal upon it, which the Shining One said he should look at as he made his pilgrimage to the Celestial City. And as I remember, he told Christian to give it to the one who would greet him when he came to the gate of the Celestial City.

The Shining Ones continued on their way. Then Christian gave three leaps for joy he went on singing:

Christian: *I have come all this way laden with my sin,*

Nothing could ease the grief that I was in until I came to this place.

What a place is this!

This is where I began to reap the joy that was given to me by Goodwill at the Small Gate. My Salvation that was sealed forever when I came in at the Door has now become sensible to me as I could not enjoy it because of my lingering fears and little faith.

This is the beginning of my bliss.

The sure promise of things accomplished when I entered the Gate have now, at the sight of this cross, grown larger than my fears and apprehension. I bless the name of the "Son of man" who was put to shame so that I might be redeemed.

Evangelist: Do you understand what Christian was saying?

Faithless: Yes, I think he was saying the cross relieved him of the sense of his burden of sin even though his sins had been forgiven by a promise that cannot be broken when he entered into the Way.

 **7** *Colossians 2:14*

Evangelist: That is an agreeable explanation to be sure.

What did you see next?

Faithless: Then, in my dream, Christian continued on the Straight Path until he came to the bottom of the hill. He saw out of the corner of his eye, a little way off the path, three men fast asleep with fetters upon their heels.

Evangelist: Do you remember their names?

Faithless: Yes, the name of one was Simple, another was Slothful, and the third was called Presumption.

Christian, noticing they were shackled in irons, went to them in order to wake them up. He cried louder and louder until finally, they stirred a little from their slumber. This is what I heard...

> **Christian**: *Let me help you off with your irons. There is one who goes about like a roaring lion and if he finds you in this condition you will become his prey.*
>
> *I Peter 5:8*

Faithless: With that, they looked upon him with some disgust and replied, each one in turn.

Evangelist: And what did they say?

Faithless: I will report what I heard...

> **Simple**: *Be gone, I see no danger.*

> **Slothful**: *Yet a little more sleep.*

> **Presumption**: *Mind your own business and leave me alone.*

Evangelist: And what did Christian say to these rebukes?

Faithless: Christian was dumbfounded by the replies of the three men as he watched them fall back asleep without saying another word.

Evangelist: Was Christian troubled that these men

Christian tries to assist Simple, Slothful and Presumption

should have so little esteem for the kindness that he freely offered to help them?

Faithless: Yes, and I think he would have tried a second time to wake them and offer them his help in taking off their irons, but just then he heard a small commotion as he watched two men come tumbling over the wall of Salvation on the left-hand side of the Narrow Way.

 Mark 6:11

While Christian was still pondering what he might do to help the three sleeping men, these other two men came up the path to meet Christian.

Evangelist: Do you know the names of these two men?

Faithless: I heard one tell Christian that his name was Formalist and the other said his name was Hypocrisy.

Evangelist: And did they enter into a discourse with Christian?

Faithless: Yes, and the discourse, as best I can recall, went something like this...

Christian warns Formalist and Hypocrisy that they will not be received in the Celestial City since they have come into the Way without going through Christ the Narrow Gate

Christian: *Where have you come from, and where are you going?*

Formalist and Hypocrisy: *We were born in the land of Vain-glory, and we are going to Mount Zion.*

Christian: *Why didn't you enter at the Small Gate that stands at the beginning of the way? Don't you know that it is written, 'He that cometh not in by the door, but climbed up some other way, the same is a thief and a robber'?*

 John 10:1

Formalist and Hypocrisy: *To go to the gate for entrance was, by all their countrymen, counted to be too far and roundabout; therefore, our usual way is to make a shortcut and to climb over the wall, as we have just done.*

 Proverbs 14:12

Christian: *But will not this be counted a trespass against the Lord of the city where we are bound? Aren't you violating His revealed will?*

Formalist and Hypocrisy: *You do not need to trouble your head about it. What we do is a well-established custom, and we can produce, if required, testimony that would bear witness to the fact that this practice had been the approved way of entering the path for more than a thousand years.*

Christian: *But, will it stand up in the King's court of law?*

Formalist and Hypocrisy: *Sir, it is a custom of long standing of over 1000 years and will be admitted as legal by any impartial judge. And besides, what does it matter how we found our way into the Way as long as we get in?*

 John 10:1, John 6:44

Hypocrisy: *If we are in, we are in and that is the end of the matter. You came in by the gate and we came tumbling over the wall. So how is your condition better than ours?*

Evangelist: Did Christian give a reply?

Faithless: Oh yes, this is what he told them, as best I can remember:

Christian: *I walk by the rule of my Master; you walk by the rude working of your fancies. You are counted thieves already by the Lord of the Way: therefore, I doubt you will be recognized as True Pilgrims when you reach the Celestial City. You come in by yourselves without the King's direction, and shall go out by yourselves without receiving the King's mercy.*

Formalist and Hypocrisy: *You go your way and we will go ours.*

Evangelist: Was that the end of the matter?

Faithless: No. Formalist yelled back at Christian as they ran ahead.

Formalist: *We keep the laws and ordinances as conscientiously as anyone, and probably better than you do. I do not see any difference between ourselves and you, except that the coat you now wear is a testimony that you have been given it by someone else in order to hide your own nakedness and shame.*

 *Matthew 7:25*

Christian: *By laws and ordinances you will not be saved since you did not come in by the door.*

 *Galatians 2:16*

And as for this coat that is on my back, it was given to me by the Lord of the place where I go; and as you say, to cover my nakedness. And I take it as a token of kindness to me, for I had nothing but rags before.

 15 *Isaiah 64:6, Romans 3:10*

And besides, when I come to the gate of the city, the Lord will know me as a friend, since I have His coat on my back; a coat that He gave me freely in the day that He stripped me of my rags.

I have a mark in my forehead of which perhaps you have taken no notice. This mark was placed there by one of my Lord's most intimate associates.

Besides that, I was given a sealed scroll to comfort as I go on the way; I was also asked to give it at the celestial gate as a token of my right to enter the Celestial City. And I doubt that you have any of these things since you did not come in at the gate.

Faithless: To these remarks, they gave Christian no answer; they only looked at each other and laughed.

Then they all walked up the Way, except Christian kept to himself, sometimes sighing and sometimes joyfully. I noticed he would often read the scroll that one of the Shining Ones gave him. This seemed to refresh him.

Then they all went on until they came to the foot of the Hill of Difficulty, at the bottom of which there was a spring.

There were two paths that went to the right and the left of the hill; there was also the Narrow Way that went straight up the steep Hill of Difficulty.

Evangelist: What did Christian do when he came to the Hill of Difficulty?

Faithless: Christian went to the spring and drank to refresh himself, and then he began to go up the hill, saying:

 16 *Isaiah 49:10*

Christian: *The hill, though high,*
I desire to ascend;
The difficulty of it will not offend;
For I see the way to life lies here:
With God's help, I neither faint nor fear.
Better, though difficult, the right way to go,
Than wrong, though easy, where
the end is woe.

Evangelist: And what did Formalist and Hypocrisy do?

Faithless: They also came to the foot of the hill.

But when they saw the hill was steep and high, that there were two other ways to go, and supposing these two ways might meet again on the other side of the Hill of Difficulty, they resolved to take the easy path.

Evangelist: I suppose these two bypaths had a name?

Faithless: Two names: the one way to the right was called Danger, and the way that went around the Hill of Difficulty on the left side was called Destruction.

Christian climbs the Hill of Difficulty

Evangelist: Which way did Formalist and Hypocrisy take?

Faithless: I saw Formalist begin to walk down the path called Danger, which led into a densely wooded forest. Hypocrisy took the way called

Destruction, which led him into a wide field full of dark mountains where he stumbled, fell, and rose no more.

Evangelist: And what about Christian?

Faithless: In my dream, I watched him go up the hill. At first he ran and then he walked, and then he crawled up, clambering on his hands and knees due to the steepness of the hill.

Then I saw that about midway to the top of the hill, there was a pleasant Arbor which I suppose was made by the Lord of the Hill for the refreshment of weary travelers.

When Christian spied the spot, he hastened his pace and sat down to rest. Then he pulled his scroll out of his bosom and comforted himself as he read; he also began to take a close look at the coat that was given to him as he stood by the cross.

 I John 5:12

Finally, Christian fell into a slumber and then into a deep sleep, which detained him in that place until it was almost night; and while he was asleep, his scroll fell out of his hand.

Christian struggles to reach the top of the Hill of Difficulty

CHAPTER 10
CHRISTIAN LOSES HIS SCROLL

Evangelist carefully listened to the dream that Faithless was retelling, while also watching the gate that led out of the City of Destruction and into the wide-open field.

Evangelist: Dear friend, I see that my next appointment is on the near horizon.

Do you see the burdened man who has just come out of the gate of the City of Destruction?

Faithless: Yes, I see him. He is moving very slowly as the burden on his back is much larger than the one that plagued Graceless.

Evangelist: I am sorry for his burden. But judging by his slow pace it does not appear that I need to run to meet him. So, my dear Faithless, please walk with me and tell me the rest of your dream.

As Evangelist and Faithless walked toward the City of Destruction, they could see the meadow where Evangelist had a divinely scheduled appointment to meet with Without-Strength.

As they walked together, Evangelist asked Faithless to continue sharing his latest dream.

Faithless: Well, as I said, Christian was fast asleep in the arbor halfway up the Hill of Difficulty.

Evangelist: I think I can guess what happened next.

Faithless: How so?

Evangelist: The King has scouts all along His path who keep watch over His Pilgrims and I would not be surprised if one of them, seeing Christian asleep, went to him to wake him up.

 Proverbs 6:4-11

Faithless: Yes, you are right. I could not see his face, but I did notice that he was a robust man. Without a word, he went up to Christian and shook him out of his slumber. He then told him without so much as a "how do you do" to consider the ant and reflect on how wise are his ways. Once Christian was awake, the man warned him not to become a worthless sluggard.

 Proverbs 6:6

Evangelist laughed out loud.

Evangelist: Yes, I know this man, he is a kinsman of mine, a man named Diligence who travels this part of the King's Path looking for Pilgrims in need of assistance.

What happened next?

Faithless: Christian awoke and thanked the man and would have entered into a long conversation with him because he was starved for good fellowship.

Evangelist: If this was my cousin, Diligence, then he would have none of that.

Faithless: It must be the very man, for this is the conversation I heard:

Diligence: *This is no time for talking but a time for action.*

Christian: *Yes, I must make haste before the sun goes down.*

Diligence: *Well, on your way, Pilgrim, and may the Lord speed you along the path before you.*

Faithless: Christian, who was all of a sudden aware of his precarious condition, started up the hill as fast as his legs could carry him, with no rest or delay. In a short space of time and before the sun went down, he was at the top of the Hill of Difficulty.

Now when he was up to the top of the hill, two men came running toward him.

Evangelist: Do you remember their names?

Faithless: Yes, the name of the one was Timorous and the other was called Mistrust.

Evangelist: I know these two brothers very well because they have a notorious reputation for discouraging and disheartening true Pilgrims. The one brother, Timorous, is weak and fearful but his brother, Mistrust, is a bully and a robber who runs with a gang of like-minded men, plundering poor pilgrims who are traveling on the King's Highway.

What did they say to Christian?

Faithless: It was Christian who first asked them what they were doing, running the wrong way. This is the answer I heard:

Timorous: *We were going to the city of Zion and had got up that difficult place; but the farther we go, the more danger we meet, wherefore we turned and are going back again.*

Christian meets Mistrust and Timorous who try and fill him with fear in order to persuade him to abandon the Narrow Way

Mistrust: *Just ahead, there lie a couple of lions in the way. I don't know if they are sleeping or waking and I don't want to find out. I am sure if we came near them, they would pull us in pieces.*

Lions of Persecution greet Christian as he approaches the House Beautiful, which is a picture of the Church

Christian: *You make me afraid; but where shall I go to be safe?*

If I go back to mine own country, that is prepared for fire and brimstone, I shall certainly perish.

If I can get to the Celestial City, I am sure to be in safety there. I must venture. To go back is nothing but death; to go forward is fear of death and life everlasting beyond it. I will yet go forward.

Faithless: Then I saw Mistrust and Timorous run down the hill, as Christian went on his way. Thinking about what he had heard from the two men, Christian began **Grubbling*** in his pocket for his scroll in order to read it and be comforted. As hard as he looked, he could not find the scroll.

Evangelist: This must have put Christian in a fever.

Timorous and Mistrust

---

* Grubbling—Grubbling is like groping, except less organized. It is a verb that usually refers to pockets, but can also be used for feeling around in your pockets or desk drawer scrounging around looking for a lost item.

Faithless: Yes, Christian was in great distress and perplexity of mind and he didn't know what to do.

At last, he must have thought about the arbor that is on the side of the hill. Perhaps, he thought, the scroll must have fallen out of his lap when he slept.

Evangelist: How do you know this?

Faithless: Because he began to retrace his steps back to the arbor but not before he fell down upon his knees and asked God for forgiveness for his foolish carelessness.

As he went back down the hill, I could hear Christian chiding himself for falling asleep in the place that was only provided by the King for a short time of refreshment for weary pilgrims and not a place where he should linger and sleep.

I saw Christian go back down the hill, carefully looking on this side and on that, all the way hoping he might find his scroll that had been his comfort so many times in his journey.

He went until he came to the arbor. Seeing the place renewed his sorrow by bringing to his mind, again his sinful carelessness.

 Revelation 2:4, 1 Thessalonians 5:6-8

Christian went on, bewailing his sinful sleep:

> **Christian**: *O wretched man that I am, that I should sleep in the daytime! That I should sleep in the middle of difficulty! That I should so indulge the flesh as to use that rest for ease to my flesh which the Lord of the Hill has erected only for the relief of the spirits of pilgrims! How many steps have I taken in vain!*
>
> *This is what happened to Israel for their sin. They were sent back again to wander in the wilderness by the way of the Red Sea; and I am made to tread these steps with sorrow, which I might have*

tread with delight, had it not been for this sinful sleep. How far might I have been on my way by this time? O that I had not slept!

Faithless: Now by this time, I saw in my dream that as he came to the arbor again, he sat down and wept. But finally (as Providence would have it), looking sorrowfully down under the bench, he spied his scroll. Christian then, with trembling, picked it up and put it into his bosom.

Christian was filled with ecstasy as he clutched the precious scroll.

Evangelist: Is that all Christian said?

Faithless: No. I heard Christian talking to himself, saying:

> **Christian**: Thank You, Lord, for helping me find my scroll. I shall preserve it and present it for my acceptance in your great City as it is my assurance of Eternal Life!

Evangelist: And is this the conclusion of your most recent dream?

Faithless: Yes.

Christian recovers his lost scroll which is his assurance of salvation

Evangelist: I thank you for sharing it with me. I am pleased to hear of the progress of Christian.

Does anything puzzle you regarding the dream?

Faithless: Yes, I am confused by the scroll since it seems to be so easily lost and yet without it, Christian cannot enter the Celestial City.

 Psalm 119:11

Evangelist: You are right about the scroll on two counts.

Firstly, it is important.

Secondly, it is an article that can be easily lost due to neglect, as you saw in your dream, or by other means that have not yet been revealed to you. But on the third count, you are mistaken.

Faithless: What have I misunderstood?

Evangelist: Let me begin to answer your question and concern by asking you a question.

Faithless nodded, notifying Evangelist that he would be happy to entertain his question.

Evangelist: What is the purpose of the scroll given to Christian by one of the Shining Ones when first he clearly viewed the cross?

Faithless: It gave Christian encouragement to read it.

Evangelist: Anything else?

Faithless: It was something of great value since Christian would risk all to retrieve it. And I suppose that it was a warrant that would gain him entry into the Celestial City.

Evangelist: Yes, and there is where it has been tangled up in your mind, like so many novices who do not fully understand the meaning and purpose of the precious scroll.

I cast your mind back to the three Shining Ones and ask you to remember the three gifts that were given to Christian.

Faithless thought for a moment and then offered up the following summary:

Faithless: The one said, "Peace be to you, your sins been forgiven you."

The second Shining One stripped him of his rags and clothed him with a change of raiment.

The third Shining One set a mark on his forehead and gave him a scroll with a seal upon it, which the Shining One said he should look at as he made his pilgrimage to the Celestial City. He told him to give it at the celestial gate.

Evangelist: So, the first declared to Christian that according to the law of the King of the Celestial City, that Graceless, who was once an enemy of the King, is now his beloved friend and further that in the courts of Heaven he has been declared forgiven of all his sins.

The second stripped him of his rags, which were the outward sign of his unrighteousness, and clothed him in the raiment of His own Son. In short, Christian is now covered with a righteousness he did not merit. He has received a free gift that covers all his own unrighteousness with the perfect righteousness of the King's Son.

The third Shining One set a mark on his forehead and gave him a scroll with a seal on it with instructions to read it as he journeyed and finally to surrender it at the gate of the Celestial City.

Now, if we were to summarize all of this and boil it down to the size of a quail's egg, might it not unfold as follows?

Faithless listened carefully.

Evangelist: When Graceless entered in through the Narrow Gate, which is a picture of Christ, the only Door, his name was written in the Lamb's book of life. No man, or angel or any other creature can remove it because the King has decreed that it remain there forever unaltered.

The death sentence hanging over Christian's head, the great debt he could not repay, has been canceled in full and forever.

Faithless: Yes, I remember that Graceless was renamed Christian and advised as to the change in his name and nature by Goodwill.

Evangelist: Yes, and from now on Christian, filled with the Spirit of God, began to be instructed by the Holy Spirit. He entered into the House of the Interpreter, an illustration of the Spirit, who is going about refashioning Christian's mind in accordance with the truth of God's Word.

Then Christian, after some period of time, had the scales of doubt and apprehension removed from his eyes so that he might fully enjoy, by way of personal experience, the reality that he had been established completely righteous, as a matter of fact in the courtroom of Heaven.

 Acts 9:17-18

Remember that it is not Christian's righteousness but the imputed righteousness of the King's Son that has established forever his eternal salvation.

With the scales now removed, Christian began to enjoy more fully the joy and peace that he could not enjoy when he was tormented by his sense of his great sin.

Faithless: Yes, I did witness the great change.

Evangelist: Yes, you did. So, now we come to the point.

The third Shining One put a mark on Christian's forehead, a sign that could not be lost or ever destroyed, and he gave Christian a scroll that could be both lost and damaged.

Faithless: I am beginning to understand.

But I must ask, can the mark on his forehead be removed?

Evangelist: There is no power in heaven or on the earth that can remove that mark. It is the guarantee that the man bearing the mark is an adopted son of God.

 Romans 8:38, Ephesians 1:13

Faithless: So, am I to understand that the mark on the forehead and the scroll serve the same purpose?

Evangelist: No, not in all respects but as it pertains to your question, they both serve the same purpose.

Faithless: I do not understand.

Evangelist: You see, the scroll is the visible and tangible evidence that the person in possession of it is a child of the King.

Faithless: But it can be lost as I saw in my dream.

Evangelist: Yes it can, but it can also be recovered, as you saw in your dream. The scroll is the evidence that should be happily provided at the entrance to the gate to the Celestial City. It is an invitation to enter into the city with all its glories and benefits.

Faithless: But what if the scroll is lost or stolen? If the Pilgrim arrives at the gates of the Celestial City without his scroll will he be granted entry?

Evangelist: Arriving at the Celestial City without your scroll at the end of your pilgrimage is evidence of a careless journey through this world. It will be something that causes shame that will not be rewarded once inside the Celestial City.

 I Corinthians 3:12-13

But the Pilgrim who is written in the Lamb's Book of Life, who has entered in through the Narrow Way, is guaranteed entry into the Celestial City even as if he were a twig snatched out of the fire.

 Jude 1:23

So, the short answer is yes, your salvation does not depend upon your scroll, but it is evidence of a faithful and careful pilgrimage.

Faithless: I think I understand.

Evangelist pulled a book from inside his coat. Faithless immediately recognized the book as he could see the charred smudge at the right-hand corner.

Evangelist: Let me read the testimony of what I have just told you in the King's own words. Remember, Faithless, that Graceless received the Spirit of God when he entered in at the Door, which is Christ. Once the Spirit enters a believing man or woman, He never departs. Consider that fact as I read the King's own testimony which is meant to both encourage us and give us a certain hope of eternal life.

Romans 8:9-10

⁹ But ye are not in the flesh, but in the Spirit, if so be that the Spirit of God dwell in you. Now if any man have not the Spirit of Christ, he is none of his.

¹⁰ And if Christ be in you, the body is dead because of sin; but the Spirit is life because of righteousness.

2 Timothy 2:11-13, 19

[11] It is a faithful saying: For if we
be dead with him, we shall
also live with him:

[12] If we suffer, we shall also reign with him:
if we deny him, he also will deny us:

[13] If we believe not, yet he abideth faithful:
he cannot deny himself.

[19] Nevertheless the foundation
of God standeth sure, having
this seal, The Lord knoweth
them that are his.

Romans 8:35-39

[35] Who shall separate us from the love of Christ?
shall tribulation, or distress, or persecution,
or famine, or nakedness, or peril, or sword?

[36] As it is written, For thy sake we are killed
all the day long: we are accounted
as sheep for the slaughter.

[37] Nay, in all these things we are more than
conquerors through him that loved us.

[38] For I am persuaded, that neither death,
nor life, nor angels, nor principalities,
nor powers, nor things present,
nor things to come,

[39] Nor height, nor depth, nor any
other creature, shall be able to separate
us from the love of God, which is in
Christ Jesus our Lord.

Evangelist: And finally, Faithless, I would like you to consider this solemn promise from the King of the Celestial City.

Philippians 1:6
Being confident of this very thing,
that he which hath begun **a good work**
in you will perform it until the day
of Jesus Christ:

Evangelist gave Faithless a manly embrace and the two parted ways. Faithless headed back to the City of Destruction and Evangelist headed for the open field outside the City of Destruction with the firm purpose in mind of pointing another poor sinner to the Small Gate, that once entered, gives a sinner the certain hope of Life Eternal.

CHAPTER 11

Christian Enters the House Beautiful

aithless returned to his home and family.

Evangelist met with and directed Without-Strength to the Narrow Gate. He then returned to the King's Cottage to report to his brother the latest chapter in the dream of Faithless. He arrived back at the King's Cottage just in time to eat a hearty dinner. That evening, Evangelist shared the rest of Faithless' dream with his brother. Early the following morning, he collected his daughter, Constance, and prepared to take the two-hour journey back to his home.

Great-Heart: I was hoping you might stay just a few days longer.

Evangelist: That would be wonderful except the King has sent word by one of His messengers to inform me that I should make a journey to the outskirts of Vanity Fair as soon as I was able. So, I need to make haste in order to deliver Constance safely home before I make the journey.

Great-Heart: Have you received any other news?

Evangelist: Yes, I have been informed that Christian was no longer making his pilgrimage alone and has been joined by another pilgrim.

Great-Heart: Do you know his name?

Evangelist: I was not told his name but that he has just recently entered through the Narrow Gate.

I can hazard a guess as to what his name is.

Great-Heart: Please do.

Evangelist: I believe this is the man Faithful, who, by the careful reading of the King's Book and without any human assistance, found his way to the Narrow Gate with little incident.

 Isaiah 55:11, John 14:26

Great-Heart: This would explain why, by reason of his great faith, he is further along the way than Christian, even though he has only just recently entered in through the Narrow Gate.

 Hebrews 5:12

Since it was not unusual at that time for pilgrims to come to the Narrow Gate through the instrument of the Word alone, only a few remarks were made.

Both brothers agreed that the faithful reading of God's Word, when directed by the Spirit of God, is the most blessed and primary path to Salvation.

 II Timothy 3:16, Hebrews 4:12, Romans 10:17

Great-Heart speculated that he would not see Faithless for about a month since the events in the life of his little brother, Evangelist, seemed to correspond to the dream of Faithless.

It was surprising when a couple days after Evangelist and Constance departed, Great-Heart heard a knock on his door. He opened the door to find Faithless wide-eyed and anxious to share the next episode in his dream.

Faithless: I am hoping that your brother is still here.

Great-Heart: I regret to tell you that Evangelist left three days ago and I do not expect to see him for the space of a month.

Faithless seemed disappointed but brightened up as soon as he was welcomed inside and seated with a cup of tea and crumpets, which appeared like clockwork within minutes after his arrival.

Faithless: Thank you, Fidelity.

Fidelity: You're most welcome.

Great-Heart retrieved the King's Book from the shelf, sat down in front of Faithless, smiled, and asked how it went with him.

Faithless bit his lip a little as if wondering how much he should reveal. In the end, he just said things were fine when it was clear they were not fine.

Great-Heart, who was a trained doctor of the soul, knew when to press in and when to give space to those who were being beckoned to enter in through the Narrow Gate. Clearly, in the mind of Great-Heart, he was not only listening to a great, miraculous adventure that arrived by an unlikely courier who, by his best reckoning, was about to follow the pilgrim, Christian, on his own pilgrimage.

 Proverbs 20:5

But clearly, today was not to be that day and so Great-Heart settled in to listen to the rest of the dream that Faithless was about to recall.

Faithless: Did Evangelist tell you about the dream I had just after I left here a couple of days ago?

Great-Heart: Yes, he carefully rehearsed every detail and I stand ready to hear what happened after Christian retrieved his scroll from the arbor, constructed by the King, halfway up the Hill of Difficulty.

Faithless was happy to hear it as he collected his thoughts so he might start at exactly the place he left off with Evangelist just three days earlier.

Faithless: Christian picked up the scroll and pressed it into his bosom. He gave thanks to God for directing his eye to the place where it lay and with joy and tears began his journey back up the Hill of Difficulty. But before he got to the top of the hill, the sun began to set.

Great-Heart: What did he say?

Christian recovers his lost scroll

Faithless: As I remember, he said he was decrying his decision to sleep.

Christian:
OH, sinful sleep!
I must walk without
the sun, darkness
must cover my path and I must listen to the noise of the doleful
creatures all because of my sinful sleep!

As he began to go down the Hill of Difficulty, he remembered the testimony of Mistrust and Timorous, how they were frightened by the sight of the lions.

Then Christian spoke again to himself.

Christian: *These beasts range in the night for their prey. If they should meet with me in the dark, how should I survive an attack? How can I escape from being torn to pieces?*

Christian was glad it was still daylight, for he was fearful of the beasts. This was on his mind as he carefully and watchfully marched up the Hill of Difficulty. While he was bewailing his unhappy circumstances, he lifted up his eyes and beheld a very stately palace just up ahead. The name of the palace, as he later learned, was the House Beautiful, and it stood by the King's Highway.

So, I saw in my dream that Christian went forward to see if it might be possible to find lodging there. Now before he had gone far, he entered into a very narrow passage, which was about a furlong off the porch to the Palace. As he looked down this narrow path, he spied two lions in the way.

Now, he thought, I see the dangers that drove Mistrust and Timorous back. (The lions were shackled, but he did not see chains.)

 Proverbs 22:13

Christian was afraid. He thought about retreating as Timorous and Mistrust had because he considered there was nothing but death waiting for him.

 Luke 9:62

While Christian was **Pitchkettled*** and fretting about what to do, the Porter of the Palace, whose name is Watchful, perceiving that Christian was frozen with fear and was considering going back, cried to him, saying:

> **Watchful the Porter**: *Is your strength so small?*
>
> *Mark 4:40*
>
> *Don't be afraid of the lions as they are chained and have been placed here as a trial of your faith to discover those who have none. Keep in the middle of the path and they cannot harm you.*

Faithless: Then I saw Christian walk down the middle of the path, trembling for fear of the lions, as he followed the directions of the Porter; the lions roared but they did no harm.

Then Christian clapped his hands and went on until he came and stood before the gate where the Porter stood.

> **Christian**: *Sir, what house is this, and may I lodge here tonight?*

---

* **Pitchkettled**—Puzzled.

Watchful the Porter: *This house was built by the Lord of the Hill, and He built it for the relief and security of pilgrims. Where did you come from and where are you going?*

Christian: *I am come from the City of Destruction and am going to Mount Zion; I desire, if I may, to lodge here tonight.*

Watchful the Porter: *What is your name?*

Christian: *My name is now Christian, but my name at the first was Graceless. I came of the race of Japheth, whom God will persuade to dwell in the tents of Shem.*

Christian encouraged to enter the House Beautiful by the Porter who is a picture of a true Gospel minister

 Genesis 9:27

Watchful the Porter: *But how does it happen that you come so late?*

Christian: *I had been here sooner, but, wretched man that I am, I slept in the arbor that stands on the hill-side! If I had not slept when I should have been traveling, I would have been here much sooner. To make matters worse, I discovered when I had gotten to the top of the Hill of Difficulty that I had lost my scroll of assurance and had to return to the arbor to find it again.*

 Matthew 26:41

Christian enters the House Beautiful
despite his fears of persecution

Watchful the Porter: *I will call out one of the maidens of this place, who will, if she likes your testimony, bring you unto the rest of the family, according to the rules of the house.*

So, Watchful the Porter rang a bell, at the sound of which a grave and beautiful maiden came out the door. Her name was Discretion.

> **Discretion**: *Why have you beckoned me?*

> **Watchful the Porter**: *This man is on a journey from the City of Destruction to Mount Zion, but being weary he has asked me if he might lodge here tonight. So, I told him I would call for you, who, after a conversation with him, may decide how to answer his request as you see fit and according to the rules of the house.*

Discretion: *What is your name, where have you come from, and where are you going?*

Christian: *My name is Christian. I am come from the City of Destruction and am going to the Celestial City.*

The porter rang a bell, at the sound
of which a beautiful maiden
came out of the door

Discretion: *How did you enter the Way?*

Christian: *I was granted entry by Goodwill and have entered through the Narrow Gate.*

Discretion: *What have you seen and met with in the way?*

Christian told her about his many adventures.

Discretion: *What do you want me to do for you?*

Christian: *I have a strong desire to lodge here tonight. I perceive this place was built by the Lord of the Hill for the relief and security of pilgrims.*

Faithless: In my dream, I saw Discretion smile as she wiped a tear from her eyes. After a little pause she said...

Discretion: *I will call forth two or three more of the family.*

Faithless: So, she ran to the door, and called out Prudence, Piety and Charity, who, after a little more discourse with Christian led him inside to meet the family.

Discretion: *Come in, you blessed of the Lord; this house was built by the Lord of the Hill on purpose to provide rest and to equip pilgrims such as yourself.*

 Hebrews 13:2

Faithless: Then Christian bowed his head and followed them into the house. He sat down and Piety gave him something to drink. She and her two sisters, Prudence and Charity, conversed together until supper was ready.

Piety, Prudence and Charity had a long discourse with Christian.

Great-Heart: Can you remember what they talked about?

Christian shares his testimony with Piety, Prudence and Charity and only after they are satisfied that he is a true pilgrim is he included in the fellowship of the assembly of believers

Faithless: The conversation went something like this as best I can remember:

Piety: *Come, good Christian, since we have been so kind to you and received you into our house, let us talk with you of all things that have happened to you on your pilgrimage.*

Christian: *I would be happy to.*

Piety: *What moved you at first to take up the life of a pilgrim?*

Christian: *I was driven out of my native country by a dreadful sound that kept ringing in my ears. I was convinced that if I stayed in that country I would meet with certain destruction.*

Piety: *But how did you happen to come out of your country and end up here?*

Christian: *It was as God would have it. When I was under the fear of destruction, I did not know where to go. But, by chance, as I was trembling and weeping, there came a man whose name is Evangelist and he directed me to the Narrow Gate. I would never have found it on my own, so he set me onto the way that has led me directly to this house.*

Piety: *But did you not come first to the House of the Interpreter?*

Christian: *Yes, I saw things in his house that I will remember as long as I live.*

Piety: *What did you learn?*

Christian: *I learned these things:*

1. I learned how Christ, despite all the schemes of Satan, maintains His work of grace in the heart;

2. I learned from the Man in the Iron Cage how the man had convinced himself he had sinned himself quite out of hopes of God's mercy; and also, the dream of another man who dreamed the day of judgment was come.

Piety: *Did you hear him reveal his dream?*

Christian: *Yes, and it was dreadful. It made my heart ache, but I was glad I heard it.*

Piety: *Was this all you saw at the House of the Interpreter?*

Christian: *No. The Interpreter showed me a stately palace and the people who lived in the castle who seemed to be clothed in gold. I saw a venturous man as he cut his way through the armed men who stood in the door to keep him out. I also witnessed how that same man asked to come into the palace and win eternal glory.*

Piety: *And what else did you see while traveling the King's Way?*

Christian: *After I left the House of the Interpreter, I went a little farther and I saw One who had been hung bleeding upon a tree. The very sight of Him made my burden fall off my back; I never saw anything like it before. While I stood looking up at the cross and at Him who was hanged on it, three Shining Ones came to me.*

Piety: *And what did they say to you?*

Christian: *One of them testified that my sins were forgiven me; another stripped me of my rags, and gave me this broidered* *coat which you see. The third set the mark, which you see in my forehead, and gave me this sealed scroll you see me holding.*

Piety: *What else did you see?*

Christian: *The things I have told you were the best: but I saw some other things also.*

I saw three men: Simple, Slothful, and Presumption lie asleep, a little out of the way with irons clapped to their heels. But do you think I could awake them? I also saw Formalist and Hypocrisy come tumbling over the wall of Salvation, pretending to be on their way to Zion.

Piety: *Pretending?*

Christian: *Yes, they were quickly lost just as I told them they would be, but they would not listen to or believe me.*

I cannot forget how hard it was to get up the Hill of Difficulty and how hard it was to pass between the two roaring lions. If it had not been for the good man, the Porter who stands at the gate, I do not know if I would be sitting here talking to you. I thank God I am here, and thank you for receiving me.

Faithless: Piety smiled at Christian and gave him a gentle pat on the shoulder as she rose to refresh his drink.

Then Prudence thought it would be good to ask Christian a few questions.

Prudence: *Do you think sometimes of the country from where you came?*

Christian: *Yes, but with much shame and sorrow, but now I desire a better country, that is, a heavenly one.*

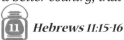 *Hebrews 11:15-16*

Prudence: *Do you not have some fond memories of the City of Destruction?*

Christian: *Yes, but against my will. These things I once loved, as my countryman did, I now find to be a grief to me. And if I could choose my memories, I would choose never to think of those things again. But I confess that even though I try and put them out of my mind, they return like unwelcome robbers to steal me of my joy and humble me.*

 Romans 7:15-16, Romans 7:20-21

Prudence: *And when this happens, what do you do?*

Christian: *I pray for help and rest in the hope that I will one day be changed to be like my Lord. I am assured by reading the King's Book that one day I will be sown in corruption and raised in incorruption and will never again struggle with these terrible things that still tug at my heart against my will.*

 I Thessalonians 4:17, I Corinthians 15:42

Prudence: *What do you find vanquishes these present struggles between the good that you would do and the evil that still entangles you in things that are unprofitable?*

 Romans 7:25

Christian: *One thing does it best.*

Prudence: *And what is that?*

Christian: *I call to my memory what I saw at the cross.*

Prudence: *Anything else?*

Christian: *Yes, when I look upon my broidered coat that was given to me to cover my own unrighteousness.*

Prudence: *Is there anything else that brings relief?*

Christian: *Yes, one last thing; when I read the scroll that I carry in my coat, that will do it.*

Prudence: *Anything else?*

Christian: *Yes, when I turn my thoughts away from this world and think about the Celestial City and the world to come, that will also do it.*

 Galatians 5:16, Psalm 119:11

Prudence: *And what is it that makes you so desirous to go to Mount Zion?*

Christian: *It is there that I hope to see Him alive who did hang dead on the cross and there I hope to be rid of all those things that to this day are inside me and an annoyance. I am informed by the Book there is no death in the place I am going, and I will dwell with wonderful company as I like best. To tell you the truth, I love Him because He took off my burden and I am weary of my inward sickness. I desire with all my heart to be where I shall never die, and with company that continually cry, Holy, Holy, Holy.*

 Isaiah 25:8, Revelation 21:4;

Prudence smiled as she touched the shoulder of her sister, Charity, who was listening carefully.

Prudence: *Dear Christian, I know my sister, Charity, would like to ask you a few questions.*

Christian fixed his gaze on the warm and inviting face of the most favored of the sisters, although to be honest, all three were fairer than any maidens that Christian had ever seen.

Charity: *Do you have a family? Are you a married man?*

Christian: *I have a wife and three small children.*

Charity: *And why did you not bring them along with you?*

Christian began weeping.

Christian: *Oh, how willingly I would have been to bring them with me! But, all of them were utterly averse to my going on this pilgrimage.*

Charity: *But you should have talked to them and endeavored to show them the danger of staying behind.*

Christian: *And so, I did. I also told them what God had shown to me of the destruction of our city, but they mocked me and refused to believe that what I was telling them was true.*

 Genesis 19:14, Matthew 10:34-36

Charity: *And did you pray to God that He would bless your counsel to them?*

Christian: *Yes, and that with much affection; for you must know that my wife and poor children are very dear to me.*

Charity: *But did you tell them of your own sorrow and fear of destruction? For, I suppose, that destruction was visible enough to you.*

Christian: *Yes, over, and over, and over. They witnessed my fears in my countenance, in my tears, and also in my trembling under the apprehension of the judgment that hung over our heads. But all that was not sufficient enough to persuade them to come with me.*

Charity: *Did they tell you why they refused to join you?*

Christian: *Yes, my wife was afraid of losing this world, and my children were given to the foolish delights of youth. So, by one thing and another, they left me to wander in this manner alone.*

Charity: *Did they not see some change in your life that would persuade them to come along with you?*

 Matthew 5:16, I Peter 3:1

Christian: *I cannot commend my life, for I am conscious of my many failings. I know also that a man, by the way he lives his life, may soon overthrow whatever he claims by argument or persuasion.*

Yet this I can say, I was very careful not to give them occasion, by any unseemly action, to make them averse to going on this pilgrimage. In fact, this was the very thing that disturbed them as they would tell me I was too precise, and that I denied myself of things (for their sakes) in which they saw no evil.

I think I may say, that if what they saw in me did hinder them, it was my great tenderness in sinning against God, or of doing any wrong to my neighbor.

Charity: *Indeed, Cain hated his brother, because his own works were evil, and his brother's righteous. If your wife and children have been offended with you for this, they thereby show themselves to be implacable to good; you have delivered your soul from their blood.*

 1 John 3:12, Ezekiel 3:19

CHAPTER 12
CHRISTIAN IS BAPTIZED

hristian listened attentively as Watchful the Porter, who was seated next to him, opened up the King's Book. He spoke of how the King's Son was not only gentle and kind, but also a great warrior who had fought and slain the one who had the power over death, but not without the great loss of His own blood!

Great-Heart: Do you know who Watchful the Porter is?

Faithless: I am not sure but I did notice that Christian seemed to know him, although at first he did not recognize him.

Great-Heart: And how did Christian discover who he was?

Faithless: I heard Christian ask Watchful if he had not met him before.

Great-Heart: And what did Watchful say?

Faithless: I will report the conversation between the two of them as best I can recall.

> **Watchful:** *My brother, Christian, did you recount to Piety ALL the things you witnessed at the House of the Interpreter?*

> **Christian:** *I think so.*

> **Watchful:** *When you entered the House of the Interpreter, did he not ask his servant to light a candle and bid you follow him into a private room?*

Christian: *Yes, it was the first thing he did.*

Watchful: *And once the door was open, what did you see?*

Christian thought for a moment and then stuttered as he finally recalled what he had witnessed.

Christian: *Yes, now I remember. I saw the picture of a very grave person framed and hanging on the wall.*

Watchful: *Describe what you saw.*

Christian: *The eyes of the man were lifted up to Heaven. He had the best of books in his hand, the law of truth was written upon his lips, the world was behind his back, and he stood as if he pleaded with men. Finally, I noticed a crown of gold hung over his head.*

Faithless: At this point Christian was a little taken back and embarrassed.

Great-Heart: How so?

Faithless: I think for two reasons.

Great-Heart: Pray tell.

Faithless: Well, first I heard him apologize to Watchful for not fully reporting what he saw while in the House of the Interpreter and secondly, for not recognizing Watchful and taking him for a humble servant.

Great-Heart: And what did my cousin, Watchful, say to all this?

Faithless: Your cousin?

Faithless was again surprised at how his dream was mysteriously connected with his desire to find its true meaning and those who were helping him discover and discern the vision.

Finally, Faithless collected his thoughts and answered Great-Heart.

Faithless: He told Christian that he was a humble servant and delighted beyond reason to be one.

And then I heard the following conversation between Christian and Watchful.

> **Christian:** *You are the man in the picture that the Interpreter showed me when I first entered his house!*
>
> **Watchful:** *The picture is one of ten thousand or more humble servants. But yes, I am one of those favored men. It is my vocation to plead with sinners to escape the wrath to come by trusting in the blood sacrifice of the King's Son, as you have done.*
>
> *And now I have a question for you.*
>
> **Christian:** *Please sir, ask it.*
>
> **Watchful:** *Since you have come in through the Small Sheep Gate, a picture of Jesus who is the only way that leads to life, what is the next thing you need to do?*

Christian thought for a moment but could not give a ready answer.

Watchful then opened up the King's Book and read from four passages.

Great-Heart: Can you remember the passages?

Faithless: I cannot give you an exact account but I do remember that the first passage instructed those who were on the King's Highway to teach others and baptize those who entered in through the Narrow Gate in the name of the King, His Son, and the Holy Spirit.

 *Matthew 28:19*

Watchful also told Christian that Peter the Fisherman, who was a beloved follower of the King's Son, told all who would listen to repent and be baptized.

 Acts 2:38-41

Great-Heart: Did Watchful tell Christian about the Ethiopian who was baptized by Phillip, the follower of the King's Son?

 Acts 8:26-38

Faithless: Yes, and he also pointed out to Christian that obeying the King's Son and being baptized was a sign of faithfulness and delighted the King and His Son.

 Acts 16:11-16, 31-34

Great-Heart: And how did Christian respond to this admonition?

Faithless: At first, he inquired as to the meaning of baptism. I heard Watchful tell Christian that just as the King's Son was killed, buried and resurrected to life, so we must also bear witness to this fact in baptism as a testimony that we are followers of the King's Son.

Great-Heart: Did Watchful tell Christian how this truth was demonstrated in baptism?

Faithless: Yes. He told Christian that baptism symbolized the death, burial, and resurrection of our Savior. And that, as a follower of the King's Son, we are to be fully covered by the water symbolizing our Lord's death and then raised up out of the water symbolizing His resurrection.

 Colossians 2:12, Romans 6:3-4

Great-Heart: And what did Christian say when he heard all these things?

Faithless: He was determined to be baptized that very evening and could not be persuaded to wait one more minute.

Christian is refreshed and nourished at the House Beautiful which is a picture of the gathered assembly of blood-bought Christians

Great-Heart: And how did Watchful respond?

Faithless: He smiled as he stood up and invited all the guests to follow him out of the house and to the little river that meandered through the property on which the House Beautiful was so prominently situated.

Great-Heart: And how did all the guests respond, the hour being so late?

Faithless: I thought there might have been some protest as the sun was just setting and there was little daylight left.

Great-Heart: Was there anyone who brought up a complaint or asked that this interruption be postponed to a more convenient hour?

Faithless: I would have thought so, but there was no complaint. To the contrary, everyone seemed overjoyed at the prospect as they had been listening in on the conversation between Watchful and Christian. It seemed to me they were all pleased with Christian's response.

Great-Heart: And what happened next?

Faithless: Christian was led out of the House Beautiful along a little lane that ended on the banks of a slow-moving river. The two men waded into the river until they came to a deep spot that put the water to the height of Christian's elbows.

Watchful then asked Christian to make a true confession of his faith in the King's Son. When he had immersed Christian, he declared to all who witnessed that he was baptizing him in the name of the King, the King's Son Jesus, and the Holy Spirit.

Great-Heart: And then what happened?

Faithless: The guests all began to sing a song about the pure love of the King's Son for His Country and the poor sinners He came to rescue.

Then all returned to the House Beautiful where Christian and Watchful stood in front of the fireplace to warm themselves and give testimony to the faithfulness of Jesus, the King's Son.

Many at the table nearby spoke of the King's Son's pure love for His country. A few at the table, whose names I cannot remember, said there was testimony in the King's Book, faithfully reported by His friends who had spoken to Him, after He died on the cross and raised Himself back to life after three days and nights. They said they heard from the King's Son's own lips how He loved poor pilgrims with a love that could not be found if you searched for ten thousand years from east to west. Hearing all this made Christian love Him even more.

 Hebrews 2:14-15

Christian heard the testimony of how the King's Son had left His dwelling place in glory in order that poor pilgrims might dwell with Him in the mountain of Zion.

Christian listened as they told how the King's Son had made many pilgrims princes, though by birth and nature they were beggars and their original condition had been like a dunghill.

 1 Samuel 2:8, Psalm 113:7

The conversation went on until late in the night after which they then committed themselves to their Lord for protection and took their leave to rest.

Christian was taken to a large upper chamber whose window opened towards the east. The name of the chamber was Peace, and it was there that he slept until the break of day at which time he awoke and sang:

> **Christian**: *Where am I now? Is this the love and care of Jesus, for the men that are pilgrims on the Narrow Way?*

I heard Christian say that in that place he felt as close as he had ever felt to Heaven itself.

Great-Heart: And was this the end of your dream?

Faithless: No, there is more to report.

The two men, Great-Heart and Faithless, decided to take a walk around the property in order to stretch their legs and give a little space for reflection and contemplation.

Fidelity inquired if they would like to have an early lunch. This was an invitation that Faithless was glad to accept.

Great-Heart snatched up the King's Book from the small bookshelf and headed for the front door. Faithless followed.

CHAPTER 13

CHRISTIAN ARMED FOR BATTLE

G reat-Heart and Faithless went out the front door of the King's Cottage but not before Great-Heart went into the kitchen where Fidelity was preparing lunch.

Great-Heart: Faithless and I are going to stretch our legs and get a little sunshine before lunch.

Fidelity: That sounds like a grand idea.

Great-Heart: Yes, indeed. When would you like us back for lunch?

Fidelity: I will have it ready to serve in about an hour.

Great-Heart gave his daughter a kiss on the forehead and thanked her for all her gracious hospitality and then headed for the door where Faithless was waiting for his company.

Fidelity: I will see you in an hour.

Great-Heart stopped and took a deep breath.

Great-Heart: As delicious as it smells now, I can only imagine what delicacies will await us in an hour.

Fidelity: Stop teasing me and go take your walk with Faithless. I will have everything prepared when you return in an hour.

With that, Fidelity began to sing one of the many "kitchen songs" she had learned from her mother so many years ago.

The lyrics were taken from Psalm 92:1. Fidelity sang it to the melody of an Irish jig.

It is a good thing
to give thanks unto the Lord,
and to sing
praises unto thy name!

Great-Heart smiled as he listened to the sweet sound that drove the kitchen hum-drum and drudgery out and away from the King's Cottage.

Great Heart: Faithless, I am happy for the chance to stretch my legs and looking forward to hearing all the progress that Christian has made on his journey to the Celestial City.

Faithless: It is my great delight to do so as I believe it is a service to both of us in ways I do not fully understand.

Great-Heart: Yes, it is an unexpected blessing to be in your acquaintance as a result of something that is both mysterious and hopeful for both of us.

Faithless: How is it hopeful for me?

Great-Heart: Do you not sense the awakening in your own heart as to the dangers that await you if you stay in the City of Destruction?

Faithless: I have tried to shut those thoughts out of my mind, but I confess that as of late I am beginning to apprehend and fear something that appears to be on the near horizon.

Graceless: What is it that you fear?

Faithless: That some great calamity is looming.

Great-Heart: And what do you think that threat is?

Faithless: It is knowledge of the fact that the City of Destruction is now under a curse and a judgment will someday, and I fear soon, result in its complete overthrow.

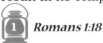 *Romans 1:18*

Great-Heart: And what else?

Faithless: That I, and my dear family, may be overthrown with it and unable to save ourselves because we have broken God's laws and are subject to His wrath.

Great-Heart: If this is true, then why don't you flee as Graceless did?

Faithless was quiet and offered no answer. Finally, a little sheepishly, he asked Great-Heart if he would like to hear the rest of his dream.

Great-Heart swept a weed aside that had sprung up on his path and graciously asked Faithless to continue the telling of his dream.

Faithless: As you recall, Christian was given sanctuary in the House Beautiful, where he was later baptized. After a full evening that included dinner and lots of conversation, he was shown to his bedroom. Here he slept in peace and tranquility until the morning light brightened the window high above his head. So, in the morning they all got up; and, after some more discourse, they told him that he should not depart until they had shown him the rarities of that place.

Great-Heart: I am most anxious to hear about this.

Faithless, encouraged by the genuine interest of Great-Heart, continued to recount his dream.

Faithless: First, they led him into the study where they showed him records of the greatest antiquity. As I remember my dream, they showed him the pedigree of the Lord of the Hill, that He was the Ancient of Days, and came by way of an eternal generation.

Here also was more fully recorded the acts that the King's Son had done, and the names of many thousands that He had taken into His service, and how He had placed them in such habitations that could neither by length of days nor decays of nature, be dissolved.

 I Corinthians 12:22-29

Then Discretion, Piety and Prudence read to him some of the worthy acts that some of His servants had done; how they had subdued kingdoms, wrought righteousness, obtained promises, stopped the mouths of lions, quenched the violence of fire, escaped the edge of the sword, out of weakness were made strong, waxed valiant in fight, and turned to flight the armies of the aliens.

 Hebrews 11:33-34

Great-Heart: I suppose this greatly encouraged Christian!

Faithless: Yes, indeed it did.

Faithless picked up his pace a little since he had fallen more than ten feet behind Great-Heart who took long strides and also seemed anxious to arrive at some unknown destination.

Faithless, now walking side by side with Great-Heart, continued.

Faithless: Then, as I recall, Discretion read again another part of the records of the house. It was shown how willing their Lord was to receive into His favor any, even any who in times past had offered great affronts to His person and proceedings.

Then Christian was taken into a grand library with more books, scrolls and artifacts than anyone could count.

Here Christian perused several other histories of many other famous things and exploits of the King and His Son.

Christian looked into things both ancient and modern, together with prophecies and predictions of things that are certain to happen in the future.

Great-Heart: And do you know what was made of all this?

Faithless: Oh yes, for it was noised about by all in the room that the things Christian was learning were both to their dread and amazement.

Great-Heart: Dread?

Faithless: Yes, dread to the enemies of the King and His Son and comfort and solace to his Pilgrims, who were assured by the King's Son that they were friends and brothers and would never experience the wrath of His Father.

The next day the three sisters and their brother, Steadfast, took Christian into the armory where they showed him all manner of equipment which their Lord had provided for pilgrims.

Steadfast was tall with a manly stature who had himself just returned from a small skirmish with agents of the Prince of Darkness, he was anxious to show Christian the sword, shield, helmet, breastplate, all-prayer, and shoes that would not wear out.

 Ephesians 6:11-18

Christian shown the armory where he is equipped for the battles that every Christian must fight in this life

Great-Heart: Yes, that sounds like my nephew, Steadfast.

Faithless stopped for a moment as he was amazed at all the family connection between Great-Heart and the noble characters in his dream.

Faithless: In my dream, I could not help but notice there was enough armory in this large room, the end of it so distant I could not see it, to arm tens of thousands and perhaps many more who desired to enter the service of their Lord. In fact, I must confess that I could not number all that was stored in this great place.

Great-Heart: What did Christian make of all this?

Faithless: I heard Steadfast tell Christian, who also marveled at the sight of all the armor, that in the future there would be men whose number, as the stars in Heaven, could not be counted, who would be equipped with the armor that was stored for pilgrims in this place.

 Genesis 32:12, II Timothy 2:3-5

Great-Heart: Yes, I know this is true. What else?

Faithless: They also showed him some of the articles with which some of the King's Son's servants had done wonderful things.

Great-Heart: Can you remember what they were?

Faithless paused for a moment as he collected his thoughts, not wanting to leave even the smallest detail out of his telling of the dream.

They showed him Moses' rod. He examined the pitchers, trumpets, and lamps used by Gideon to put to flight the armies of Midian.

Then they showed him the ox-goad used by Shamgar to slay six hundred men.

 Judges 3:31

They showed him also the jawbone with which Samson did such mighty feats.

They showed him, moreover, the sling and stone used by David to slay Goliath of Gath, and also the sword with which their Lord will kill the Man of Sin in the day that he shall rise up in order to be slain.

They showed him many excellent things with which Christian was much delighted.

From morning to dusk Christian was occupied with all these matters.

Great-Heart: And then he rested?

Faithless: He should have rested, but instead, after dinner he begged Steadfast to show him how to use the sword.

Great-Heart: And did he?

Faithless: Steadfast was most anxious to train Christian in the art of swordsmanship because he said, he was certain it would be a skill he would need as he continued his journey.

So, in my dream, I saw that for many days Christian applied himself to the recounting and memorization of the disciplines that made for the right and proper use of the sword.

 Ephesians 6:17

Great-Heart: And was he successful?

Faithless: At first, I thought he handled the sword rather clumsily. On a few occasions he carelessly managed to do injury to himself, which smarted but did not dampen his determination to be a skilled swordsman.

 II Corinthians 4:2, II Timothy 2:3

Great-Heart: And what of Steadfast?

Faithless: To look at the man you would fear to be in a battle with him. But his nature was kind and with longsuffering, he bore all Christian's mistakes as he patiently instructed him since he was eager to become a skilled handler of the sword.

Great-Heart: And do you know what the sword is?

Faithless: I thought I did, but after watching Christian train tirelessly with Steadfast, I learned that my opinion needed to be altered and improved.

Great-Heart: What changed your mind?

Faithless: I can better describe it. When Steadfast raised his sword and gave it a slice through the air, it produced the sound of words that I could hear. It was as if the sword was alive and speaking to the enemy.

 Hebrews 4:12

Great-Heart: I am anxious to hear an example of what you heard.

Faithless: Well, on one occasion, Christian asked Steadfast what to do if an enemy attacked him from his left side.

Great-Heart: And what did Steadfast tell him?

Faithless: That was just it, he did not speak a word; the sword spoke as it was skillfully handled by Steadfast.

Great-Heart: And what did the sword say?

Faithless: It was a sound like a rushing wind and it said, as best I can recall:

> *There is none righteous, no, not one.*

And when Steadfast swung it again the sword said:

> *For all have sinned, and come short*
> *of the glory of God.*

Great-Heart: And what else did you hear?

Faithless: At first, I only heard the sword speak threats and admonitions but then, strangely, it also spoke words of peace and comfort.

Great-Heart: Do tell!

Faithless: Steadfast was instructing Christian how to care for his sword and keep it sharp. As he polished the sword, it glowed and spoke words of peace and joy. I thought this to be very strange indeed.

Great-Heart: Can you remember what came forth from the sword while it was viewed and polished?

Faithless: It was almost like a song with a hundred verses. But I can only remember one or two.

Great-Heart: I would be glad to hear them.

Faithless: I can remember one verse in particular since it seemed to be so strange to me.

Great-Heart: Pray tell.

Faithless: Steadfast held his sword up and bowed to it as you bow to a master. Then he held it with one hand above his head and polished one little edge of it. Next I heard these words come forth:

Therefore, being justified by faith,
we have peace with God through
our Lord Jesus Christ:

Great-Heart: And what else?

Faithless: Steadfast polished his sword in another spot while holding it above his head, a custom I have never witnessed before and would like to know what it means.

Great-Heart: And I will be most glad to tell you, but first tell me what other words you heard as the sword was being attended to by Steadfast.

Faithless: As if it were a song carried by the wind, I heard the sword announce: **though your sins be as scarlet, they shall be as white as snow.** Then again I heard it say: **Neglect not the gift that is in thee.**

Great-Heart: And what about Christian?

Faithless: As I said, Steadfast was patient with Christian and after three days of intense study and practice, Christian was beginning to handle the sword with more confidence.

 II Corinthians 4:2

I do remember that Steadfast was kind and gentle and only on one occasion did he rebuke Christian most sternly.

Great-Heart: And what prompted the rebuke?

Faithless: It was over something that seemed a trivial matter to me. Christian, instead of holding the sword up over his head, put it in his lap and began to polish it. It seemed a trivial matter but Steadfast became much exercised with Christian and rebuked him most harshly.

Great-Heart: How did Christian take the rebuke?

Faithless: He was miffed at first but after considering the words that followed his stern rebuke, he took it well and mended his behavior. I witnessed that from that point on Christian put the sword above his head, holding it awkwardly at first, as he rubbed it and caressed its sharp edge with a polishing stone.

 II Timothy 4:2-4

I was hoping you could enlighten me as to the reason for this strange custom. I have never in my life seen anyone care for his sword in this way.

Great-Heart: Understanding the mystery of the sword and why Steadfast attended to it while holding it over his head can only be revealed once you know what the sword is.

Faithless: And what is it?

Great-Heart: Cannot you guess?

Faithless could not answer.

Great-Heart: The Sword is the very **WORD OF GOD.** The lesson is to remind men they are mistaken if they think they can polish it up while holding it under their own heads; as if their mind and all the fanciful nonsense that occupies the space between a man's two ears can inform them like the supernatural power that is the very Word of God. And the sheath, which is but a covering, is marred, soiled, and bears the marks of the flame in the right-hand corner.

Faithless was speechless as he considered and marveled at the insight he had just been given by one who he now imagined was himself a master swordsman, a warrior in the army of the King and His great Son.

 *Hebrew 4:12*

CHAPTER 14

The Valley of Humiliation

Great-Heart and Christian continued to walk the pathway that made a winding circle around the King's Cottage. Up ahead Faithless could see a little wooded area with what looked like a mile of blackberry hedges. Just then, a small rabbit scampered across the path. "I wondered if I might see you little fella," said Great-Heart, who was not only well acquainted with the path but all the creatures that inhabited the meadow and woods that surrounded the King's Cottage.

Great-Heart stopped for a minute to let Faithless catch up with him as they came upon the first few blackberry bushes.

Great-Heart: They are ripe and sweet this time of the year and I can see that my little friends have been busy feasting on the bottom of this little bush.

Great-Heart rustled through the blackberry bush and managed to find a handful of large, ripe berries which he proudly presented to Faithless.

Faithless popped the berries in his mouth, savoring the sweet juice that colored his lips a dull purple color as it dripped down his chin.

Great-Heart: I hope you will continue telling me your dream.

Faithless wiped his chin and smiled.

Faithless: The next thing I saw in my dream took place in a large room just off the armory of the House Beautiful the morning that followed the final lesson in swordsmanship.

I saw in my dream that early in the morning, very early, Christian got up and waited for the rest of the household to awaken. He then greeted and thanked everyone for their hospitality and instruction, paying special attention to Steadfast, whom he had come to both admire and respect.

But the entire household protested and desired that Christian stay for one more day because they wanted to show him the Delectable Mountains which, they said, would further comfort him on his long journey.

Steadfast persuaded him to stay with the promise of one last lesson in swordsmanship.

So, Christian consented to stay.

Early that afternoon they led Christian to the top of the house and asked him to look south. As he did, off in the distance he saw a most pleasant mountainous country, beautified with woods, vineyards, fruits of all sorts, flowers, springs and fountains. It was very delectable to behold.

 Isaiah 33:16-17

Great-Heart: What did Christian have to say about all these wonders?

Faithless: As best I can recall, Christian asked this:

> **Christian:** *What is the name of this fair country?*

> **Charity:** *It is called Immanuel's Land.*

> **Piety:** *It is a land kept especially for Pilgrims.*

Christian given a glimpse of the
Celestial City, which is heaven

Prudence: *Yes, and when you arrive in Immanuel's Land, you will be greeted by the King's shepherds.*

Steadfast: *And that is not all, my brother Christian. From Immanuel's Land, on a clear day, you can see the gates of the Celestial City.*

Christian: *This is all wonderful to consider. And it makes me even more eager to go forward, as I am anxious to enter Immanuel's Land.*

Steadfast: *Yes, Christian, you are ready to continue your journey, right after we make one more visit to the armory.*

Faithless: So, in my dream, they made their way back to the armory where, all together, they harnessed Christian from head to foot with armor.

Then I heard Christian protest:

Christian: *Is all this really necessary?*

I don't think I am going to war.

Steadfast: *You don't think you're going to war?*

Christian: *I didn't think I was.*

Steadfast: *Let me disabuse you of that idea. You are going into a battlefield that will test both your skill and your will.*

 II Timothy 2:3-4

Faithless: Steadfast, Piety, Prudence and even Charity all began to tell war stories to Christian; true tales of poor pilgrims who did not think they were going to war and were not armed or ready for the onslaught of the many enemies of the true pilgrim.

All the tales ended badly with sorrows heaped upon sorrows. It did not take long before Christian realized that all the armor they were clapping on him was not a precaution for something that might befall him but a necessity in order to face what he would certainly encounter in the days to come. Steadfast and Prudence told him chilling tales of how dozens of pilgrims had been ambushed and assaulted after leaving the House Beautiful.

 Ephesians 4:12

Christian: *It was the King's gracious providence that I have taken some refuge in this place. I know now that it was not just the immediate sanctuary that I needed, but much more: things I had not even considered in order to prepare me for the arduous and dangerous journey ahead.*

Steadfast: *This is certainly true. I advise you to remember the lessons in wielding the sword; your most valuable defense is a good offense. Keep your sword sharp and yourself in practice by diligently attending to it with prayerful reverence and diligence.*

Christian armed by Prudence, Discretion, Piety and Charity

Christian is equipped for the battle that all true believers must face in this world

Prudence: *Yes, Christian, my brother is giving you wise counsel. And, may I add this? Test everyone you come upon, and do not be beguiled by those who make a show of religion but have not entered in through the Narrow Gate. As we tested you in order to discover your true heart, so test others before you become their companions. There are many true pilgrims on that path who will be blessed by your company and there are many others who only desire to lead you off the path into darkness and despair. Be careful whose company you keep!*

 I Timothy 1:10, I Corinthians 5:11-13, 1 Thessalonians 5:21

Soon everyone in the room, including the porter and a couple of young lads who were nephews of Prudence, showed up to fasten and fix Christian with a helmet, shoes, breastplate, gloves and a sheath to hold his sword. They were all convinced that he was going to meet with enemies who, they kept repeating, would show him no mercy.

I remember Christian saying:

Christian: *I have received so many instructions it has made me dizzy just trying to keep them all in my mind.*

Piety: *Don't worry, dear Christian.*

The Spirit of God Who now indwells you will bring it to your mind when the occasion arises.

Faithless: After an hour or so, Christian and the small band of new friends who now attended him walked out to the gate.

Prudence: *Have any other pilgrims passed by?*

The Porter Watchful: *I will ask my assistant.*

The young lad, Watchful's youngest son, was eager to report that he had seen a pilgrim pass by just an hour ago.

The Porter Watchful: *Did you attempt to wave him into the house?*

The Young Lad: *Yes, father, I waved and waved and yelled in order to get his attention, but he just kept going on his way.*

 Hebrews 10:24

The Porter Watchful: *Did you assure him that the Lions were chained and they would do him no harm?*

The Young Lad: *Yes, father, I did. But as I said, he paid me no heed. And he was not alarmed at all by the Lions.*

The Porter Watchful: *I wonder why he did not come to the porch so we could interview him?*

The Porter Watchful: *Did you ask him his name, son?*

The Young Lad: *Yes, indeed I did. And he told me his name was Faithful and he was going to the Celestial City.*

Christian: *Oh, I know the man. He is my townsman, my near neighbor; he comes from the place where I was born.*

Christian receives final instruction from the Porter, who is the picture of a Gospel minister

How far do you think he may have traveled by now?

The Porter Watchful: *By this time, he will be at the bottom of the Hill of Difficulty.*

Christian: *Well, may the Lord be with you and add to all your blessings which I pray will increase in proportion to the kindness that you have shown me.*

Faithless: Then Christian began to go forward; but Discretion, Piety, Charity, and Prudence insisted on accompanying him down to the foot of the hill.

So, they went on together, reiterating their former conversations until they came to the little brow that marked the spot where the hill began to descend.

> **Christian**: *Just as it was difficult coming up the Hill of Difficulty, I can see that it is also dangerous going down.*

> **Prudence**: *Yes, so it is; for it is a hard matter for a man to go down into the Valley of Humiliation without slipping along the way.*

Faithless: Then I saw in my dream that Christian's companions continued to go with him all the way down to the bottom of the Hill of Difficulty. When he reached the bottom of the hill they gave him a loaf of bread, a bottle of wine, and a cluster of raisins; then Christian went on his way.

CHAPTER 15

CONFLICT WITH APOLLYON

As Faithless continued to unfold the dream, Great-Heart was quietly listening with thoughtful intent.

Faithless: It was not long before Christian came to a dreadful valley. As I remember, it was called the Valley of Humiliation. Christian had no sooner entered the place when he spied the foul fiend coming over the field to meet him. His name was Apollyon.

Christian is assaulted by Apollyon, who is a picture of the god of this world

Christian, seeing the fiend approach him, began to be fearful and wondered if he should go back or stand his ground. As Christian considered his choices, he realized he had no armor for his back and thought that to turn his back to this fiend might give him a greater advantage to pierce him with his darts.

I Corinthians 10:13

Christian resolved to stand his ground, hoping it was the best way to save his life.

 Ephesians 6:13

Apollyon was soon standing face to face with Christian. The monster was hideous to behold. He was clothed with scales like a fish and they were his pride. He had wings like a dragon, feet like a bear, and out of his belly came fire and smoke. His mouth was as the mouth of a lion. When he was come up to Christian, he looked at him with a disdainful countenance, and began to question him:

> **Apollyon**: *Where did you come from, and where are you bound?*

> **Christian**: *I have come from the City of Destruction, which is the place of all evil, and I am going to the City of Zion.*

> **Apollyon**: *By this, I perceive you are one of my subjects; for all that country is mine, and I am the prince and god of it. How is it, then, that you have run away from your king?*

> *Were it not that I hope you may do me more service, I would strike you to the ground with one blow.*

> **Christian**: *I was, indeed, born in your dominions, but your service was hard, and your wages such as a man could not live on; for the wages of sin is death.*

 Romans 6:23

> **Apollyon**: *There is no prince that will take lightly the loss of one of his subjects, neither will I lose you; but since you are complaining about your service to me and your wages, be content to go back, and I will increase your wages and improve your position.*

Christian: *I have given myself to another, even to the King of princes. How can I with fairness go back with you?*

 I Corinthians 6:19-20

Apollyon: *You have done this according to the proverb, changed a bad for a worse. But it is ordinary for those who have professed themselves His servants, after a while to give Him the slip, and return again to me. Do that and all shall go well with you.*

 Romans 8:6-7

Christian: *I have given Him my faith and sworn my allegiance to Him; how then can I go back now and not be hanged as a traitor?*

Apollyon: *You did the same by me, and yet I am willing to let it pass if you will now turn again and go back.*

Christian: *The promises I made to you were made when I was not of age. Besides, I know that the Prince, under whose banner I now stand, is able to absolve me and to pardon me of what I did when I was in your service.*

And besides, O you destroying Apollyon, to speak truth: I like His service, His wages, His servants, His government, His company, and country, better than yours. Therefore, quit trying to persuade me to come back into your service. I am now His servant, and I will follow Him alone.

Apollyon: *Calm down and think about what you are doing. Do you know what you are likely to meet up with if you continue on the way that you are now going? You do know that for the most part, His servants come to an ill end because they are transgressors against me and my ways. How many of them have been put to shameful deaths!*

 Philippians 3:8-10

And besides, you count His service better than mine; whereas He has never left His place to deliver any who served Him out of their enemies' hands. But as for me, how many times, as all the world very well knows, have I delivered, either by power or fraud, those who have faithfully served me?

 Revelation 12:9-11

I am not willing to let you go!

Christian: *My King's forbearance, at the present time, is for the purpose of discovering who truly loves Him and will trust Him to the end, whether that end be good or ill.*

His pilgrims do not expect so much present deliverance because they know they will have future glories that will last forever. And when you compare the fleeting moments of this present world with Eternity, the answer to your argument becomes foolish.

Apollyon in a rage attacks Christian

And besides, the day is coming when He will return in glory to this dominion with all His angels and saints.

Apollyon: *You have already been unfaithful in your service to Him and now you foolishly think you will receive wages from Him?*

Christian: *Is it true, O Apollyon, that I have been unfaithful to Him?*

Apollyon: *You fainted when you first set out on*

this fool's errand when you were almost choked in the Swamp of Despair. You attempted to be rid of your burden in the wrong way.

You sinfully slept and lost choice things.

You were also almost persuaded to go back at the sight of the lions at the House Beautiful.

And when you talk of your journey and of what you have seen and heard, you are inwardly desirous of vain-glory in all that you say and do.

Christian: *All that you accuse me of is true, and much more which you have left out, but the Prince whom I serve and honor is merciful and ready to forgive. And to be clear, most of these infirmities overtook me while I was in your country. It is true that while a citizen of the City of Destruction I was persuaded to relish in its vices, policies and practices, and I groaned under them. But I have repented of them all and have obtained pardon of my Prince.*

 I John 1:9, I Corinthians 6:9-11

Faithless: Then Apollyon broke out into a grievous rage, saying:

Apollyon: *I am an enemy to this Prince; I hate His person, His laws, and people. I am come out to meet you for the purpose to either persuade you to reenter my service or to kill you.*

Christian: *Beware, Apollyon, what you do for I am in the King's Highway, the way of holiness; therefore, take heed to yourself.*

Faithless: Then Apollyon straddled himself over the whole breadth of the Narrow Way.

Apollyon: *I am void of fear in this matter. Prepare to die! I swear by my infernal den that you will go no farther; here will I spill your soul.*

Faithless: And with that, he threw a flaming dart at his breast; but Christian had a shield in his hand with which he caught it, preventing it from doing any harm.

Then I saw Christian pull out his sword because he saw it was time to defend himself.

Apollyon attempts to overcome Christian

Apollyon quickly charged him, throwing darts as thick as hail. The barrage overcame Christian for a moment and Apollyon gave Christian a wound in his head, his hand and foot.

This made Christian back up a little. Apollyon pushed forward but Christian, filled with courage, resisted him as best he could.

 I Peter 5:8

This combat lasted for above half a day.

Christian was almost quite spent. The many wounds he received made him grow weaker and weaker.

Then Apollyon, seeing his opportunity, moved up close to Christian and, wrestling with him, which caused Christian's sword to fly out of his hand.

   Apollyon: *I have you now.*

Faithless: And with that, he almost pressed him to death. Christian began to despair of life. But, as God would have it, while Apollyon was gathering strength for his last blow in order to make a full end of this good man, Christian nimbly reached out his hand for his sword, and snatched it up.

Christian: *Rejoice not against me, O mine enemy; when I fall, I shall arise.*

 Micah 7:8

Faithful: And with that, gave Apollyon a deadly thrust which made him retreat, having received a mortal wound. Christian, perceiving his advantage, once again thrust his sword into the side of the beast.

Christian prevails relying on the sure promises of God

Christian: *No, in all these things we are more than conquerors through Him that loved us.*

 Romans 8:37

Faithless: And with that final blow, Apollyon spread forth his dragon wings and sped away. Christian saw him no more.

 James 4:7

Faithless turned to Great-Heart who was listening intently to the description of the battle between Christian and Apollyon.

Faithless: I have never seen anything like this before in my life. You could not imagine it unless you had seen it as I did in my dream.

The yelling and hideous roaring Apollyon made during all the time the battle lasted; he spoke like a dragon. On the other side, what sighs and groans burst from Christian's heart. I never saw him all the while give somuch as one pleasant look until he perceived he had wounded Apollyon with his two-edged sword; only then did he smile and look upward! But it was the most dreadful sight I have ever seen.

Great-Heart: What did Christian do after the battle was over?

Faithless: Christian said this:

> Christian: *I will give thanks to Him Who has delivered me out of the mouth of the lion, to Him Who helped me against Apollyon.*

Great-Heart: What happened next?

Faithless: I saw a young, fair man dressed in white apparel come and nurse Christian's wounds with leaves from the Tree of Life. Once he received the leaves and pressed them against his wounds, they immediately healed. He also ate bread and drank the cool, clear water from the bottle that he was given by Charity when he began his journey into the Valley of Humiliation.

 *Matthew 4:11*

Then another young man with white apparel came to him carrying with him some more of the leaves of the Tree of Life, which Christian took and applied to his remaining wounds and they were healed.

Great-Heart: Then what happened?

Faithless: After he was refreshed, he began his journey again but this time with his sword in his hand, he spoke to it out loud.

> Christian: *I will keep you ready at all times from this moment on since I do not know if some other enemy may be at hand.*

 I Peter 5:8

Christian recovers from the battle with Apollyon

Faithless: Then I heard a gentle voice say, "I will be a light to your path. You need not fear what flesh can do you if you will not forget My Word."

Great-Heart: Is this where your dream ended?

Faithless: Oh no, there is much more to tell.

Great-Heart: Did Christian make it through the Valley of Humiliation without meeting any more foes?

Faithless: No, and I am anxious to tell you what happened next.

CHAPTER 16

CHRISTIAN ENTERS THE VALLEY OF THE SHADOW OF DEATH

reat-Heart led Faithless up the lane a little further. They were both soon in front of a large stand of small Maple trees that had been overgrown with vines loaded with ripe, succulent blackberries.

Great-Heart produced a large woven jute cloth out of his jacket. It was about four foot wide and six feet long. He smoothed a spot on the ground and then scooped out a small bowl. He then spread the jute canvas over the spot and began picking ripe blackberries. Great-Heart gently laid his harvest of blackberries into the middle of the canvas.

Faithless soon joined into the task as it was modeled by Great-Heart who told him to pluck and gobble, pluck and gobble. The plucking produced a large number of berries in a short time, the volume of which was greatly decreased by the gobbling.

Before a quarter of an hour had passed, the jute canvas was filled with berries. Great-Heart folded the four corners together and tied them with a little bit of jute string he produced from the pocket of his coat.

Great-Heart: Now *that,* my dear Faithless, is what I consider time well spent.

Great-Heart carefully, so as not to crush the overripe blackberries, placed the bundle over his right shoulder and headed back to the King's Cottage by a way that was different but within eyeshot of the original path.

Great-Heart: Faithless, please continue the telling of your dream as I am most anxious to hear what happens next.

Faithless grabbed one more handful of blackberries and put them in his mouth, making it impossible for him to continue the narrative. Within a couple minutes, with lips purple from the berries and a trail of reddish-purple trailing down his chin, Faithless began again to reveal his dream. But it was not without giving one more fond look toward the bounty of blackberries that were growing pretty much unmolested about two miles away from the King's Cottage. As Faithless and Great-Heart strode down the gentle lane that led back to the King's Cottage, Faithless continued telling his tale.

Faithless: After Christian had gotten through the Valley of Humiliation without further incident, he entered another valley.

Great-Heart: And did you hear the name of the valley?

Faithless: Yes, it was called the Valley of the Shadow of Death, and Christian must go through it because the way to the Celestial City lay right through the middle of it.

 Psalm 23:4

Great-Heart: What sort of place was it?

Faithless: In my dream, it appeared to be a very solitary place. I heard Christian remark that the prophet Jeremiah had described it as, "A wilderness, a land of deserts and pits, a land of drought, and of the Shadow of Death, a land that no man (but a Christian) passeth through, and where no man dwelled."

 *Jeremiah 2:6*

Now if you can believe it, the place was worse for Christian than his fight with Apollyon.

Great-Heart: How so?

Faithless: In my dream, I saw that Christian got to the borders of the Shadow of Death, he met two men. They were, as Christian said later, children of them who brought up an evil report of the good land.

 *Numbers 13:32*

These two men were making haste to go back but they stopped long enough to talk to Christian.

And here is an account of the conversation between Christian and the two men, one stout and the other short.

Great-Heart: Do you remember their names?

Faithless: Yes, the stout man was named Fearful and the other was called Faltering.

Great-Heart: And you say Christian conversed with them?

Faithless: Yes, for the space of about a quarter of an hour.

I cannot remember all that was said but the gist of it was as follows:

> **Christian**: *Where are you going?*

> **Faltering**: *Back, back, and we would have you do so too, if either life or peace is prized by you.*

> **Christian**: *Why, what's the matter?*

> **Fearful**: *We were going the way you are now going and as far as we dared. Indeed, we were almost past the point where we could return back for had we gone any further, we would not be here to bring this fearful news to you.*

> **Christian**: *But, what did you meet?*

> **Faltering**: *Why, we were almost in the Valley of the Shadow of*

Death, but by chance, we looked before us and saw the danger before we came to it.

 Psalm 44:19, 107:19

Christian: *But what have you seen?*

Fearful: *Why, the valley itself is as dark as pitch; there were hobgoblins, satyrs, and dragons sent from the pit. We also heard a continual howling and yelling, as if people were trapped in unutterable misery. We saw many who were bound in affliction and irons and over the entire valley hangs the discouraging clouds of confusion. And, Death has his wings spread over it.*

 Isaiah 41:10

Faltering: *In a word, it is every bit of it dreadful, being utterly without order.*

 Job 3:5, 10:22

Christian: *What you have said sounds alarming, but you have said nothing to persuade me that this is not the way to the Celestial City, which is the haven I desire to reach.*

 Psalm 44:18-19, Jeremiah 2:6

Christian studies and meditates on God's Word (Sword Drawn) as he enters the Valley of the Shadow of Death

Faltering: *That may be true enough, but we will not choose to go any further in that way.*

Fearful: *Come now Faltering, we must flee before we are swallowed up by this hideous place.*

Great-Heart: What happened next?

Faithless: The two men went their way and Christian went his way, but cautiously with his sword drawn in his hand, just in case he should be assaulted.

I then saw in my dream that as far as the valley reached there was on the right hand a very deep ditch; the ditch that the blind have led the blind into for all ages, and both have miserably perished there.

 *Matthew 15:14*

Great-Heart: And what did you see on the left side?

Faithless: On the left side there was a very dangerous cliff into which, if even a good man falls, he will find no bottom or any place to get a footing to stand on.

I heard Christian say that this was the cliff that King David did fall off once and no doubt would have been smothered, had not He Who is able plucked him out.

 *Psalm 69:14*

The pathway through the ditch and the cliff was exceeding narrow and knowing this made good Christian move slowly and carefully.

I saw that when Christian tried to avoid the ditch on the one side, he came perilously close to the cliff that would pitch him into the mire on the other side.

That is how Christian continued to slowly go forward as I heard him sighing bitterly. Besides the danger mentioned, the pathway was so dark that Christian had no confidence that his next step would not send him hurling over the two perilous edges.

In the middle of this valley, I saw what looked like the mouth of Hell and it stood right next to the narrow way through the Valley of the Shadow of Death.

This is when I heard Christian speak to himself, or to another, I am not sure which, as he said:

Christian: *What shall I do?*

As Christian was dismayed and crying for help, the flame and smoke would come out of the pit in such abundance, with sparks and hideous noises, that he was forced to put up his sword and take up another weapon.

Great-Heart: And what weapon is that?

Faithless: It was a weapon called All-Prayer.

 Ephesians 6:18

I then heard Christian begin to cry out with a loud voice.

Great-Heart: And did you hear what he said?

Faithless: Yes, he cried:

Christian cries out to the Lord for help

Christian: *O Lord, I beseech you to deliver my soul.*

 Psalm 116:4, Psalm 22:20

Christian continues to pray for assistance in his time of deep trouble

Faithless: This went on for a great while, but still the flames leaped out of the pit and towards him. I also heard doleful voices, as if creatures were rushing to and fro.

It seemed to me that Christian thought that he should be torn in pieces, or trodden down like mire in the streets.

I witnessed all these frightful sights and sounds as I watched Christian slowly make his way through the valley. They continued for several miles and then I heard other dreadful noises for several more miles. I am sure Christian must have thought a company of fiends was coming toward him to meet him and cut him into pieces.

Great-Heart: And what did Christian do?

Faithless: He stopped and began to muse what he should do next. Sometimes he said, out loud, that he had half a mind to go back; then again, he thought he might be half-way through the valley.

He refreshed himself a little as he remembered and spoke of how he had already vanquished many dangers; and that the danger of going back might be much worse than going forward.

So, it seemed to me that after a while he must have decided to go forward even though the sound of the fiends seemed to come nearer and nearer.

Great-Heart: And then what happened?

Faithless: Just when it seemed that the fiends were ready to pounce on Christian, he cried out with a most vehement voice.

    Christian: *I will walk in the strength of the Lord, God.*

Great-Heart: And then?

Faithless: The fiends retreated and did not return to terrorize him anymore.

One more thing I did notice in my dream is that poor Christian was so confounded that he did not know his own voice. I perceived that just when he was come over against the mouth of the burning pit.

Christian could not see what I saw from the vantage point in my vision.

Great-Heart: And what did you see?

Faithless: I saw one of the wicked ones creep up softly behind Christian and whisper suggestions that were grievous blasphemies.

Great-Heart: Yes, this is a tactic of the enemy. And what effect did it have on Christian?

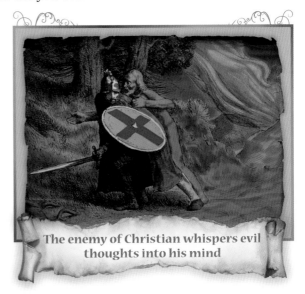

The enemy of Christian whispers evil thoughts into his mind

Faithless: Well at first, he thought that the muttering and blasphemies proceeded from his own mind. This put Christian in more distress than any trial he had experienced so far on his journey.

Great-Heart: What distressed him?

Faithless: The very thought that he should now blaspheme Him Who he loved so much. If he had known the voice was not His own but a trick of the enemy, he would have been fine, but he lacked the discernment to either stop listening or to understand where these blasphemies came from.

When Christian had traveled in this horrible condition for some considerable amount of time, he thought he heard the voice of a man going before him, saying, "Though I walk through the Valley of the Shadow of Death, I will fear no evil, for you are with me."

 Psalm 23:4

Great-Heart: Did this cheer Christian?

Faithless: Oh, yes! It seemed to make him glad for three reasons.

First, because he understood from that point on there were others who feared God who were also in this valley.

 Acts 1:8

Secondly, he perceived God was with them through that dark and dismal state.

 Job 9:11

Thirdly, he hoped he could overtake the pilgrim ahead of him on the path in order to have a companion on his journey.

So, Christian went on and called out to the pilgrim who was ahead of him but received no answer.

By and by the day broke, then Christian said:

Christian: *He has turned the shadow of death into the morning.*

 Amos 5:8

Once morning light overcame the darkness, Christian looked back to see, by the light of the day, what hazards he had gone through in the dark.

Christian saw more of the ditch that was on the one hand, and the cliff that was on the other; he saw how narrow the way was that went between them. He saw off in the distance, a long way from where he now stood, the hobgoblins, satyrs, and dragons that inhabited the pit. He "discovereth deep things out of darkness, and bringeth out to light the shadow of death."

 Job 12:22

Christian, seeing the danger through which he had safely passed, was much affected with this deliverance from all the pitfalls and traps of this solitary way. Dangers he feared while on his journey, he now saw more clearly because the light of the day made them conspicuous.

 Romans 8:37-39

About this time, the sun rose revealing another great mercy. For though the first part of the Valley of the Shadow of Death was dangerous, the second part he was about to travel was far more dangerous.

From where he stood, Christian could see the end of the Valley of the Shadow of Death. He saw that all along the way it was full of snares, traps, gins, and nets. He also saw there were pits, pitfalls, deep holes, and shelvings.

Had it been dark, Christian, I am certain, would not have made the journey without being cast away as a thousand souls had before him.

But, as I said, the sun was rising.

Then I heard Christian say:

> **Christian**: *His candle shineth on my head, and by his light I go through darkness.*
>
> *Job 29:3*

Now in the light, Christian passed safely and without incident until he came to the end of the valley. I saw in my dream that at the end of the valley lay blood, bones, ashes, and mangled bodies of men, even of pilgrims who had gone this way formerly; and while I was musing what should be the reason for all this carnage, I spied a little before him a cave, where two giants lived.

Great-Heart: Yes, I know these giants well.

Christian passes by
the den of Giant Pope

Faithless: I did not hear Christian mention their names. Do you know who they are?

Great-Heart: Oh yes, the one giant is named Pope and the other is named Pagan. They have been dwelling in these caves next to the Valley of the Shadow of Death for over a thousand years. The bones, blood and ashes you see are there by the power and tyranny of these two giants, Pope and Pagan.

Was Christian attacked by either of these giants?

Faithless: No, it appeared he went without much danger: I somewhat wondered about that.

Great-Heart: Each of the giants has a season it seems. Sometimes they appear to be helpless to attack pilgrim travelers and then at other times they seem to gain their strength by reason of the general unbelief of all. In those seasons they both rage and cause a great deal of death and suffering.

Did either of the giants say anything to Christian?

Faithless: The one giant did speak, who I suppose is the one named Pope, since I noticed he wore the headdress of Dagon, the fish god.

He shouted at Christian.

Great-Heart: Do you remember what he said?

Faithless: He told Christian that he would never mend until he and ones like him were burned up.

Christian held his peace and went on his way without an incident, singing as he traveled.

> **Christian:** *O world of wonders (I can say no less),*
> *That I should be preserved in that distress*
> *That I have met with here! O blessed be*
> *That hand that from it, has delivered me!*
> *Dangers in darkness, devils, Hell, and sin*
> *Did compass me, while I this vale was in;*
> *Yea, snares, pits, traps, and nets did lie*
> *My path about, that worthless, silly I*
> *Might have been caught, entangled, and cast down;*
> *But since I live, let Jesus wear the crown.*
>
> JB

CHAPTER 17
CHRISTIAN MEETS FAITHFUL

 reat-Heart and Faithless were now only 100 feet from the King's Cottage and it was just about lunch time. Great-Heart could feel the wet blackberry juice that had soaked through the jute canvas, his jacket and shirt.

Great-Heart: Fidelity is not going to be very well-pleased with me.

Faithless, who was following close behind, could not help but notice the blackberry juice seeping through the jute makeshift knapsack staining the coat of Great-Heart.

Faithless: You're probably right.

Great-Heart: So, Faithless, we have just about finished our walk and completed our mission. I am sure our efforts will result in a half dozen pies, a dozen jars of jam and enough blackberry crisp to feed the three of us with an abundance left over.

Faithless smiled at the prospect of blackberry crisp.

Great-Heart: Is that the end of your dream? I suppose you must now return home after lunch?

Faithless: Well, I do not want to presume upon your time, but as to the dream, there is much more to tell.

Great-Heart: I would have thought it finished by now.

Faithless: No, my last dream lasted from when my head lay on my goose down pillow until my wife stirred me for breakfast. And strangely, it seemed to me that I was awake during some of the dream, although I do not know how that is possible.

 Job 4:13, II Corinthians 12:2

Great-Heart knew how it was possible but thought it best to leave that topic for another time.

Great-Heart: I wonder when you need to be home?

Faithless: If I leave an hour before dusk, I will be home in time for dinner. The days are getting longer so I suppose I might stay here for at least four more hours, give or take. If that is convenient, of course?

Great-Heart: I am happy to have your company and since the dream is fresh in your mind, I think we both need to hear it out loud before the memory of it fades away.

Faithless had no fear of his dream fading away since it was branded on his mind. He was happy to hear that he would be welcome to stay until the dream, or at least this long episode of his dream, was concluded.

Great-Heart and Faithless were greeted at the door by the warm smile of Fidelity who changed immediately to dutiful concern.

Fidelity: Oh Father, you have blackberry juice all over your jacket. Please go and take it off and put something else on so I can immediately attend to it.

Great-Heart was happy to have escaped with such a light rebuke and did as Fidelity requested.

Fidelity: I will have lunch ready for the three of us in half an hour.

Great-Heart: Faithless, please make yourself comfortable and I will join you in a few minutes.

As Great-Heart went to change his jacket and shirt, Faithless made his way into the living room where he spent a few minutes looking at the titles of the two dozen or so books that Great-Heart had collected and stored in his little library.

He then made his way to his familiar chair and patiently waited for Great-Heart to return, but before he did, Faithless was presented a cup of tea and several generous slices of dried apples.

Great-Heart arrived about a minute later with a fresh shirt and a clean jacket.

Faithless waited for Great-Heart to collect the King's Book from his little bookshelf and sit across from him.

Faithless: Should I continue?

Great-Heart: Yes, I am most anxious to hear what happened after Christian finally made his way out of the Valley of the Shadow of Death and past the two giants, Pope and Pagan.

Faithless: Well, as Christian went on his way, he came to a little ascent, which had been built in order that pilgrims might see what was up ahead of them. Christian went and stood on this little rise in order to see what lay ahead and that is when he saw another pilgrim on the path just ahead of him. I will tell you what happened next.

Christian yelled to the pilgrim:

Christian: *Hold up, please; stay! I will be your companion.*

At that, the pilgrim looked behind him.

Christian cried again...

Christian: *Stay, stay, until I can catch up with you!*

Great-Heart: Was it as we guessed, the pilgrim named Faithful who was ahead of Christian on the way?

Faithless: Yes, it was Faithful who answered.

> **Faithful**: *No, I am escaping for my life, and the avenger of blood is behind me.*
> *II Timothy 2:22*

Faithless: When Christian heard this, he was stirred in his spirit and somewhat moved. It appeared to me that he gathered up all his strength and with a look of determination ran as fast as he could. In fact, he ran so fast that he quickly caught up with Faithful, and then ran past him. So, the last was now first.

Great-Heart: What happened next?

Faithless: I saw Christian look back at Faithful with a vain, glorious smile because he had gotten ahead of his brother; but not paying attention to his feet, he suddenly stumbled and fell and was not able to rise again until Faithful came up to help him.

 Proverbs 16:18

Then, in my dream I saw the two pilgrims travel on together, having an unceasing conversation about all the things that had happened to them on their pilgrimage.

Faithful helped Christian to rise

Great-Heart: Did you hear what they said?

Faithless: I heard Christian begin the conversation by saying:

> **Christian**: *My honored and well-beloved brother, Faithful, I am glad that I have overtaken you and that God has so tempered our spirits that we can walk as companions on this pleasant path.*

 Amos 3:3

> **Faithful**: *I thought, my dear friend, to have had your company from the beginning. But you began your journey before I was able to begin mine. So, I was forced to come this far alone.*

> **Christian**: *How long did you stay in the City of Destruction before you set out after me on your pilgrimage?*

> **Faithful**: *Until I could stay no longer; for there was a great talk presently after you were gone out, that our city would, in a short time, be burnt to the ground with fire from Heaven.*

> **Christian**: *Did your neighbors share this opinion?*

> **Faithful**: *Yes, for a while everyone was talking about it.*

> **Christian**: *I must wonder then why more of your neighbors did not come with you to escape the danger.*

> **Faithful**: *Though there was, as I said, a lot of talk about it, I think few firmly believed it. In the heat of the debate, I heard some of them speak ill of you and your desperate, dangerous journey. They called it YOUR pilgrimage. But I did believe the reports that our city will come to an end with fire and brimstone. So, I made my escape.*

> **Christian**: *Did you hear no talk of neighbor, Pliable?*

> **Faithful**: *Yes, Christian, I heard that he followed you until he came to the Swamp of Despair, where, as some said, he fell*

in. He would not admit to it, but I am sure he did since he was soundly bedabbled with the muck and slime from the swamp.

Christian: *And what did his neighbors say to him?*

Faithful: *He has, since his going back, been held in derision among all sorts of people; some mock and despise him, and will scarcely give him the time of day. He is seven times worse than if he had never gone out of the city.*

 Luke 11:25

Christian: *But why should they be so set against him, since they also despise the way that he himself forsook?*

Faithful: *Oh, they say, hang him, he is a turncoat; he was not true to his profession! I think God has stirred up even his enemies to hiss at him, and make him a proverb because he has forsaken the Way.*

 Jeremiah 29:18-19

Christian: *Did you talk with him before you began your pilgrimage?*

Faithful: *I met him once in the streets, but he crept away to the other side as if he was ashamed of what he had done. So, I never spoke with him.*

Christian: *Well, at first, I had hopes for Pliable, but now I fear he will perish in the overthrow of the city. For it has happened to him according to the true proverb, the dog is turned to his vomit again, and the sow that was washed has returned to wallowing in the mire.*

 2 Peter 2:22 , Proverbs 28:9

Faithful: *These are my fears also, but who knows what will be?*

Christian: *Well, neighbor Faithful, let us talk of things that* *are more of an immediate concern. Tell me now what you have encountered in the way. I know you have had adventures and if you have not, I would be amazed.*

Faithful: *I escaped the Swamp of Despair, that I perceive you fell into, and got up to the gate without that danger. Then I met with one whose name was Wanton who was determined to do me mischief.*

Christian: *It was well you escaped her net; Joseph was hard put to it by her and he escaped her devices but it almost cost him his life.*

 Genesis 39:11-13

Faithful narrowly escapes
the lustful desires of Wanton

But what did Wanton do to you?

Faithful: *I think you know what a flattering tongue she has; she tried everything she could to turn me aside, promising me all manner of luxuries and contentment.*

Christian: *I will wager that she did not promise you the contentment of a good conscience.*

Faithful: *You know what I mean, all carnal and fleshly contentment.*

Christian: *Thank God that you escaped her; the abhorred of the Lord will fall into her pit.*

 Proverbs 22:14

Faithful: *To be honest, I do not know if I completely escaped her.*

Christian: *I am sure you did not consent to her desires.*

Faithful: *No, I did not defile myself; for I remembered an old writing that I had seen, which said, her steps take hold on Hell.*

 Proverbs 5:5

I shut my eyes so that I would not be bewitched with her looks.

 Job 31:1

Then she railed against me and I went my way.

Christian: *Did you meet with any other assault as you traveled on the King's Path?*

Faithful: *When I came to the foot of the Hill of Difficulty, I met with a very aged man who asked me who I was, and where I was bound. I told him that I was a pilgrim, going to the Celestial City.*

Then said the old man: "You look like an honest fellow; will you be content to come work with me for the wages that I will give you?"

Then I asked him if his name was Adam.

He said his name was Adam the First, and that he dwelled in the town of Deceit. I asked him what work he wished me to do and what were the wages that he would pay me.

 Romans 5:12

He told me his work held many delights, and his wages would be that I should be his heir.

I further asked him where his house was and what other servants he employed.

He told me that his house was maintained with all the dainties of the world and that his servants were those of his own flesh.

Then I asked how many children he had?

He said that he had but three daughters, the Lust of the Flesh, the Lust of the Eyes, and the Pride of Life, and that I could marry them all if I so desired.

 13 *1 John 2:16*

Then I asked him how long of a time he would have me live with him. He told me, as long as he himself lived.

Christian: *Well, and what conclusion did you finally come to about the old man?*

Faithful: *Why, at first, I found myself inclined to go with the man, for I thought his offer sounded good. But as I talked with him I had a chance to look on his forehead where there was a warning written.*

Christian: *And what did the warning say?*

 14 *Colossians 3:9*

Faithful struggles with his old sin nature, which is the result of the fall of Adam

Faithful: *Put off the old man with his deeds.*

 15 *Ephesians 4:22*

Christian: *And what happened next?*

Faithful: *Then it was revealed to me that whatever he said, and however*

he flattered me, the truth was that when he got me into his home he would sell me for a slave.

I asked him to stop talking because I would not come near the door of his house. Then he reviled me and told me that he would send someone after me that would make my soul bitter.

I turned to go away from him; but just as I turned to go, I felt him take hold of my flesh and give me such a deadly grip that I thought he had pulled my flesh off. This made me cry out, O wretched man!

 Romans 7:24, I Peter 5:8

So, I went on my way up the Hill of Difficulty.

Now, when I had got above half-way up, I looked behind me and saw someone coming after me, swift as the wind.

He overtook right about where the arbor stands.

Christian: *That is where I sat down to rest and soon fell asleep, and while sleeping my scroll fell out of my coat and rolled under the arbor seat.*

Faithful: *Dear brother, hear me out. As soon as the man overtook me, he said hardly one word before he struck me with a blow that knocked me out. I laid there for a while, as if dead, and finally regained my consciousness. I asked him why he set upon me and beat me.*

Christian: *And what did the man say?*

Faithful: *He said he struck me because of my secret inclining to Adam the First. And with that, he struck me another deadly blow on the breast and beat me down backward. I lay at his foot, stunned and near death. When I came to myself again I cried, "have mercy," but he said, "I do not know how* to show mercy," and with that he knocked me down again. He had doubtless made an end of me, but another one came and asked him to stop beating me.

 Galatians 3:24

Christian: *Who asked him to stop beating you?*

Faithful: *A man who had holes in His hands and in His side. Then I knew that He was our Lord. After that, I continued up the hill.*

Christian: *The man who overtook you was Moses. He does not spare anyone and he does not know how to shew mercy to those who transgress the law.*

Faithful: *I know that now; it was not the first time he has met with me. It was Moses who came to me when I dwelled secure-*

The Law shows no mercy, the Savior is full of grace

ly at home and told me he would burn my house over my head if I stayed there.

Christian: *But did you not see the House Beautiful that stood there on the top of the hill?*

Faithful: *Yes, and I saw the lions also, but I think they were asleep. It was about noon and because I was so early in the day, I passed by the young lad who was waving me to come in. I decided to come down the hill.*

Christian: *The young lad you saw was the Porter's apprentice, his young son. He told us he saw you go by. I wish you had called at the house, for they would have shown you so many rarities that you would scarce have forgot them to the day you died. But please tell me, did you meet anyone in the Valley of Humiliation?*

Faithful: *Yes, I met a man whose name was Discontent, who would willingly have persuaded me to go back with him. His reason for going back was that the Valley of Humiliation was altogether without honor. He told me that to go there was the sure way to insult all my friends such as Pride, Arrogance, Self-Conceit, and Worldly Glory, along with others, whom he knew would be very much offended if I made such a fool of myself as to wade through this valley.*

Christian: *Well, how did you answer him?*

Faithful: *I told him that although all these whom he named might claim they were my kinsmen, and rightly so (for indeed they were my relations according to the flesh), since I became a pilgrim, they have already disowned me and I also have rejected them. Therefore, they meant no more to me than if they had never been of my lineage.*

 Luke 6:22

I told him, moreover, that as to this valley, he had quite misrepresented the true facts; for before honor is humility and a haughty spirit comes before a fall. Therefore, I said that I would rather go through this Valley of Humiliation in order to ultimately receive the honor that is given only to the wisest than choose the esteem of the fellows that he so esteemed.

Christian: *Is there anything else you can report as you traveled through the Valley of Humiliation?*

Faithful: *Yes, I did meet with Shame; but of all the men that I have met with so far in my pilgrimage, I think he bears the wrong* name. *The others I met would, after a little persuasion, never have been as bold-faced as Shame.*

Christian: *Why, what did he say to you?*

Faithful: *He objected to my faith. He said it was a pitiful, low, sneaking business for a man to mind spiritual things and that a tender conscience was an unmanly thing. He also said that for a man to watch over his words and ways, so as to tie himself up from that hectoring liberty that the brave spirits of the times had accustomed themselves, would make me the ridicule of the times.*

Christian: *What else?*

Faithful: *He objected to the fact that few of the mighty, rich, or wise were of my faith and opinion; nor were any of them so foolish as to venture the loss of all for nobody knows what.*

 19 *1 Corinthians 1:26, 3:18, Philippians 3:7-9, John 7:48*

He, moreover, objected to the base and low estate and condition of those who were chiefly the pilgrims of the times in which they lived. He objected to what he called the ignorance and lack of understanding of all natural science. He said it was a shame to sit whining and mourning under a sermon and a shame to come sighing and groaning home under the conviction of sin; that it was a shame to ask my neighbor forgiveness for petty faults, or to make restitution when I had taken anything from one of my neighbors and not returned it. He also said that my faith made me a great stranger and outcast because I was unwilling to abide a few vices, which Shame called by finer names that made what is base sound like something respectable and a thing to be cherished. And when it came time for him to finish talking he finally said, "is not everything that I have accused you of a shame?"

 **20** *Romans 6:21-22*

Christian: *And what did you say to him?*

Faithful: *Say? I didn't know what to say at first. He made me so angry that my blood came up in my face causing Shame to criticize me for my passion against his counsel I thought he was going to beat me to the ground. But at last I began to consider; that which is highly esteemed among men is an abomination with God.*

 Luke 16:15

And I thought again, this Shame tells me what men are; but he tells me nothing about what God or the Word of God is.

And I also thought that at the day of doom we shall not be condemned to death or given life according to the mocking hectoring spirits of the world, but according to the wisdom and law of the Highest. Finally, I thought, what God says is best, though all the men in the world rail against it and mock it.

 Romans 3:4, Galatians 1:10

Seeing, then, that God prefers my faith in Him and His Son; knowing that God prefers a tender conscience; seeing those who make themselves fools for the Kingdom of Heaven are the wisest, and that the poor man that loveth Christ is richer than the greatest man in the world who hates Him,

I finally told Shame that he was an enemy of my salvation and to depart.

I asked him if I should listen to his vain counsel or the counsel of my sovereign Lord.

How then shall I look Him in the face when He comes again to gather His followers if I have been ashamed of Him and not looking for His coming?

 Mark 8:38

Should I in this present age be ashamed of His ways and His servants, how can I expect any blessings?

 Matthew 10:33

I will say this for the scoundrel Shame, he was a bold villain. I could scarcely shake him out of my company. He was always hounding and haunting me, continually whispering in my ear with one thing or another about the other regarding the infirmities that attend those who have true saving faith.

I finally told him he was wasting his time trying to bring me around to his way of worldly thinking. After I thought about it I realized that the very ones he disdained were the very ones in which I saw the most glory; and so, at last, I broke his will and he left a defeated foe. When I had finally shaken him off, I began to sing:

> *The trials that those men do meet withal,*
> *Who are obedient to the heavenly call,*
> *Are manifold and suited to the flesh,*
> *And come, and come, and come again afresh;*
> *That now, or sometime else, we by them may*
> *Be taken, overcome, and cast away.*
> *O let the pilgrims, let the pilgrims then,*
> *Be vigilant, and quit themselves like men.*
>
> JB

Christian: *I am glad, my brother, that you withstood this villain so bravely. As you have said, I think he has the wrong name; for he is so bold as to follow us in the streets and to attempt to put us to shame before all men, that is, to make us ashamed of that which is good. But if he was not himself audacious, he would never attempt to do as he does.*

But let us continue to resist him; for, notwithstanding all his bravadoes, he promotes the fool, and nothing else.

The wise shall inherit glory, said Solomon; but shame shall be the promotion of fools.

 Proverbs 3:35, James 4:8

Faithful: *I think we must cry to our LORD for help to withstand and defeat Shame. I do not wish to be ashamed but rather to be valiant for truth upon the earth.*

Christian: *What you say is true. Did you meet anybody else in that valley?*

Faithful: *No. I had sunshine all the rest of the way through that, and also through the Valley of the Shadow of Death.*

Christian: *I am glad it went well for you. It was not sunshine for me but utter darkness and a long season of fear and trembling as I inched along the way. I had no sooner entered into that valley than I entered into dreadful combat with that foul fiend, Apollyon. I thought truly that he would have killed me, especially when he got me down, and crushed me under him. He desired with all his strength to crush me to pieces. When he first threw me to the ground, my sword flew out of my hand. He told me he was about to finish me off, but I cried to God and He heard me and delivered me out of all my troubles.*

 Philippians 2:13

Then I entered into the Valley of the Shadow of Death and had no light for almost half the way. I thought I should have been killed many times but at last, day came and the sun rose, and I went through what was left of the journey through the Valley of the Shadow

CHAPTER 18

Christian and Faithful Encounter Talkative

reat-Heart and Christian continued to discuss the conversation that took place between Christian and his newly found companion, Faithful. There was a pause as Great-Heart considered the last words of Christian as reported in the dream of Faithless. Great-Heart was happy to hear that Christian had made it through the Valley of the Shadow of Death with ease. He thought about all the bedsides he had sat beside, witnessing the journey from this life to the next, not all filled with ease to be certain.

Just then Fidelity came into the living room.

Fidelity: Father, lunch is ready to be served.

Great-Heart and Faithless rose from their chairs, stretched and made their way to the kitchen table. Fidelity had prepared a savory vegetable soup, hot biscuits and a jar of strawberry jam that had just arrived that morning as a gift from one of the neighbors.

They spent most of lunch listening to Fidelity read the

mail that was delivered the day before. One special letter received her particular attention. It was a letter from her cousin, Constance, and it contained news from her dear mother, who had just arrived back from a mission of mercy attending to another relative of hers, a widow whose name was Assurance. She had taken ill and had just that week gone to be with her Lord, carried by the angels to the Celestial City.

Faithless wondered that the news of this person's death was received by Great-Heart and Fidelity with what seemed to him to be a cheerful and slightly careless response.

 I Thessalonians 4:13

Faithless: Did you know the widow, Assurance?

Fidelity: Oh yes, and very well. She was a dear friend and a close relative of mine as she was my aunt, my mother's sister.

     Faithless, not wanting to offend, tried to stay silent on the matter but finally could not keep from asking.

Faithless: If the widow, Assurance, was a close friend and relative, I wonder why her death has not had more of an effect on you. In my neighborhood, when a relative dies it is a cause for great sorrow and grief that sometimes goes on for weeks.

 I Thessalonians 4:17

     Fidelity was unruffled by the inference as she looked at Faithless and smiled and answered him straightly.

Fidelity: When I first read the news yesterday I was greatly affected and could not stop the tears. But then, my confidence rose up within me as I thought of how my dear aunt's condition has changed from the constant sorrows that attend this world to the peace and joy that is the birthright of all who have put their faith in the promises of the King's Son.

Faithless: Yes, and it is the same in my city. When a near relative or friend dies, everyone comforts their neighbor by saying, "They have gone to a better place."

Fidelity: When that person was living did they constantly talk about the better place you speak of?

Faithless: No, they were occupied with the important things of this world and had not the time or inclination to speak or speculate about such matters as it would quench their enthusiasm for this present life. It is considered impolite to speak of such things except when it is unavoidable.

Fidelity: But then you say the mourning and sorrow for a loved one who dies goes on for weeks on end?

Faithless: Yes, and there is often one or two in the family who never quite recover from the shock of it.

Fidelity: If the proverb they recite is true—if they truly believe that the dead friend or relative has gone to a better place—then I wonder why the sorrow should be so severe and occupy such a space of time?

Faithless: I suppose because it is such a great shock. And I am sure the loss of a friend leaves an empty space in your heart that can never again be filled.

Fidelity: Never filled? How is this so? Don't you have confidence that you will also go to that "better place," and once there be reunited with your dead friend?

Faithless: Some say it, but I don't know anyone that truly believes that to be the case.

Fidelity: So, the proverb that "all the dead go to a better place" is better said than actually believed?

Faithless: I suppose there is some truth in what you have just said.

Fidelity: You have now discovered why my grief and the grief of my father, upon hearing the news, seems to you to be so unnatural and unfeeling.

Fidelity could see the tears form in her father's eyes and she knew without being told that some of those tears were reserved for the loss of his wife's sister, Assurance. She also knew a few of those tears were for Faithless who was without real hope in this world and had no certain hope of the world to come.

 II Corinthians 5:8-9

Faithless: It is a natural thing to grieve for a lost loved one.

Fidelity: Yes, it is, and I have bottled my tears for my dear aunt and will feel her loss but not as keenly as you might imagine in the natural because I read in the King's Book that the King Himself rejoices in the death of the righteous saints.

 Psalm 116:15, Exekiel 33:11

To this, Faithless had no answer and was relieved when he was given leave to think about it no more when Great-Heart spoke.

Talkative

Great-Heart: I see you have finished your soup; would you like another bowl?

Faithless: No, I am quite satisfied. And then he thanked Fidelity who received the compliments of Faithless with a smile.

Great-Heart: Would you like to continue the telling of your dream here at the table or would you like to retire to the living room?

Just then a dish of hot blackberry crisp was exchanged for the empty soup bowl and the decision to stay was made without any further discussion.

Faithless: Now, where were we?

Great-Heart: We had just finished listening to Christian and Faithful each share their adventures as they traveled the King's Highway.

Faithless: Yes, I remember.

The next thing I saw in my dream as they continued on the way was Faithful turn his head and look behind him. There he saw a man whose name was Talkative, walking at a little distance in back of them.

 Ecclesiastes 5:3

He was a tall man and something more handsome when viewed from a distance than when he was close at hand.

The two pilgrims slowed their pace in order to let this man catch up to them. Then Faithful addressed himself in this manner:

Faithful: *Friend, where are you headed?*

Are you going to the heavenly country?

Talkative: *That is where I am going.*

Faithful: *Good, then I hope we shall enjoy your good company.*

Talkative: *I am happy for the company and happier still to be your companion.*

Faithful: *Come, let us go together and spend our time talking about things that are profitable.*

Talkative: *To talk of things that are good, to me is very acceptable, with you or with any others. I am glad I have met with those who are inclined to do a good work. To speak the truth, there are few who care to spend their time as such while they are in their travels, choosing much rather to be speaking of things of no profit. This has always troubled me.*

 Ephesians 5:5

Faithful: *That is something to be lamented, for what better use of the tongue and mouth than to speak about the God of Heaven?*

 Psalm 19:14

Talkative: *I like what you are saying and I like that you say it with such conviction. And to add to what you have said about how profitable it is to talk about the things of God, let me add that it is also pleasant. For instance, if a man delights to talk about history, or the mystery of things; or of miracles, wonders, or signs, where will he find things recorded so delightful, and so sweetly penned, as in the Holy Scripture?*

 I Timothy 4:7

Faithful: *That is true; but to profit by the things we talk about should be our chief design.*

Talkative: *That is what I said; to talk of such things is very profitable, for by so doing a man may get knowledge of many things such as the vanity of earthly*

Faithful and Talkative

*things, and the benefit of things above. By talking, a man may
learn about the necessity of the new birth, the insufficiency
of our works, the need of Christ's righteousness, etc. Besides
this, a man may learn what it is to repent, to believe, to pray,
to suffer, and the like. By this, also, a man may learn what are
the great promises and consolations of the Gospel, to his own
comfort. By talking, a man may learn to refute false opinions, to
vindicate the truth, and also to instruct the ignorant.*

Faithful: *All this is true and glad am I to hear you say them.*

Talkative: *Because there is not enough talk about these things is
the reason so few understand the need of faith, and the necessity
of a work of grace in their soul in order to have eternal life. They
ignorantly live in the works of the law through which a man can
by no means obtain the Kingdom of Heaven.*

Faithful: *But I must add that heavenly knowledge of these things
is the gift of God; no man can attain them by human industry, or
only by the talking about them.*

 I Corinthians 2:14

Talkative: *Yes, I know all this very well; for a man can receive
nothing, except it be given him from Heaven: all is of grace, not of
works. I could give you a hundred scriptures that confirm this truth.*

Faithful: *Well, then, what is that one thing that we should talk
about at this time?*

Talkative: *Whatever you want to talk about. I will talk of things
heavenly, or things earthly; things moral, or things evangelical;
things sacred, or things profane; things past, or things to come;
things foreign, or things at home; things more essential, or things
circumstantial,provided that all be done to our profit.*

Now Faithful began to wonder at the fine words of Talkative and
stepping to Christian (for he was walking a little distance away by

himself), he said to him, but softly, *what a brave companion we have here! Surely, this man will make a very excellent pilgrim.*

At this, Christian modestly smiled, and said:

> **Christian**: *This man, with whom you are so taken, will beguile with this tongue dozens of pilgrims who don't know him.*

> **Faithful**: *Do you know him?*

> **Christian**: *Know him? Yes, better than he knows himself.*

> **Faithful**: *I pray you tell me who he is.*

> **Christian**: *His name is Talkative. He lives in the City of Destruction and I am surprised that he is a stranger to you.*

> **Faithful**: *Whose son is he and where does he live?*

> **Christian**: *He is the son of one, Say-Well. He lives in Prating-Row where he is known to all as Talkative of Prating-Row and, notwithstanding his fine tongue, he is a sorry fellow.*

> **Faithful**: *Well, he seems to be a very good man.*

Prating Row

> **Christian**: *Only to those who do not have a thorough acquaintance with him, for he is best abroad but the nearer to home he gets, the uglier he becomes. He is like the painter*

who paints a portrait that looks good from a distance but once you get up close, it looks like a mess.

 James 1:8, James 1:22-24

Faithful: *Are you jesting with me?*

Christian: *God forbid. I will give you a further insight into him.*

This man is for any company, and for any talk. As he talks now with you, so will he **Brabble*** *when he is on the ale-bench and the more he drinks, the more evil comes out of his mouth.*

The true faith that binds us together has no place in his heart, house, or lifestyle. All he has is in his tongue, and his religion is to make a big high-sounding noise.

Faithful: *If what you say is right, then I have been greatly deceived.*

Christian: *Deceived! You can be sure of it.*

Remember the proverb: They say, and do not; but the kingdom of God is not in word, but in power.

 Matthew 23:3, 1 Corinthians 4:20

He talks of prayer, of repentance, of faith, and of the new birth; but he knows but only to talk of them.

I have been in his family and have observed him both at home and

Notwithstanding his fine tongue, he is a miserable person

---

* **Brabble**—To brabble is to argue loudly about matters of no importance.

abroad. I know what I say of him is the truth. His house is as empty of true faith as the white of an egg is of savor. In his home there is neither prayer, nor sign of repentance for sin. A dumb mule serves God far better than he does.

He is the very stain, reproach, and shame of our faith to all who know him.

 Romans 2:24-25

There is not one good report of him in all of the town where he dwells.

The common people who know him say that he is a saint abroad, and a devil at home. His poor family finds it so; he is such a foul man with a profane temper often given to fits of rage. He is so unreasonable with his servants that they do not know how to, nor do they dare, to speak to him.

Talkative is a saint abroad and a devil at home

Men that have any dealings with him say it is better to deal with a Turk than with him, for he is a cheat and a liar when it is to his advantage.

This man Talkative (if it be possible) is worse than the worst of men who defraud, beguile, and overreach and besides all that, he brings up his sons to follow in his footsteps. If he finds in any of them even the slightest sign of ethics, honesty or a tender conscience, he calls them fools and blockheads and takes away their means for making a living.

For my part, I am of the opinion that he has, by his wicked life, caused many to stumble and fall; and will be, if God does not intervene, the ruin of many more.

Faithful: *Well, my brother, I am bound to believe you, not only because you say you know him, but also because, like a Christian, you make your reports of men in light of the truth. For I cannot believe that you speak these things out of ill-will, but because they are true.*

Christian: *Had I made his acquaintance as you just have, I might have thought of him as you did. If I had heard a report about him from those who hate Christ and those who follow Him, I might have thought it a slander by his enemies. But all these things, yes, and a great many more just as bad from my own personal knowledge prove him guilty. Besides, good men are ashamed of him; they do not call him brother or friend. When they hear his name spoken it makes them blush.*

 II Timothy 3:5-7

Faithful: *Well, I see now that saying and doing are two different things and from now on, I will observe this distinction more carefully.*

Christian: *Yes, saying and doing are two different things indeed, and are as diverse from each other as the soul and the body. As the body without the soul is just a dead carcass so it is with saying a thing that is not connected with the doing of a thing. If the saying stands alone, it is a dead thing.*

 James 2:18

The soul of our faith is the practical part. Pure religion and undefiled before God the Father is this, to visit the fatherless and widows in their affliction, and to keep himself unspotted from the world.

 James 1:27

Talkative is not aware of this and he thinks that hearing and saying will make a good Christian; by this error he deceives his own soul. Hearing is like sowing of the seed; talking is not sufficient to bring forth living fruit.

And we both know that at the day of doom, men shall be judged according to their fruits.

 Matthew 13:23

On that day it will not be asked, did you believe? But, were you doers of the Word of God or talkers only? And accordingly all shall be judged by the true Gospel that always produces fruit in a man's life.

 John 5:39, James 2:19-20

The end of the world is compared to a harvest, Matthew 13:30, and you know that the men who do the harvesting are looking for nothing but fruit. Not that anything can be accepted that is not of faith, but faith without works reveals itself to be a false faith of no value. I am telling you this to show you how insignificant the profession of Talkative will be on the final day of judgment.

 Matthew 7:11

Faithful: *This brings to my mind what Moses said when he described the beast that is clean as one that parts the hoof and chews on the cud.*

 Deuteronomy 14:7

Not one who parts the hoof only or that chews the cud only.

The hare chews the cud but is still unclean because he does not part the hoof. Truly this resembles Talkative who chews the cud, seeks knowledge and chews upon the Word, but he does not divide the hoof.

Faithless stopped at this point in the dream and asked Great-Heart if he would explain the meaning of what sounded to his ears to be a mystery.

Great-Heart: The chewing of the cud is a picture and type of someone who reads the Word of God and meditates upon it both day and night. Yes, it is true that he loves to discuss the things written in the Bible, but not just for the sake of talking about them.

 Romans 10:2

The parting of the hoof is a picture of departing from the sinful ways of the world and living a life free from its policies and wicked practices.

The one thing, chewing the cud, is necessary because without it we would not be acquainted with God's warnings or His promises.

Without the Word to light our path, we would not find the true testimony of how God's Son came to rescue the sinner and how by faith we can receive His free gift of salvation.

 Romans 10:9-10

Without meditating on God's Word, we would never know the mind of God the Father or His Son. And if we do not know His mind, then we do not know to do His will.

What God would have us do is not something we are meant to always be reading, as if we are young lads in school under the tutelage of the schoolmaster. No, we are to eagerly devour God's Word in order that we may know His mind and then with that in our heart we understand what to do when presented with both the opportunities and trials of life. Of course, none of this is even possible except that the Spirit of God indwells and enables all those who have trusted in the atoning work of His Son.

The one thing leads to the other. A true knowledge and love for God's Word and His testimony of salvation and redemption, once received by faith, produces a work in the heart that also produces a life that is changed and can be seen as distinctive and different from the lives of the earth-dwellers who love the world and the things in the world.

 1 John 2:16

Do you understand?

Faithless: Yes, thank you, I understand.

Shall I continue telling my dream?

Great-Heart: Please do!

Faithless: This is what I heard Christian say to Faithful:

> **Christian**: *You have spoken the truth and now I am certain you understand that our faith is not just about talk, but it manifests itself in deeds as well.*
>
> *And I will add one more thing: Saint Paul, the Apostle to the Church, called some men who were great talkers, sounding brass and tinkling cymbals.*
>
> *1 Corinthians 13:1-3*
>
> *In another place, Saint Paul says that talk alone is like things without life giving sound: things without life. That is, without the true faith and grace of the Gospel, and consequently things that are only talk, without true life, shall never enter into the Kingdom of Heaven or be found among those who are the children of life; even if their sound be as it were the tongue or voice of an angel.*
>
> *1 Corinthians 14:7*

Faithful: *Well, I was not so fond of this man's company at first, but I am sick of it now.*

What shall we do to be rid of him?

 Matthew 7:25

Christian: *Take my advice, and do as I say, and you shall find that he will soon be sick of your company too, except God shall touch his heart, and turn it.*

 I Peter 4:4

Faithful: *What would you have me to do?*

Christian: *Why, go to him, and enter into some serious discourse about the power of religion. Ask him plainly (when he has approved of it, for that he will), whether these things are manifesting themselves in his heart, are seen to be operating in his house and unfolding in his life.*

Faithless: Then, in my dream, I saw Faithful step forward and say:

Faithful: *How are you doing?*

Talkative: *Very well indeed; but I thought by now we might have had a great deal to talk about.*

Faithful: *Well, if you will allow me, I will propose a question that is worthy of discussion.*

Talkative: *Very good! Yes, let's consider your worthy question.*

Faithful: *Since you left it with me to state the question, let it be this:*

How does the saving grace of God discover itself when it is in the heart of man?

Talkative: *This is a very good question.*

Yes indeed! I perceive that you want to talk about the power of things. Well, that is something I am willing and able to answer you.

In brief, first, where the grace of God is in the heart, it causes there to be a great outcry against sin. And secondly...

Faithful: *Wait a minute, hold on; let us consider your answers one at a time. I think you would be more accurate to say it shows that grace, when it is in the heart, inclines the soul to abhor its own sin.*

 Job 42:2

Talkative: *What difference is there between crying out against and abhorring of sin?*

Faithful: *Oh! A great deal of difference. A man may cry out against sin as a principle or policy; but he cannot truly abhor it except by virtue of a Godly hatred of it.*

I have heard many cry out against sin in the pulpit who let the same sin abide happily in their own heart, house, and conduct.

 Genesis 39:15

Joseph's mistress cried out with a loud voice, as if she was very holy; but she would willingly, notwithstanding that, have committed fornication with Joseph. Some cry out against sin, even as the mother cries out against her child in her lap, when she calls it a naughty girl, and then immediately begins hugging and kissing it.

Talkative: *I can see that you are trying to trick me.*

Faithful: *No, I am only for setting things right. But what is the second thing that you believe would prove the discovery of a work of grace in the heart?*

Talkative: *Great knowledge of Gospel mysteries.*

Faithful: *This sign should have been first: but, first or last, it is also false; for knowledge, great knowledge, may be obtained in the mysteries of the Gospel without the attending work of grace in the soul.*

Even if a man has all knowledge, he may yet be nothing and so, consequently, he may not be a child of God.

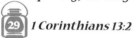 *1 Corinthians 13:2*

Christ Himself said, "Do you know all these things?" and the disciples answered, "Yes!"

Then Jesus added, "Blessed are ye if ye do them."

Christ did not pronounce the blessing in the knowing of them, but in the doing of them. For there is a knowledge that is not attended with doing: he who knoweth his Masters will, and does it not.

 James 4:17

A man may know like an angel and not be a Christian; therefore, your second sign that signifies the work of grace in the soul is not true.

To know is something that pleases talkers and boasters; but to do is that which pleases God.

Do not misunderstand what I am saying. The heart cannot be good without knowledge, for without knowledge the heart is ignorant.

There are two sorts of knowledge: knowledge that relies on the bare speculation of things, and knowledge that is accompanied with the grace of faith and love, which results in a man doing the will of God from the heart.

The first kind of knowledge will serve the talker; but without the other, the true Christian is not content.

"Give me understanding, and I shall keep your law; yea, I shall observe it with my whole heart."

 Psalm 119:34

Talkative: *You are trying to catch me in a lie and this is not edifying.*

Faithful: *Well, if you please, propose another sign of how the work of grace discovers itself in the heart of man.*

Talkative: *No, I will not, for I see that we will not agree.*

 Amos 3:3

Faithful: *Well, if you will not, will you give me permission to do it for you?*

Talkative: *You are free to do whatever you wish.*

Faithful: *A work of grace in the soul discovers itself both to him who has it, and to standers-by.*

To him who has God's grace, it gives him conviction of sin and exposes the defilement of his nature along with the sin of unbelief. It is grace that first convinces a man that he will surely be damned if he does not find mercy by God's hand and by faith in Jesus Christ.

This sight and sense of things works in him sorrow and shame for sin.

 Psalm 38:18, Jeremiah 31:19, John 16:8, Romans 7:24, Mark 16:16, Galatians 2:16, Revelation 1:6

He finds revealed to him the Savior of the world, and the absolute necessity of being bound to Him in order to obtain life.

He finds himself hungry and thirsty for Christ alone.

These are signs that true grace is at work in the heart of a man and this is the man to whom the promises are given.

Now, according to the strength or weakness of his faith in his Savior, in the same proportion he will receive joy and peace.

His love of holiness will be the thing that causes him to desire to know Him more, and also to serve Him in this world.

But even though, I say, this is the way grace is discovered in a man, yet it is seldom the case that the man will conclude at the time that it is grace at work. The corruption of man confuses his ability to reason.

The man awakened to his guilt will find himself confused and will misjudge what is happening to him.

Man, under the conviction of sin, is often the first witness to the fact that God's grace is at work in his heart. But the man under conviction almost always misjudges what is actually happening in his own soul. It is only after his reason and a sound mind is restored by God's grace, followed by faith in the finished work of God's Son, that he is able to conclude that a work of grace has taken place in his soul.

So, anyone having had this work of grace cannot judge it until God has restored very sound judgment. Then, with steadiness, he can conclude that what has taken place is a true work of grace.

 John 16:9, Galatians 2:15-16, Acts 4:12, Matthew 5:6, Revelation 21:6

Now to the question of how others perceive that a work of grace has taken place in a man's heart; to others the grace of God demonstrates itself and is discovered in the heart and soul.

1. *By an outward confession of his faith in Christ.*

2. *By a life answerable to that confession; a life of holiness, heart-holiness, family-holiness, (if he has a family), and by conduct-holiness in the world. This in general teaches him inwardly to abhor his sin in himself and in his family, and to promote holiness in the world: not by talk only, as a hypocrite or a talkative person may do, but by a practical demonstration of faith and love of the power of the word.*

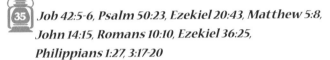 *Job 42:5-6, Psalm 50:23, Ezekiel 20:43, Matthew 5:8, John 14:15, Romans 10:10, Ezekiel 36:25, Philippians 1:27, 3:17-20*

And now, Talkative, to this brief description of the work of grace, and also the discovery of it, if you have a reason to object then please do so now. If not, then I will propose to you another question.

Talkative: *No, for my part I am not here to debate but to listen, let me hear your question.*

Faithful: *The question is this: Have you truly experienced the grace of God at work in your life? Does your life and conduct testify to the fact that this work is a genuine work of God?*

 *II Corinthians 5:17*

Or is your religion only to talk in words and not in deed and truth?

Please give me your answer to this question and only tell the truth as you can be sure that God is listening. Also, only tell me things that your own conscience can justify. Remember that the one who commends himself is not approved, but only those whom the Lord commends. To say that you are such and such and so and so when your conduct, witnessed by all my neighbors who know it to be a lie, is great wickedness.

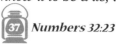 **Numbers 32:23**

At first Talkative began to blush but then, recovering himself, he replied:

Talkative: *You talk about experience, about conscience, about God, asking me to appeal to Him for justification of what is spoken. This kind of discourse I did not expect, nor am I disposed to give you an answer to such questions.*

I do not consider myself under any obligation to answer your questions. I refuse to allow you to be my judge. But I would like you to tell me why you ask me such questions.

Faithful: *Because I noticed that your quick and bold talk is just talk. I have heard of you and know that you are a man whose religion lies in talk only, and that your conduct proves your mouth-profession to be a lie.*

They say you are a spot among Christians and that true religion is the worse off because of your ungodly conduct.

 Jude 1:12

*I hear that some have already stumbled because of your wicked ways, and that more are in danger of being destroyed by the way you live your life. Your religion is not mixed up with **Adam's Ale*** but with the spirits of the ale-house where your talk is not so holy but carnal, foul, full of covetousness, uncleanness, swearing and lying.*

 *Ephesians 5:5*

---

* Adam's Ale—A light hearted term for water, the only drink for Adam and Eve.

*I also know that the company you keep is with vain and worthless men and that you are notorious for your **Bawdreaming**.**

The proverb is true of you which is said of a harlot, to wit, that she is a shame to all women; so are you a shame to all those whose lives match their testimony, as yours does not.

Talkative: *Since you are so ready to take up reports and to judge so rashly as you do, I cannot but conclude you are some peevish or melancholy man, not fit to be discoursed with and so, I bid you good-bye.*

Then Christian came up to Faithful and said:

Christian: *I told you how it would happen; your words and his lusts could not agree. He would rather leave your company than reform his life.*

 John 3:18-19

But now he is gone, as I said he would be. Let him go, the loss is his alone. He has saved us the trouble of going with him and by so doing would seem to be condoning his behavior which would be a blot on us. Besides, the apostle says, from such withdraw yourself.

 I Corinthians 5:11

Faithful: *I am glad I had this little discourse with him; it may happen that he will think of it again. I have dealt plainly with him and so am clear of his blood if he perishes.*

 Ezekiel 3:18

Christian: *You did well to talk to him as plainly as you did.*

---

* **Bawdreaming**—Bawdy misbehavior.

There is very little plain speaking or faithful dealing with men now-a-days, and that causes religion to stink.

There are plenty of these talkative fools whose religion is only in word, who are debauched and vain in their conduct. Why these men are admitted into the fellowship of the godly is a puzzle to me since they are a blemish on Christianity and a vexation and discouragement to the sincere believers.

I wish that all men would deal with such talkers as you have done with Talkative. If this was the general practice among true Christians, then these fakers and frauds would soon leave the company of the saints and both would be better off for it.

 Jude 1:16

Faithful: *Both? I know the true Christian would be better off but how would it improve the Talkatives of this world?*

Christian: *They would discover that for all their talk, godly men see them for what they really are and that disclosure might cause them to repent.*

Remember how Talkative at first lifts up his plumes?

Consider how bravely he speaks of things without experience!

Notice how he presumes to drive down all before him!

*He truly is a **Cockalorum**!**

And yet, in one discourse, he is driven from true pilgrims.

That is a good thing for us and him, since his conduct is now revealed as the proof that his talk is insincere and worthless.

---

* Cockalorum—A small man with a big opinion of himself.

It would be a good thing to drive these fellows from our fellowship. But I doubt it will happen, generally since the policy of the age is to accept all things without any discernment. This policy has been the ruin of many a Christian who sees the life of the talkers in their midst and think that if it is alright with them, then they need pay little attention to the conduct of their own lives.

And then I saw in my dream that Christian and Faithful went ahead of Talkative who held back until he was a good distance away from them.

Great-Heart: And is this the end of your dream so far?

Faithless: Yes, it is.

The two men chatted as Fidelity cleared and cleaned the table. After the space of about half an hour, Faithless bid goodbye and returned to the City of Destruction. There he spent much time meditating upon all that had been revealed to him in his dream as he anxiously waited for the next episode.

CHAPTER 19

VANITY FAIR

Great-Heart was busy working in his garden when he spied Faithless coming up through the meadow and toward the King's Cottage. As soon as he saw Faithless, he went to the kitchen window and tapped to get Fidelity's attention. Fidelity, who was busy baking biscuits, wiped her brow and cheerfully opened the window.

Fidelity: What is it, Father?

Great-Heart: I just saw Faithless coming up the meadow and he should be here in no less than a quarter of an hour. I need to get cleaned up, so if he arrives before I am ready to greet him, please bring him into the kitchen and serve him a biscuit with what is left of the blackberry jam.

Fidelity laughed.

Fidelity: Father, you ate the last of the blackberry jam this morning, but I do have a jar of plum preserves that just arrived yesterday from one of our near neighbors.

Great-Heart: Ah, that will do nicely.

Great-Heart made his way to the back door, clapped his boots together and then gingerly made his way through the kitchen and into his room. He soon made himself ready for his guest and then plunged to his knees as he prayed out loud that the King would give him the wisdom to know how to minister to Faithless.

 James 1:5

Great-Heart made his way back to the kitchen where he found Faithless seated and sipping a hot cup of tea as he nibbled on a biscuit lavished with plum preserves.

Great-Heart: How goes it with you, my dear friend?

Faithless: I am fine, although my latest dream is most distressing.

Great-Heart: How so?

Before Faithless began to tell the story of his dream, Great-Heart ushered him into the living room where they were seated in front of a small fire, as the weather had turned from mild to chilly.

Faithless began to share his dream with Great-Heart.

Faithless: In my dream, just when Christian and Faithful were almost out of the wilderness, Faithful chanced to look back and spied someone coming after them.

Great-Heart: Who was it?

Evangelist reminds Christian and Faithful that they will have persecution in this world

Faithless: It was someone we all know, and I am surprised he is not here to tell the tale himself.

Great-Heart: Please tell me what you witnessed in your dream.

Faithless: This is what I saw and heard:

> **Faithful**: *Someone is coming to meet us.*

Christian looked back behind himself.

Christian: *It is my good friend, Evangelist.*

Faithful: *Indeed, and my good friend also, for it was Evangelist who set me on the way to the Narrow Gate.*

Christian and Faithful then slowed their pace in order that he might catch up with them. After a few minutes, Evangelist came up and saluted them.

Evangelist: *Peace be with you, my friends.*

Christian: *Welcome, welcome, the sight of you reminds me of all your kindness and unwearied labors for my eternal good.*

Faithful: *And a thousand times welcome! Your company refreshes my soul!*

Evangelist: *How has it fared with you, my friends, since the time of our last parting?*

What have you met along the way and how have you con-
ducted yourself?

Faithless: Christian and Faithful told him of all things that had happened to them in the way; and how, with great difficulty, they had finally arrived at this place.

> **Evangelist**: *I am glad to hear it, not that you have met with*
> *trials, but that you have been victorious, and despite your*
> *weakness, continued in the way faithfully to this very day.*
>
> *Philippians 4:13*

> *I am glad about this not just for my own sake but also*
> *for yours. I have sowed, and you have reaped. The day is*
> *coming when both the one who sows, and those who reap*
> *will rejoice together.*
>
> *John 4:36*

> *That is, if you hold out; for in due season ye shall reap,*
> *if ye faint not.*
>
> *Galatians 6:9*

> *The crown is before you, and it is an incorruptible crown;*
> *so, run that ye may obtain it.*
>
> *1 Corinthians 9:24-27*

> *Some set out to obtain this crown, and after a little while some-*
> *one comes along and takes it from them. Hold fast to what you*
> *have; let no man take your crown from you.*
>
> *Revelation 3:11*

Then Evangelist paused from speaking to them as he gathered the two of them together as a hen would gather her chicks.

Evangelist: *Brothers, I am here to give you encouragement and a warning.*

You are not yet out of the gunshot of the devil; you have not resisted unto blood, striving against sin.

Let the kingdom be always before you and believe steadfastly concerning the things that are now invisible.

Let nothing that is on this earth get between you and the world to come.

And, above all, look well to your own hearts and to the lusts thereof; for the heart of man is deceitful above all things, and desperately wicked.

 Jeremiah 17:9

Set your faces like a flint; you have all power in heaven and earth on your side.

 Proverbs 4:27

Christian: *Thank you for your exhortations. Please stay with us as we walk along the way in order to help us.*

Faithful: *We know you are a prophet and can tell us not only about things that might happen to us, but how we can resist and overcome.*

Evangelist: *I will do as you have requested for a little while since I am here to warn you about just such a matter.*

My sons, you have heard in the Word of the truth of the Gospel, that you must go through many tribulations before you enter into the Kingdom of Heaven; and again, that in every city, bonds and afflictions will follow you. There-fore, you cannot expect that you should go long on your pilgrimage without trials and tribulation.

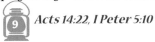 ***Acts 14:22, I Peter 5:10***

You have already found the truth about what I am telling you. And I am here to inform you that more tribulation is just up ahead of you.

As you can see, you are almost out of the wilderness. You will soon come to a town where you will be assaulted by many enemies who will try and kill you, and you can be sure that one or both of you must seal the testimony which you hold with your own blood.

Great-Heart: How did Christian and Faithful treat this news?

Faithless: Not as I thought they would.

Great-Heart: And how did you think they would greet the news that one or both of them would soon be facing death?

Faithless: I thought they would have fainted at the news and sought some other way to get around the city. But since the path went right through the middle of it, they did not even consider taking a byway in order to escape. And I might add, they received the news without any fear; it actually seemed to make them more resolute and determined than ever to prove themselves loyal followers of the King.

Great-Heart: What did you see next?

Faithless: I can tell you what I heard Evangelist say to the two pilgrims.

> **Evangelist**: *You must be faithful even unto death; the King will give you the crown of life. Even though one of you should die in this wicked city and under circumstances that may be filled with pain and end in a death that is unnatural, be assured that the one who dies will be better off than the one who is spared.*

Great-Heart: Did you hear my brother, Evangelist, tell them why it would be better for the one who died than for the one spared?

Faithless: Yes, I did. This is what your brother told the two pilgrims:

> **Evangelist:** *It will be better for the one who dies because you will arrive at the Celestial City sooner than your fellow pilgrim.*
>
> *Not only will one of you enter into the kingdom before the other, but the one who escapes death will meet with many miseries that the other will not meet during the rest of his journey.*
>
> *Philippians 1:23*
>
> *I want to encourage you both to be steadfast and courageous, giving your soul over to our God and faithful Creator.*

Faithless: In my dream, when they were out of the wilderness, they soon saw a town before them with the name, Vanity. In the town there is a Fair called Vanity Fair. I heard Evangelist instruct Christian and Faithful.

> **Evangelist:** *The Fair is kept open all year-long. It has the name of Vanity Fair because the town where it is kept is lighter than vanity.*
>
> *Psalm 62:9*

We must go through this world before we arrive in Heaven

And also, because everything that is sold in the town is vanity.

 Ecclesiastes 11:8, 1:2-14, 2:11-17, Isaiah 40:17

The Fair is nothing new; it has been standing since ancient times.

Christian: *Please tell me when and why this town with its Fair was first built?*

Evangelist: *Almost five thousand years ago there were pilgrims walking to the Celestial City just as you are now. Spying this Beelzebub, Apollyon, and Legion, along with their companions, and also seeing that the path the pilgrims must travel went right through the town of Vanity, they conspired together to set up a fair; a fair where all sorts of vanity should be promoted and sold.*

Faithful: *What is being promoted and sold in Vanity Fair?*

Evangelist: *Among the fair merchandise sold are houses, lands, trades, places, honors, preferments, titles, countries, kingdoms, lusts, pleasures and delights of all sorts. Additional merchandise sold includes harlots, wives, husbands, children, masters, servants, lives, blood, bodies, souls, silver, gold, pearls, precious stones, and whatnot.*

Moreover, at this fair you can see at any time juggling, cheats, games, plays, fools, apes, knaves, and rogues, and that of every kind.

This is also the place where there are thefts, murders, adulteries, false-swearers and the like.

Faithful: *Is that all that awaits us?*

Evangelist: *No. as in other fairs of less prestige, there are several rows and streets under their proper names where such and such unique wares are vended. There are streets named after countries and kingdoms where particular wares, common to that country, can be found and purchased.*

Christian: *Pray tell.*

Evangelist: *For an example, you are likely to see in Vanity Fair the Britain Row, the French Row, the Italian Row, the Spanish*

Row and the German Row where several other sorts of peculiar vanities are offered for sale.

But, as in other fairs, one commodity is the most highly promoted above all others. So, it is in Vanity Fair where the wares of Rome and her merchandise are greatly promoted.

Our English nation, along with some others, have taken a dislike to the prominence of Rome but they still abide it without much complaint.

Christian: *And you say our path goes through the middle of this wicked city with all its amusements, distractions, and temptations?*

Evangelist: *I must add one more thing because it is the summary of all you have mentioned and much more.*

Faithful: *And what would that be?*

Evangelist: *Vanity Fair is a trap, a pit, a place meant to capture your soul and make you unfit to enter the Celestial City. It is a gilded snare. Now, as I said, the way to the Celestial City lies just through this town, where this lusty Vanity Fair is standing; and if anyone would desire to go to the Celestial City he must go through this town and the only escape from it is death.*

 1 Corinthians 4:10

The Prince of princes, the King's Son Himself, when He was here, went through this town to His own country, and that also upon a fair-day. It was Beelzebub, the chief lord of this fair, that invited him to buy of his vanities and would have made him lord of the fair if only he would show him reverence and worship him as he went through Vanity Fair.

 *Matthew 4:9*

Beelzebub led him from street to street and showed him all the kingdoms of the world in an instant of time that he might, if possible, allure that blessed One to be tempted and buy some of his vanities. But the King's

Christian and Faithful enter Vanity Fair

Son had no regard at all for the merchandise or for Vanity Fair, and He left the town without paying out so much as one penny for its vanities.

 Matthew 4:8-9, Luke 4:5-7

Great-Heart: What happened next?

Faithless: The two pilgrims, Christian and Faithful, entered the fair. As soon as they entered there was a disturbance throughout the entire fair.

Great-Heart: Why was there a disturbance?

Faithless: First, the pilgrims were clothed with raiment that was different from the raiment of any who traded in the Fair. The people of the fair gazed upon them; some said they were fools, some that they were bedlams and others that they were outlandish men.

 1 Corinthians 4:9-10

Secondly, as the men of Vanity Fair gazed and wondered about the apparel worn by Christian and Faithful, they also wondered at their speech because no one could understand what they said.

Christian and Faithful spoke naturally the language of Canaan; but those who kept the fair were the men of this world. So, from one end of the fair to the other, they each seemed barbarians to the other.

 17 *1 Corinthians 2:7-8*

Thirdly, Christian and Faithful paid little attention to the wares of Vanity Fair. They could not be bothered to even look at the merchandise. When the merchants called out to them to come to look and buy the merchandise, Christian and Faithful would put their fingers in their ears and cry out, "Turn away my eyes from beholding vanity," and look upward, signifying that their trade and traffic was in Heaven.

 18 *Psalm 119:37, Philippians 3:20-21*

Christian and Faithful refuse to love this world and all its vanities

Great-Heart: What else do you remember?

Faithless: I do remember one incident and I will report it to you as I witnessed, but first I would like to ask you a question.

Great-Heart: I will be glad to answer if I can.

Faithless: The first thing that the townsfolk of Vanity Fair noticed was that Christian and Faithful wore different apparel.

Why is that and what does it mean?

Great-Heart: You have asked an important question.

The clothing worn by Christian and Faithful is a picture of their character. It is character that is being changed by the continual work of the indwelling Spirit of God.

There is, or there certainly should be, a great difference between the way those who are on the King's Highway headed for the Celestial City conduct themselves and how the men of this world conduct themselves.

This difference is pictured in your dream as apparel. The apparel worn by Christian and Faithful is an outward sign of an inward work that should be noticed by all as it distinguishes them from the general character of those who dwell in Vanity Fair. Vanity Fair is a picture of the world all dressed up to go to a ball or party. It is the glamour and pride of the ages.

 I Peter 3:3, I Peter 4:4

Faithless: That is helpful and I am beginning to understand, but why are the citizens of Vanity Fair so exercised and agitated by behavior that should be lauded as good and decent?

Great-Heart: Do you mean things like honest dealings with your neighbor, covenant keeping, keeping your tongue from gossip, truth-telling, fidelity and purity of heart, not speaking evil, shunning what is vile and unholy, and the like?

Faithless: Yes, and I could add being peaceful and not given to fits of temper and violence.

Great-Heart: Yes, I see that together we could recite a very long list of things that make up a man's good character. As to why it so agitated the citizens of Vanity Fair, the answer is simple.

Faithless: I am anxious to hear it.

Great-Heart: It can all be summed up in one word.

Faithless: And what word is that?

Great-Heart: Censure!

A holy life lived in accordance with the Word of God, enabled by the Holy Spirit, to love what is good and hate what is evil is an affront to all those who are carnal and living lives full of sin. The man or woman with Godly character is an offense because they stir up the conscience of evil men who resist anything that condemns them, even without a word being spoken.

Christian and Faithful resist the temptations of this world

The King's Son told all those who would follow Him that as He was hated by the world, so those of us who love and follow Him will be hated also.

 John 15:18

Unfortunately, in this time of great spiritual laxness, there is too often little difference between the character of Christians and the men of the world.

We will talk more about this later. I would like to hear the one incident you wanted to report.

Faithless: Yes. In my dream I heard one of the merchants in Vanity Fair mockingly yell to Christian, "What will you buy?" And this is what I heard Christian say:

> **Christian**: *We buy the truth.*
>
> *Proverbs 23:23, Matthew 13:45-46*

Faithless: What so surprised me is how quickly that one simple answer gave rise to an occasion for mocking and taunting. Some even called on the men of the fair to strike Christian and Faithful.

This caused a hubbub and a great stir in the fair, so much so that chaos broke out all over Vanity Fair.

News of this hubbub was brought to the Great One of the fair who quickly came down and deputized his most trusted friends to arrest both Christian and Faithful and bring them into the town hall to be investigated.

So, before long Christian and Faithful were brought in and interrogated by the leaders of Vanity Fair. While it is vivid in my memory, I will report what I heard and saw in my dream.

Christian and Faithful are hated by those that serve the god of this world

Mr. Hate-Good: *Where have you come from and where are you going?*

Mr. Scorn: *Why are you wearing such outrageous garb?*

Christian: *We are pilgrims and strangers in this world and we are going to our own country, which is the Heavenly Jerusalem.*

 Hebrews 11:13-16

Faithful: *We have given no occasion to the men of the town, nor any of the merchandisers, any reason to abuse us.*

Mr. Love-the-World: *Did you or did you not insult one of our esteemed merchants telling him that you would not buy his wares as you were only interested in buying the truth?*

 I John 1:4

Christian: *Yes, this is true.*

Mr. Sneering: *I don't believe that you two rascals are anything but bedlams and madmen.*

Mr. Suspicion: *I think you are spies who have been sent here by the enemies of our fair in order to create confusion and cause us to lose our profit from trading in the luxuries that grace our fair.*

 Romans 14:16-19

Great-Heart: And what happened next?

Faithless: They took Christian and Faithful into the public square where they beat them and smeared them with dirt, and then put them into a cage in order to make a spectacle of them in front of all the citizens of Vanity Fair.

Great-Heart: How long did they leave them in the cage?

Faithless: They were left there for some time and were made the objects of many man's sport, malice, or revenge. The Great One of the fair was the worst of them all, as he bragged and laughed continually.

Great-Heart: What did he brag about?

Faithless: He bragged to all who would listen to him, how the circumstances of Christian and Faithful had gone from bad to worse, with the worse yet to come.

Great-Heart: How did Christian and Faithful conduct themselves?

Faithless: Like true men. They were patient and did not respond to the verbal abuse except to bless and give good words for bad and kindness for injuries. Some men in the fair were more observing and less prejudiced than the rest.

 *Matthew 5:12*

Great-Heart: What did they do and say?

Faithless: Some of them began to blame the baser citizens of the fair for their continual abuse and did what they could to check their behavior.

Great-Heart: And how was that received?

Faithless: The bullies got angry with the kinder citizens of Vanity Fair and began cursing and insulting them and calling them traitors and confederates of Christian and Faithful.

The others replied they could see that Christian and Faithful were quiet and sober men who intended nobody any harm; and that there were many who traded in their fair that were worthier to be put into the cage, yea, and pillory too, than were the men whom they were abusing.

 II Peter 2:12

After many insults had passed between both sides, things went from angry words to fighting among themselves with fists and sticks, with many being injured.

This hubbub resulted in Christian and Faithful being brought up before their examiners again, where they were charged with being guilty of causing an insurrection in the town.

Great-Heart: And what happened next?

Faithless: They beat Christian and Faithful without any pity and then clapped them in irons. Then they led them in chains up and down the fair as an example and a warning to others not to speak in their behalf, or join themselves to them.

Christian and Faithful behaved themselves wisely and received the ignominy and shame that was cast upon them with so much meekness and patience, that it won to their side several more men in the fair.

 *Acts 17:32-34*

Great-Heart: Did this calm things down a little?

Faithless: No, indeed, it did not. As a matter of fact, this put the other party yet into an even greater rage, so much so that they concluded that the death of Christian and Faithful was the only thing that would put an end to the disturbance they had caused. They were further charged with causing treason in the town by seducing and subverting all those in the fair who had a good opinion of them.

They were then remanded to the cage again until further orders were forthcoming. So, they put them in and made their feet fast in the stocks.

Faithful and Christian in the cage

While in the cage, Christian and Faithful called to mind what they had heard from their faithful friend, Evangelist, and were even more confirmed in their determination to suffer as they had been told they must.

They also now comforted each other with speculation about whose lot it was to suffer the most. Christian and Faithful, secretly wishing that he might suffer the most, committed themselves to the all-wise disposal of Him Who rules over things.

When the time was come, they were brought before their enemies and arraigned for a trial.

 *Matthew 10:22*

Great-Heart: Do you remember the name of the presiding judge?

Faithless: I will never forget him. The judge's name was Lord Hate-good.

Great-Heart: I know this man very well and he is a disgrace to all who love true justice. He is from a family of Mugwumps and has become the chief **Mugwump*** among them in both name and nature.

And what were the charges filed in the indictment of Christian and Faithful?

Faithless: The charges were the same for both of them. They were charged with being enemies of and disturbers of the trade of Vanity Fair. They were charged with causing a commotion and divisions in the town, and with subverting a group of citizens of the town by spreading their own dangerous opinions, in contempt of the law of their prince.

Great-Heart: How did they answer these charges?

Faithless: Faithful was the first to answer the charges and this is what he said:

> **Faithful**: *I am only against those things that set themselves higher than the Highest. As for the disturbances, I deny the charges as I am a man of peace. As far as the parties who were won over, they were won over as they beheld the truth and innocence of myself and my brother, Christian. And as to the king you talk about, since he is Beelzebub, the enemy of my Lord, I defy him and all his angels.*

---

* **Mugwump**—A derogatory term for somebody in charge who pretends to be above petty squabbles and factions when actually he is neither impartial nor fair-minded.

Christian and Faithful rebuked and mistreated by the leaders of Vanity Fair

Faithless: Then a proclamation was made that anyone who had anything to say in favor of their lord Beelzebub and against the prisoner at the bar, should forthwith appear and give their evidence.

Great-Heart: Who appeared in the courtroom to testify against Faithful and Christian?

Faithless: Three witnesses appeared in the courtroom to testify: Envy, Superstition, and Pickthank.

All these three were then asked if they knew the prisoner at the bar and what they had to say for their lord, the king Beelzebub, and against Faithful. I will give you a faithful account of what they said and did.

Envy was the first one to take the stand.

Great Heart: Is there a more **Fliperous*** man in all of Vanity Fair? Please tell me what you witnessed.
Faithless: This is what he said:

> **Envy:** *I have known this man who calls himself Faithful a long time, and will attest upon my oath before this honorable bench, that he is...*

> **Judge:** *Hold on! You need to be sworn in before giving your testimony.*

---

* **Fliperous**—A proud gossip, a prattler.

Faithless: So, they swore Envy in.

> **Envy**: *My lord, this man Faithful, notwithstanding his plausible name, is one of the vilest men in our country. He neither regards prince nor people, law nor custom, but does all that he can to possess everyone he meets with certain of his disloyal notions, which he, in the general, calls principles of faith and holiness.*
>
> *I heard Faithful once say, that Christianity and the customs of our town of Vanity were diametrically opposite and could not be reconciled. By saying this, my lord, he not only condemns all our laudable works, but also those of us who do them.*
>
> **Judge**: *Have you any more to say?*
>
> **Envy**: *My lord, I could say much more, only I fear it would be tedious for the court. But if needs be, when the other gentlemen have given their evidence, in order that the charges against Faithful be complete, I will gladly appear again to give my enlarged testimony.*

Faithless: So, Envy was asked to stand by.

Then the Judge called Superstition to the stand and asked him to look at the prisoner. Then he was asked what he had to say for their lord, the king Beelzebub, and against Faithful.

Superstition was sworn in and gave his testimony.

> **Superstition**: *My lord, I have no real acquaintance with this man, nor do I desire to have further knowledge of him. However, this much I do know, he is a very pestilent fellow. Just the other day I heard him say that our religion was worthless and would not, in the end, be pleasing to God.*
>
> *In other words, Faithful believes our worship is in vain, we are yet in our sins, and finally shall be damned.*

Faithless: Following the testimony of Superstition, Pickthank was sworn in and asked what he knew on behalf of their lord, the king Beelzebub, and against the prisoner at the bar.

> Pickthank: *My lord, and you gentlemen of the jury, I have known this fellow for a long time and have heard him speak things that ought not to be spoken. I have heard him rail against our noble prince, Beelzebub, and he has also spoken contemptibly of his honorable friends whose names are: the Lord Old Man, the Lord Carnal Delight, the Lord Luxurious, the Lord Desire of Vain Glory, my Old Lord Lechery, and Sir Greedy, along with all the rest of our nobility.*
>
> *I heard Faithful once say that if all men were of his mind there would not be one of these noblemen left in the town. Besides, he has not been afraid to rail on you, my lord, who is now appointed to be his judge, calling you an ungodly villain, with many other such like vilifying terms, with which he has bespattered most of the gentry of our town.*

Faithless: When Pickthank was finished with his testimony, the judge directed his speech to the prisoner, Faithful, saying:

> Judge: *You runagate, heretic, and traitor; have you heard what these honest gentlemen have witnessed against you?*
>
> Faithful: *May I speak a few words in my own defense?*
>
> Judge: *What do you say? Speak!*
> *You do not deserve to live but to be slain immediately after this trial; yet, that all men may see our gentleness towards you, let us hear what you, a vile traitor, have to say.*
>
> Faithful: *1. In answer to what Mr. Envy has said, I never said anything but this, that whatever rules, laws, custom, or people are opposed and against the Word of God, they are diametrically the opposite of true Christianity. If I have spoken in error, convince me of my error and I am ready right here and now to recant.*

2. As to the second witness, Mr. Superstition, and his charge against me. What I actually said was that in the worship of God there is required a divine faith, but there can be no divine faith without a divine revelation of the will of God. Therefore, whatever is thrust into the worship of God that is not agreeable to divine revelation cannot be done except by a human faith, which is not the kind of faith that will result in eternal life.

3. As to what Mr. Pickthank has said, I deny the charge of railing and the like because it is a lie. As to that the prince of this town, with all the rabblement and his attendants, named by Mr. Pickthank, they are more fit for Hell than in this town and country. And so, the Lord have mercy upon me.

Faithless: Then the judge called to the jury, (who stood by to hear and observe all that had been said against Faithful):

Judge: *Gentlemen of the jury, you see this man, Faithful, who has caused such a great uproar in our town and you have also heard the charges these worthy gentlemen have brought against him. Also, you have heard his reply and confession. It is now up to you to hang him, or save his life; but before you deliberate on his fate, I need to instruct you in the ways of our law.*

First, be aware that there is a statute made in the days of Pharaoh the Great, servant to our prince, that, in case those of a contrary religion, such as the one held by Faithful, should multiply and grow too strong, their males should be thrown into the river.

 Exodus 1:22

There was also a statute made in the days of Nebuchadnezzar the Great, another of our lord's servants, that whoever would not fall down and worship his golden image, should be thrown into a fiery furnace.

 Daniel 3:6

There was also a statute made in the days of Darius, that whoever called upon any god but Darius should be cast into the lion's den.

 Daniel 6:7

Now, the substance and spirit of these laws this rebel Faithful has broken, not only in thought, which is bad enough, but also in word and deed, which is intolerable.

Furthermore, Pharaoh's law was made upon a supposition to prevent mischief, no crime being yet apparent; but here is a crime apparent.

For the second and third laws of Nebuchadnezzar and Darius, you can clearly see that Faithful disputes and slanders our religion; and for that treason, he has already confessed his guilt. In a word, the law demands that Faithful be put to death as he deserves to die.

Great-Heart: What happened next?

Faithless: It is hard for me to report as it saddens and troubles me.

Great-Heart: Please continue.

Faithless: The jury went out to deliberate.

Great-Heart: Do you remember the juror's names?

Faithless: I can hardly ever forget them because some are my relatives.

There were: Mr. Blindman, Mr. No-good, Mr. Malice, Mr. Love-lust, Mr. Live-loose, Mr. Heady, Mr. High-mind, Mr. Enmity, Mr. Liar, Mr. Cruelty, Mr. Hate-light and Mr. Implacable.

Great-Heart: And what did they decide?

Faithless: I think you already know.

But I will continue as you wish.

Every one of these men gave his private verdict against him. Afterward, they all unanimously concluded to bring Faithful before the judge where they condemned him as guilty and deserving death. This is what they said:

Mr. Blindman: *I see clearly that this man is a heretic.*

Mr. No-good: *Away with such a fellow from the earth.*

Mr. Malice: *I hate the very looks of him.*

Mr. Love-lust: *I could never endure him.*

Mr. Live-loose: *I agree with Mr. Love-Lust and would also add that this sorry man would make for bad company with all my noble companions.*

Mr. Heady: *Hang him, hang him!*

Mr. High-mind: *A sorry scrub.*

Mr. Enmity: *My heart rises up against him.*

Mr. Liar: *He is a rogue. Hanging is too good for him.*
Mr. Cruelty: *Let us dispatch him out of the way.*

Mr. Hate-light: *Yes, yes away with him.*

Mr. Implacable: *He is guilty and should be put to death.*

Great-Heart: It saddens me to hear this report.

What happened next?

Faithless: Faithful was taken from that place to the pillory where he was publicly humiliated and beaten. Faithful was then taken, half dead, to the place of execution where he was put to the cruelest death that could be invented.

According to their law, they first scourged him, then they buffeted him, then they lanced his flesh with knives; after that, they stoned him with stones, then pricked him with their swords; and last of all, they burned him to ashes at the stake.

Great-Heart: And how did you feel having witnessed this horror in your dream?

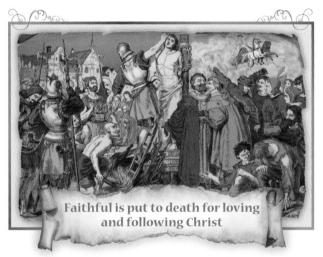

Faithful is put to death for loving
and following Christ

Faithless: Sir, it sickened me to see my kinsmen treat Faithful in this way. I was grieved in my spirit and even though it was in my dream, when I woke my pillow was soaked with my own tears.

Great-Heart: And then what happened?

Faithless: I beheld something that cheered and amazed me.

Great-Heart: Pray tell.

Faithless: I saw in my dream a crowd who mocked and railed against Faithful up until he lost consciousness. But then I saw a great multitude standing behind Faithful. I did not recognize them as they were not from Vanity Fair. They were dressed in white robes and some shone like the stars.

Great-Heart: Do you know who they are?

Faithless: I was hoping you could tell me.

Great-Heart: This is the cloud of witnesses that cheers on the saints of God, unseen in the heavens.

Faithless: So, I wonder why I saw them?

 Hebrews 12:1-2

Great-Heart: You were given a vision to see what most men, including myself, have never seen, at least not yet.

Faithless: And what is that?

Great-Heart thought for a moment before giving his answer.

Great-Heart: What you saw was a host of saints and angels who are there to welcome pilgrims into the Celestial City.

 Acts 7:55-56

Faithless: That helps me understand what I saw next in my dream.

Great-Heart: And what was that?

Faithless: I saw a chariot and a couple of horses arrive as if they were waiting for Faithful. And then I saw that as soon

Faithful ascends to the Celestial City

as his adversaries had dispatched him, Faithful took his last breath on this earth and disappeared into the ashes. He was taken up by angels and stood alive again; alive and no longer clothed in bloody spoiled garments, but adorned in splendid apparel as he was carried up through the clouds with the sound of a trumpeter.

Great-Heart: Did you see where he was taken?

Faithless: Yes, and for the first time I believe I witnessed what you had a vision of on the little hill outside your cottage, the one with the bench and the spyglass you named "Old Faithful."

Great-Heart: You saw the gates to the Celestial City?

Faithless: Sir, I saw his flight and then I saw a sight that almost blinded me even in my dream. I saw Faithful fly to the gates of the Celestial City.

Fidelity, who had been listening to the telling of the dream, burst into tears.

Faithless was touched by the outburst, and felt obliged to say:

Faithless: Fidelity, I am sorry that my vision has caused you such distress and sorrow. I am sorry for your tears.

Fidelity: Oh sir, do not be sorry as these are not tears of sorrow or pain but tears of overwhelming joy!

And now, my friend Faithless, you may begin to understand the nature of a true Christian's sorrow when a dear saint is taken to glory. Tears of sorrow mixed generously with tears of overwhelming joy and hope. Now you begin to understand the heart of the matter when it comes to death, that it is the only door to either everlasting peace and glory or to everlasting sorrow and torment.

Faithful has ended his journey in this world and has been gloriously ushered into the world to come where there is no more sorrow or tears.

Faithless was moved by the confession of Fidelity as he bowed his head and wondered what sort of greeting his death would bring. He feared it would not be the glorious parting as he witnessed with Faithful, but rather a solemn occasion that opened the door to Hell itself. This made him tremble and fear.

Great-Heart: And what about Christian?

Faithless: As for Christian, he had some respite and was remanded back to prison where he remained for a space of time. Then I saw Him Who overrules all things, having power over all things, alter the events that were aimed at the destruction of Christian, putting his enemies into a state of confusion. He then sent one of His mighty angels to release Christian and to escort him safely to the outskirts of Vanity Fair where Christian once again, absent his brother, Faithful, went his way up the King's path.

 Acts 12:5-11

And as he went, he sang:

> *Joy of every joy, the best*
> *Joy that brings the Pilgrim's rest.*
> *I will miss my Faithful friend,*
> *But only briefly for in the end*
> *I will be where he has gone,*
> *Joining Heaven's glorious throng!*
> CJL

Faithless: And this is where my dream ended.

Great-Heart: I have inquired of my King regarding your dream and he has sent me a messenger.

Faithless: And what did this messenger tell you?

Great-Heart: He told me that your dream, so far, has been about things that are for the present time. He further told me that your dream from this day going forward will be a vision of things that have not yet, but certainly will with the passage of time, unfold.

Faithless: What does this mean?

Great-Heart: To put it briefly, your dream has been about the past and the present and now begins to unfold the future of Christian as he takes his journey to the Celestial City.

CHAPTER 20
CHRISTIAN MEETS HOPEFUL

Fidelity entered the living room with a tray full of delicacies and a fresh pot of tea. She could see that her father and Faithless were lost in thought as they considered what seemed to Faithless to be a hard to understand episode in his dream.

Great-Heart: What happened after Christian left Vanity Fair?

Faithless took a sip of tea and then settled himself into the chair as he recounted the dream, still obviously a little shaken by what he viewed as the misfortune of Faithful.

Hopeful follows Christian out of Vanity Fair and they become brothers and companions in Christ

Faithless: I saw in my dream that Christian went out from Vanity Fair but not alone. There was a man named Hopeful who soon followed Christian out of Vanity Fair.

Great-Heart: Do you know why he followed Christian?

Faithless: Yes, he watched Christian and Faithful suffer with patience and joy, and it filled him with hope.

It was not long before Hopeful caught up with Christian as he made his way up the King's

Highway, and soon after, they entered into a brotherly covenant and became companions.

Great-Heart: So, one died to bear testimony to the truth, and another rises out of his ashes to be a companion with Christian on his pilgrimage.

Faithless: It would seem so. Hopeful also told Christian there were many more of the men in the fair whom he believed would follow after him in time.

Soon Christian and Hopeful were out of the district of Vanity Fair. It was then that they overtook a man who was going before them whose name was By-Ends.

Christian and Hopeful were soon in the man's company and Christian asked him:

> **Christian**: *What country do you come from, sir? And how long have you been in this way?*

> **By-Ends**: *I have come from the town of Fair-Speech, and I am going to the Celestial City.*

Faithless: In my dream I noticed something a bit odd.

Great-Heart: What was that?

Faithless: The man did not tell Christian his name. That aside, I will continue to report what Christian said to the man.

> **Christian**: *From Fair-Speech? Is there anyone good who lives there?*
> *Proverbs 26:25*

> **By-Ends**: *Yes, I hope so.*

> **Christian**: *Pray, sir, what may I call you?*

By-Ends: *I am a stranger to you and you to me; if you be going this way, I shall be glad of your company; but if not I must be content to continue on my own.*

Christian: *This town of Fair-Speech I have heard about and, as I remember, they say it's a wealthy place.*

By-Ends: *Yes, I can assure you that it is, and I have very many rich relatives who live there.*

Christian: *Pray, who are your kinsmen?*

By-Ends: *Almost the whole town and in particular: my Lord Turn-about, my Lord Time-server, my Lord Fair-Speech from whose ancestors that town first took its name. Also: Mr. Smooth-man, Mr. Facingboth-ways, Mr. Any-thing, and the parson of our parish, Mr. Two-tongues, who was my mother's own brother by father's side. To tell you the truth, I am become a gentleman of good quality and yet my great-grandfather was but a waterman, looking one way and rowing another; I made most of my fortune by the same occupation.*

Christian: *Are you a married man?*

By-Ends: *Yes, and my wife is a very virtuous woman, the daughter of a virtuous woman. She was my Lady Feigning's daughter and came from a very honorable family. She has arrived to such a height of breeding that she knows how to conduct herself in any company, be they princes or peasants.*

It is true that we somewhat differ in religion from those of the stricter sort in two small points.

Christian: *And what are those minor points?*

By-Ends: *First, we never strive against wind and tide. Secondly, we are always most zealous when religion goes about in his silver slippers; we love to walk with him in the street, if the sun shines and the people applaud him.*

Faithless: In my dream I saw Christian step a little aside to his fellow Hopeful, saying this:

>Christian: *It comes into my mind that By-Ends, of Fair-Speech, is an imposter.*

>Hopeful: *Ask him why he is ashamed of his name.*

Faithless: So, Christian came up to him again and said:

>Christian: *Sir, you talk as if you knew something more than all the world. Unless I am wrong, I believe your name is Mr. By-Ends of Fair-Speech?*

>By-Ends: *This is not my name, but indeed it is a nickname that has been given to me by some who cannot abide me. Therefore, I must be content to bear it as a reproach, as other good men have borne theirs before me.*

>Christian: *But did you never give an occasion to men to call you by this name?*

>By-Ends: *Never, never! The worst that ever I did to give them an occasion to give me this name was that I always had the luck to adjust my judgment with the winds and fashion of the times. By so doing I was able to receive the greatest benefit, but if that is considered a shame, let me count it as a blessing. It certainly should not be an occasion for reproach.*

>Christian: *I thought so, you are the man I heard about. And to tell you the truth, I believe your name, By-Ends, fits you more properly than you think it does.*

>By-Ends: *Well, if that is what you imagine I cannot help it. However, you shall find me to be good companion, if you will still admit me into your company.*

>Christian: *If you go with us, you will have to go against wind and tide and I think that is going to be contrary to your opinion.*

You must also own true religion in your rags as well as when in silver slippers. And, you must stand by your faith in Him when bound in irons as much as when you are walking in the streets receiving the applause of men.

 Philippians 4:11-12

By-Ends: *You must not impose, nor lord it over my faith; leave me to my liberty and let me go with you.*

Christian: *Not a step farther, unless you are willing to walk against the wind and all that is contrary to the popular opinion of men.*

 Ephesians 4:14

By-Ends: *I shall never desert my old principles since they are harmless and profitable.*

If I may not go with you then I must go by myself, until someone else overtakes me that will be glad to have my company.

Faithless: In my dream I saw that Christian and Hopeful forsook him, and kept their distance from him.

By-Ends finds good company in the world

Great-Heart: What happened next?

Faithless: I saw Hopeful look back because he heard footsteps.

Great-Heart: What did he see?

Faithless: I will report it in his own words.

Hopeful: *Look Christian, By-Ends has three new companions. Do you know who they are?*

Faithless: Just then I saw By-Ends give the three men a deep bow.

Then I heard Hopeful ask Christian if he knew the names of the three men who had become the companions of By-Ends.

Christian: *Oh Yes, I am very familiar with these three men. The tall one with the golden embroidered vest is Mr. Hold-the-World. The smartly dressed man with the top hat is Mr. Money-Love.*

 I Timothy 6:10

Hopeful: *And the third man?*

Christian: *Oh yes, now I recognize him. That is Mr. Save-All. These are all men whom Mr. By-Ends would have formerly known in his youth since they were all schoolfellows taught by Mr. Gripeman, a schoolmaster in the little market town of Love-Gain in the county of Coveting.*

This Schoolmaster, Professor Gripeman, taught them that the aim in life was getting whatever you wanted, either by violence, cozenage, flattering, lying, or by putting on a guise of religion. I have heard that these four gentlemen had attained much in this world and could now out teach their teacher.

Faithless: As I said, they saluted each other.

Great-Heart: Could you manage to hear what they said?

Faithless: Oh yes, I can recall it with ease.

Mr. Money-Love: *Who are those men up the road before us?*

By-Ends: *They are a couple of country-men, who, after their own mode, are going on a pilgrimage.*

Mr. Money-Love: *Why did they not stay so that we might have had their good company? For they, we, and you, sir, I hope, are all going on the same pilgrimage.*

By-Ends: *We are indeed. However, the men before us are so rigid, loving their own notions while lightly esteeming the opinions of others, that let a man, be he ever so godly, not agree with them in all things, they thrust him out of their company.*

Mr. Save-All: *That is bad. We have read about some who are overly righteous and such men's rigidness causes them to judge and condemn all but themselves. But please tell me, Mr. By-Ends, in how many ways did they differ from you?*

By-Ends: *Why, they concluded that it was their duty to rush on their journey in all weathers, while I am for waiting for convenient wind and tide. They are for hazarding all for God at a moment's notice while I am for taking all advantages to secure my life and estate. They are for holding their beliefs, though all other men be against them; but I am for a religion that is in step with the times when all is safe and secure. They are for religion when in rags and contempt; but I am for him when he walks in his silver slippers, in the sunshine, and with applause.*

 Matthew 6:25

Mr. Hold-The-World: *Yes, and keep that thought Mr. By-Ends. For my part, I can count them but fools, who having the liberty to keep what they have, shall be so unwise as to lose it.*

Let us be wise as serpents. It is best to make hay while the sun shines. You see how the bee lays still in winter, and bestirs her only when she can have profit with pleasure.

 *Proverbs 6:6*

Sometimes God sends rain, sometimes sunshine. If they are such fools to go through the first, let us be content to take fair weather along with us.

For my part, I like that religion best that will stand with the security of God's good blessings on us; for how can anyone, imagine who is ruled by reason, imagine that since God has bestowed good things upon us in this life, that He would not have us keep them for His sake?

Abraham and Solomon grew rich in religion; and Job says that a good man shall store up gold as dust.

Mr. Save-All: *I think we are all agreed in this matter; therefore, there need be no more words about it.*

Mr. Money-Love: *No, there need be no more words about this matter. Indeed, for he who believes neither Scripture nor reason (and you see we have both on our side), neither knows his own liberty nor seeks his own safety.*

By-Ends: *My brethren, as you can see, we are all going on a pilgrimage. For a diversion from anything bad, let me propose a question to you.*

Suppose a man, a minister, or a trades-man, etc., should have an advantage lay before him to get the good blessings of this life. How-ever, he can by no means receive this blessing except, in appearance at least, he becomes extraor-dinarily zealous in

By-Ends, Mr. Money-Love,
Mr. Save-All, Mr. Hold-The-World

some points of religion, even though it is not something he is genuinely interested in. May he not use this means to attain his desired end, and at the end of it be a right honest man?

Mr. Money-Love: *I understand the bottom of your question and with these gentlemen's good leave, I will endeavor to give you an answer.*

First, to speak to your question as it concerns a minister; suppose a minister, a worthy man endowed with a very small income, has his eye on something greater, fatter and plumper.

Now suppose he has the opportunity of getting it by being more studious, by preaching more frequently and zealously and, because the temper of the people requires it, by altering some of his principles.

For my part, I see no reason why a man may not grasp the opportunity to better his financial condition, provided he has a calling into ministry. And why should he not grasp the opportunity to better himself and yet be an honest man?

1. His desire of a greater income is lawful (this cannot be contradicted), since it is set before him by Providence; so then, he may get it if he can, making no question for conscience sake.

 Hebrews 13:5

2. Besides, his desire to seek after that benefit makes him more studious, a more zealous preacher, etc., and so makes him a better man, yea, makes him better improve his vocation, which is according to the mind of God.

3. Now, as for his complying with the temper of his people, by deserting, to serve them by deserting some of his principles, this proves:

1. That he has a self-denying temper.

2. *He has a sweet and winning deportment.*

3. *He is then more fit for the ministerial function.*

4. *I conclude, then, that a minister who changes a small for a great, should not, for doing so, be judged as covetous. Rather, since he is improved in his parts and industry thereby, be counted as one who pursues his call, and the opportunity put into his hand to do good.*

And now to the second part of the question, which concerns the tradesman you mentioned. Suppose such a person has a poor job in the world, but by becoming religious he may improve his trade, perhaps get a rich wife, and more and far better customers to his shop; for my part, I see no reason that this may not be lawfully done. Consider the reasons why:

1. *To become religious is a virtue, by whatever means a man becomes so.*

2. *Nor is it unlawful to get a rich wife, or more customers to his shop.*

 I John 2:15-16

3. *Besides, the man who gets these by becoming religious gets that which is good from those who are also good, by becoming good himself. The results are that he has a good wife, good customers, a good trade, and all of these accomplished by simply becoming religious. Therefore, to become religious to get all these is a good and profitable thing.*

Great-Heart: Did By-Ends and his new companion agree with what Mr. Money-Love proposed?

Faithless: Oh yes, and quite heartily so; he was highly applauded by them all. As a matter of fact, this line of reasoning was both wholesome and advantageous.

By-Ends and his companions conspire
to compromise the Godly principles
of Christian and Faithful

Then I heard Mr. Save-All say:

Mr. Save-All:
I do not think that any right-thinking man is able to contradict the clear reasoning put forth by Mr. Money-Love.

Mr. Hold-the-World: *I believe you are absolutely correct and perhaps we should see if the two overly strict pilgrims before us can answer anything to contradict our opinion of the matter.*

Faithless: Christian and Hopeful were within calling distance. By-Ends suggested they all catch up with them in order to put the question to them and by so doing, humble them and bring them in line with what they called, "sound reason and irrefutable logic."

So, they called ahead and soon caught up with Christian and Hopeful who stopped and stood still until they were all together.

The four agreed ahead of time that it should not be By-Ends who proposed the question to them but rather old Mr. Hold-the-World. They

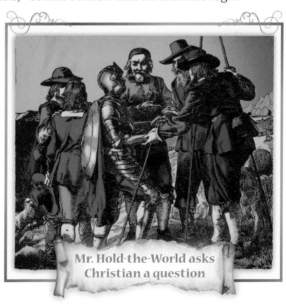

Mr. Hold-the-World asks
Christian a question

supposed that if Mr. Hold-the-World asked the question it would not alarm Christian and Hopeful as much as it might if it was asked by Mr. By-Ends, who had argued with them earlier.

So, they came up to them and after a short salutation, Mr. Hold-the-World propounded the same question to Christian and Hopeful, asking them to answer, if they could.

Great-Heart: I am most anxious to hear how Christian answered them.
Faithless: In my dream I heard Christian say:

> Christian: *Even a babe in faith can answer ten thousand such questions.*
>
> *For if it be unlawful to follow Christ for loaves, as it is, how much more abominable is it to make of Him and religion a stalking-horse to get and enjoy the world! Nor do we find any other than heathens, hypocrites, devils, and wizards who are of this opinion.*

 John 6:26

> **1.** *Heathens: for when Hamor and Shechem had a mind to the daughter and cattle of Jacob, and saw that there was no way for them to come at them but by being circumcised, they said to their companions, if every male of us be circumcised, as they are circumcised, shall not their cattle, and their substance, and every beast of theirs be ours? Their daughters and their cattle were that which they sought to obtain, and their religion the stalking-horse they made use of to come at them.*

 *Genesis 34:20-24*

> **2.** *The hypocritical Pharisees were also of this religion: long prayers were their pretense, but to get widows houses was their intent; and greater damnation was from God their judgment.*

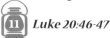 *Luke 20:46-47*

3. Judas, the devil, was also of this religion: he was religious for the bag, that he might possess what was put therein; but he was lost, cast away, and the very son of perdition.

Christian answers Hold-the-World

4. Simon, the wizard, was of this religion too. He would have had the Holy Ghost so that he might have got money therewith. His sentence from Peter's mouth is recorded in the King's book.:

 Acts 8:19-22

A man who takes up religion for the world, will throw away religion for the world; for so surely as Judas desired the world in becoming religious, so surely did he also sell religion and his Master for the same. Therefore, to answer the question affirmatively, as I perceive you have done, and to accept your opinion as authentic is heathenish, hypocritical and devilish. Your reward will be according to your works.

Great-Heart could not help from laughing out loud.

Great-Heart: I wish my brother, Evangelist, could have been here to listen to this defense of the true and everlasting Gospel. So, what did these covetous, money grubbers say to Christian's rebuttal?

Faithless: They stood staring at one another, having nothing with which to answer Christian. Hopeful's approval of the soundness of Christian's answer created a great silence among them.

Mr. By-Ends and his company staggered and kept behind so that Christian and Hopeful could go ahead of them.

Then I heard Christian say to his companion Hopeful:

> **Christian**: *If these men cannot stand before the argument of a mere man, what will they do in the presence of God? And if they are mute when dealt with but vessels of clay, what will they do when they shall be rebuked by the flames of a devouring fire?*

Great-Heart: What happened next?

Faithless: Christian and Hopeful went ahead of them until they came to a delicate plain, called Ease, where they traveled without any difficulty. The plain was narrow and they soon arrived at the other side.

Now at the furthest side of that plain was a little hill called Lucre, and in that hill there was a silver-mine, which some pilgrims had turned aside to investigate.

The rim around the silver-mine was near a pit and although it looked like good ground, it was deceitfully unstable. It would often collapse, sending many pilgrims to their death while leaving many more maimed and never fully recovered.

Then next in my dream, I saw that a little off the road and over against the silver-mine stood Demas.

Great-Heart: You saw Demas in your dream, the same man who deserted the Apostle Paul in order to chase after the wealth and luxury of this world?

Faithless: Yes, the very man. And I heard him also.

Great-Heart: What did he say?

Faithless: He was calling those pilgrims that passed by.

Great-Heart: What did Christian and Hopeful do?

Faithless: This slowed the two pilgrims down as they heard the **Trumpery*** of Demas, but Christian was determined to continue on their way. Then I heard Demas cry out:

> Demas: *Hold up gentleman, turn aside and come here and I will show you something that will dazzle your imagination.*

> Christian: *What possible thing could be so deserving as to entice us to turn out of the way to see it?*

> Demas: *Here is a silver-mine. If you will come and do some digging in it for treasure, with a little effort you may richly provide for yourselves.*

> Hopeful: *Let us go see.*

> Christian: *Not I. I have heard of this place and how many have been slain. Besides, that treasure is a snare to those who seek it because it hinders them in their pilgrimage.*

Faithless: Then Christian called to Demas:

> Christian: *Is not this a dangerous place? Has it not hindered many on their pilgrimage to the Celestial City?*
>
> *Hosea 9:6*

> Demas: *Not very dangerous, except to those who are careless.*

Faithless: In my dream I saw Demas blush as he spoke.

> Christian: *Let's not miss a step, but keep on our way.*

> Hopeful: *I will guarantee you, when By-Ends comes up, if he hears the same invitation as we just heard, he will turn out of the path.*

---

* **Trumpery**—Things that look good but that are actually worthless.

Demas tries to entice Christian and Hopeful to stop their pilgrimage and pursue worldly riches

Christian: *No doubt you are right, for his principles lead him in that direction, and a hundred to one he dies there.*

Demas: *Won't you come over and at least give it a look?*

Christian: *Demas, you are an enemy to the right ways of the Lord. You have already been condemned for turning aside out of the straight path by one of His Majesty's judges.*

 2 Timothy 4:10

So, why do you seek to bring us into your condemnation?

Besides, if we turn aside, our Lord the King will certainly hear about it and put us to shame.

How could we then stand with boldness before him?

Demas: *I was also one of the King's pilgrims. If you will wait just a little, I will walk with you.*

Christian: *What is your name? Is it not the same by which I have called you?*

Demas: *Yes, my name is Demas; I am the son of Abraham.*

Christian: *I know you. Gehazi was your great-grandfather, Judas your father and you have followed in their steps. It is but a devilish prank you are enticing us with. Your father was hanged* *as a traitor and you deserve no better reward. Be assured that when we come to the King, we will tell Him of your behavior. So, do not waste your breath as my companion and I will hasten our pace to be away from you.*

 2 Kings 5:20-27, Matthew 26:14-15, 27:3-5

Faithless: By this time, By-Ends and his companions were coming up to the silver-mine, and after only the first request by Demas, they went to investigate. Whether they fell into the pit by looking over the brink, whether they went down to dig, or whether they were smothered in the bottom by the vapors that commonly arise, I am not certain; but this I observed, they were never seen again in the way.

Then I heard Christian sing:

*By-Ends and Demas
for silver both agree;*

*One calls, the other runs,
hoping soon to be,*

*A sharer in his lucre:
seeing Demas as a friend*

*Taking up this world will
always badly end!*

CHAPTER 21

Christian and Hopeful Discover a Monument

Faithless: Now I saw in my dream that, just on the other side of this plain, the pilgrims came to a place where an old monument stood right next to the way. I could not make it out in my dream but listening to the conversation between Christian and Hopeful helped me understand what would otherwise have been a great mystery.

Great-Heart: I am anxious for you to recite the conversation between Christian and Hopeful.

Faithless: Seeing this monument, Christian and Hopeful were concerned because of the strangeness of its form. So, they approached it with caution and then Christian said:

Christian and Hopeful discover
the monument that warns
them about loving this world

> **Christian**: *It seems to me this is a woman who has been transformed into the shape of a pillar.*

Faithless: They both stood looking and looking at it, but it took a while before Hopeful could make it out.

> **Hopeful**: *Ah, I think I see it now. Yes, it does look like the shape of a woman.*

And look here Christian, here is something written upon the head in an unusual script.

Since I am no scholar, can you decipher the meaning?

Christian: *Let me see. Yes, it is written in the Hebrew script.*

Faithless: Christian was a learned man fluent in several languages including Latin, Greek and Hebrew. I saw Christian bend down and pick up a sharp rock and begin tracing the Hebrew letters on the ground, one by one from right to left.

Christian: *See here Hopeful, I have traced the Hebrew letters in the dirt.*

Hopeful: *Are these the same letters scribed by Moses?*

Christian: *Yes, they are. We are looking at ancient Hebrew.*

Hopeful: *They look like small pictures.*

Christian: *They are indeed small pictures. Each letter is a picture.*

Hopeful: *And you can read what this says?*

Christian: *I think I may be able to figure it out, if my wits do not escape me.*

Faithless: Christian then knelt down and began to decipher the message that was left scribed on the head of the pillar, reading it from right to left.

Christian: *Let me see. Yes, it says:*

She is looking

Women of him

From behind

Hopeful: *A women looking from behind?*

Faithless: Christian did not answer Hopeful's question as he continued deciphering the message written on the head of the pillar.

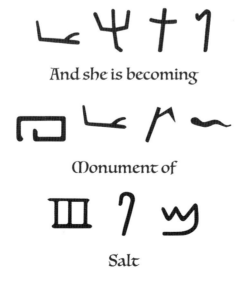

And she is becoming

Monument of

Salt

Faithless: Christian stood up and after a few moments announced:

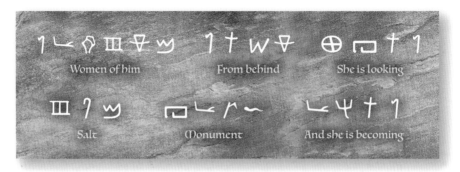

Christian: *She is looking...woman of him...from behind..and she is becoming...monument of...salt...*

Of course, I should have realized this right away.

Hopeful: *Realized what?*

Christian: *Do you have the King's Book in your possession?*

Hopeful: *It is my most valuable possession.*

Faithless: I then saw Hopeful take the King's Book from his bosom and as Christian instructed, opened up and read to himself from Genesis, chapter 19.

Christian: *Have you found the answer yet?*

Hopeful: *Yes Indeed! Shall I read it to you?*

Christian: *Of course, my brother, there is nothing ever so profitable as reading the King's Book.*

 II Timothy 3:16

Hopeful: *"Then the Lord rained upon Sodom and upon Gomorrah brimstone and fire from the Lord out of heaven; And he overthrew those cities, and all the plain, and all the inhabitants of the cities, and that which grew upon the ground. But his*

wife looked back from behind him, and she became a pillar of salt."

Christian: *This monument is placed here in order that we remember Lot's wife.*

Hopeful: *You are right, the King of the hi-way does not want us to forget that Lot's wife was turned into a pillar of salt after she looked back with a covetous heart when she was going from Sodom to safety.*

 Genesis 19:26

Faithless: Then, in my dream I saw that this sudden and amazing sight gave Christian and Hopeful occasion for a discourse.

Great-Heart: Can you remember what they discussed?

Faithless: Yes, as I recall it went something along these lines:

Christian: *Hopeful, this is a fortunate sight for us to come upon. It comes at an opportune time just after the invitation which Demas gave us to come over to view the hill, Lucre. If we had gone over, as he desired and as you were inclined to do, my brother Hopeful, we had likely been made like Lot's wife, a spectacle for all those who come after to behold.*

 Hebrews 3:19

Hopeful: *I am sorry I was so foolish, I wonder that I am not now as Lot's wife; for where was the difference between her sin and mine? She only looked back and I had a desire to go see. Let grace be adored and let me be ashamed that ever such a thing should be in my heart.*

Christian: *Let us take notice of what we see here to remind and warn us in the future. This woman escaped one judgment because she did not fall by the destruction of Sodom and yet* *she was destroyed by another. As we see, she was turned into a pillar of salt.*

Hopeful: *True, and she may be to us both a caution and an example; caution, that we should shun her sin, and a sign of what judgment will overtake such who will not be informed by this caution.*

But above all, I am reminded of one thing and that is how Demas and his fellows can stand so confidently yonder to look for that treasure. This woman perished by just looking behind and was turned into a pillar of salt (for we read not that she stepped one foot out of the way). The judgment that overtook her made her an example within sight of where Demas is right now. He cannot help but see her, all he needs to do is lift up his eyes.

Christian: *It is something to be wondered at and it persuades me that he and those who follow him have hearts that have grown desperate and hard. I would compare Demas and those who listen to him to pickpockets who ply their wicked trade in the presence of the judge.*

It is said of the men of Sodom, who were sinners exceedingly because they were sinners before the Lord, that is, in His eyesight and despite the kindness He had shown them. The land of Sodom was like the Garden of Eden before it was destroyed.

 Genesis 13:10-13

This open rebellion provoked the LORD all the more to jealousy and made their plague as hot as the fire of the Lord out of Heaven could make it. It is logical to conclude that, just like the Sodomites who sinned in His sight, and despite all the examples He placed before them to warn them to repent, they did not. Instead of repenting, they

mocked and rebuffed Him, and that is the reason for their severe judgments.

 I Samuel 15:23

Hopeful: *There is no doubt what you say is true; but what a mercy is it, that neither of us has been made an example of this kind! This salt monument has given us an occasion to thank God, to fear Him and to always remember Lot's wife.*

 Luke 17:32

I then saw them continue on their way to a pleasant river which David the king called the River of God, and the Apostle John called the River of the Water of Life.

 Psalm 65:9, Revelation 22:1, Ezekiel 47:1-9

Then, in my dream, I saw that the pilgrim's way lay just next to the bank of this river. Here, Christian and Hopeful walked with great delight. They drank the clear, cool water of the river which was pleasant and enlivening to their weary spirits.

On both sides of the banks of this river were green trees with all manner of fruit. They ate the leaves to prevent illness and disease that are common to those who travel for long distances. And, on either side of the river there was a meadow, curiously beautified with lilies that stayed green all the year-long.

In this meadow they lay down and slept, for it was safe to do so.

 Psalm 23:2, Isaiah 14:30

When they awoke, they gathered the fruit of the trees and drank again from the crystal-clear water of the river and then they lay down again to sleep. Christian and Hopeful continued this practice for several days and nights.

Then they sang:

Behold ye, how these
crystal streams do glide,
to comfort pilgrims
by the highway-side.

The meadows green,
besides their fragrant smell,
yield dainties for them;
And he that can tell

What pleasant fruit, yea,
leaves these trees do yield,
will soon sell all, that he
may buy this field.

Soon they decided to continue their pilgrimage, for they were not as yet at their journey's end. So, they ate and drank and then departed.

CHAPTER 22

GIANT-DESPAIR

aithless continued on with the dream as he relayed it to Great-Heart with such great detail, one might believe he was actually there. Great-Heart leaned in with great anticipation to hear what happened next in the unfolding of this dream.

Faithless: Now the way that departed from the river was rough and difficult to travel. After a while of struggling along the path, the pilgrims became more and more discouraged as their feet became increasingly tender and raw.

  Numbers 21:4

Christian persuades Hopeful to seek an easier path

Before long they both wished for a better and easier way.

Now, a little ahead of them and on the left-hand side of the straight path, there was a meadow separated from the King's Way by a tall stone fence. The meadow on the other side of the stone wall was called By-path Meadow. Then I heard Christian say:

Christian: *Hopeful, if this meadow goes right along the path, let us go over the fence and walk along it. It looks* *to be lush sod that will help us mend our pace and arrive at our destination all the sooner.*

Come here and look. See the hard path we are now on lays right alongside the stone wall that separates us from the easy way. Let's go over the fence in order to speed along our journey with ease.

Hopeful: *Yes, I can see that the stone fence and our present pathway seem to go in the same direction.*

Christian: *It is as I wished! Before us is the easiest way. Come, good Hopeful.*

Hopeful: *But the fence is very high and I fear I do not have the strength or skill to climb over it.*

Christian: *Look just down the way, a few paces from where we now stand there are steps for our convenience, a stile, by which we can climb over this stone wall.*

Let us go over the fence and follow the easy way that is right next to the straight way.

 Proverbs 14:12

Hopeful: *But what if the King desires us to keep on the hard road for a season?*

 1 Peter 1:6, 1 Thessalonians 3:3

What if this path should lead us out of the way?

 Psalm 107:7

Christian: *That is not likely. Look again, as you can see the meadow goes right alongside the narrow path.*

 Proverbs 14:12

Faithless: Hopeful was persuaded by Christian and followed him up the steps and over the fence. When they were over the fence and on the path, they found it very easy on their feet.

After traveling a short distance, they spied a man walking as they were. They ran to catch up with him. I then heard Christian speak.

Christian: *Sir, what is your name?*

Vain-Glory: *My name is Vain-Glory.*

 1 Samuel 12:21

Christian: *Do you know where the path we are on now leads?*

Vain-Glory: *Why sir, as you must have noticed, it lays snug up next to the path and any fool can see that by simple logic and reason it will lead us to the Celestial City in comfort and ease.*

Christian: *Look Hopeful, did I not tell you this path goes alongside the straight path and will lead us to the Celestial City? I was right.*

Hopeful: *Yes, but this man's words are too smooth and do not match the words of your own testimony that the way will be difficult at times.*

Christian: *At times this is certainly true, and I have had some terrible times, but this is a season for ease and comfort.*

 Proverbs 10:17

Hopeful: *I trust you are right.*

Faithless: So, in my dream I saw them following after Vain-Glory.

But soon the sun was setting and it was night, a very dark night that seemed to grow darker and darker. They lost sight of Vain-Glory which was by God's providence since in the darkness Vain-Glory, whose surname is Vain-Confidence, fell into a deep pit that was prepared to catch trespassers by the prince of the grounds. Vain-Glory was dashed to pieces in the fall and died in agony.

 Job 21:34, Isaiah 9:16

Now, Christian and Hopeful heard him fall and they listened for a moment as he cried out in agony, then in groans and then it was silent. They called after Vain-Glory but he could not answer for he was now dead. Then Hopeful spoke.

Hopeful: *Where are we now?*

Christian was silent, ashamed that he had led Hopeful out of the way. Then it began to rain and there was thunder and lightning in a most dreadful manner. Soon the water began to rise.

Hopeful: *Oh, that we had kept on the true way!*

Christian: *Who could have thought this path would have led us out of the way?*

Hopeful: *I was afraid it might, at the very first, and therefore gave you that gentle caution. I would have spoken plainer, but you are older than I.*

Christian: *Good brother, be not offended. I am sorry I have brought you out of the way and put you into such imminent danger.*

Pray, my brother, forgive me; I did not do it out of any evil intent.

Hopeful: *Be comforted, my brother, for I forgive you and I believe this will work out for our good.*

 Romans 8:28

Christian: *I am glad I have you as a merciful brother. However, we must not stand here but try to go back to where we first committed our error.*

Hopeful: *But, good brother, let me go first.*

Christian: *No, if you please, let me go first so if there be any danger, I may be the first to meet with it. It is because of my bad judgment that we are both out of the narrow way.*

Hopeful: *No, you shall not go first. Your mind is troubled and, in that condition, you may lead us out of the way again.*

Faithless: Then for their encouragement, they heard the voice of one saying, "Let thine heart be toward the highway, even the way that you wentest, turn again."

 Jeremiah 31:21, Jeremiah 6:16

By this time, the waters were greatly rising and going anywhere was dangerous.

They would have ventured back to where they had climbed over the wall, but it was so dark, and the flood was so high they concluded that going back in the dark would be too dangerous.

They also reasoned that with all the skill it had taken to get over the fence in the daylight, what chances of success they might have in the night.

They stumbled around until, at last, they finally found a little shelter where they sat down waiting for the sun to come up. They tried to stay awake but, being weary, they both fell fast asleep.

Now, not far from the place where they were, there was a castle that I later learned was called Doubting Castle. The owner was Giant-Despair and it was on his grounds that Christian and Hopeful were now fast asleep.

In my dream, early in the morning I saw Giant-Despair get up and walk up and down his grounds in search of trespassers.

 I Peter 5:8

It did not take him long to discover Christian and Hopeful asleep on his grounds.

Then I heard Giant-Despair, with a grim and surly voice, command Christian and Hopeful:

Giant Despair discover Christian and Hopeful trespassing on his domain

Giant-Despair: *Wake up, vile trespassers! What do you think you are doing? Why are you on my grounds?*

Christian: *We are weary pilgrims who have lost our way.*

Giant-Despair: *You have this night trespassed on my property, trampled my meadow and now you are laying on my grounds. By the law you must come with me.*

Faithless: So, Christian and Hopeful were forced to go with him because he was stronger than they. Also, they had little to say, for they knew they were indeed trespassers and in the wrong.

Giant-Despair drove them before him and put them both into a dark dungeon that stood in the middle of his castle.

Upon entering the dungeon, Christian and Hopeful began to gag, cough and wheeze, holding their hands over their mouths. It must have been a nasty and stinking place to the spirits of these two men.

Here Christian and Hopeful were kept imprisoned from Wednesday morning until Saturday night. No nourishment was provided all that time, not one bit of bread, or drop of drink except for the little bit of moisture they licked from the weeping dank stones. There was a tiny ray of light from a small window that was too small to crawl out of, and no one was about to ask how they were doing.

Then Christian spoke to Hopeful after a long period of silence.

> **Christian**: *Here we are in an evil place with no friends and no one to rescue us.*
>
> *Psalms 88:18*

> *Now this place is a double sorrow to me because it was through my unadvised counsel that we were both brought into this **Dretch**.**

Faithless: In my dream, I saw that Giant-Despair had a wife and her name was Dissidence.

When the Giant was gone to bed, he told his wife he had taken a couple of prisoners and cast them into his dungeon for trespassing on his grounds. He asked his wife:

> **Giant-Despair**: *My Turtledove, what do you think I should do with them?*

> **Dissidence**: *Who are they, my best beloved, where did they come from and where are they going?*

> **Giant-Despair**: *My Sweeting, their names are Christian and Hopeful, they come from the City of Destruction and are bound for the Celestial City.*

> **Dissidence**: *This is what you should do, my squire. When you arise in the morning, you should beat them without mercy.*

---

* Dretch—Torment.

Faithless: So, when Giant-Despair arose in the morning, he went down into the dungeon and began insulting them as if they were dogs.

He beat them without mercy with a grievous crab-tree cudgel. Then he left them to console each other in their misery.

So, all that day Christian and Hopeful spent their time in nothing but sighs and bitter lamentations.

The next night, I heard in my dream the following conversation between Dissidence and her husband, the giant:

Christian and Hopeful are imprisoned inside Doubting Castle

Dissidence: *Darling, did you do as I requested, my love?*

Giant-Despair: *Yes, Honey Cake, I railed upon them and beat them without mercy.*

Dissidence: *Are they still alive, my True Penny?*

Giant-Despair: *Yes, my Snuggery, I beat them with all my fury and yet they still live.*

Dissidence: *Listen Lambkin, this is what you must do next.*

Faithless: I could not hear what she said because it was almost a whisper, but it became clear the following morning what advice Dissidence had given to her husband, the Giant-Despair.

Great-Heart: How so?

Faithless: Early the next morning, Giant-Despair went into the dungeon and in the same surly manner as he had done before, told them that since they were likely to never come out of that place alive, their only way out would be to make an end of themselves. They could accomplish this by cutting their wrist or throat, hanging themselves with a rope, or by poisoning themselves in order to bring the misery to an end. He continued by asking them why they should choose to live, seeing it is attended with so much suffering, pain and bitterness?

 13 *Matthew 5:25-26*

He beat them without mercy

Great-Heart: And how did Christian and Hopeful respond to this advice?

Faithless: They begged the Giant to let them go.

Great-Heart: And what did Giant-Despair do when he heard their bitter cries for mercy?

Faithless: He showed them no mercy but instead rushed upon them and would have killed them except he fell into one of his fits.

Great-Heart: Fits, you say?

Faithless: Yes, I heard Dissidence warn her husband to stay away from sunshiny weather so that he did not have one of his fits which paralyzed him and caused him to shake without any control over his limbs.

Great-Heart: So, what happened next?

The next morning, Giant-Despair went into the dungeon

Faithless: After the Giant had recovered a little, groaning and grumbling, he stumbled out of the dungeon leaving Christian and Hopeful alone, once again, to consider their fate.

Great-Heart: Did you hear what Christian and Hopeful said?

Faithless: Oh yes. I heard Christian ask:

Christian: *What shall we do?*

The life that we now live is miserable. For my part, I don't know if I would not be better off dead. My soul chooses to be strangled rather than go on living in this stinking dungeon. I think the grave would be easier for me.

 Job 7:15

Shall we take the advice of Giant-Despair?

Hopeful: *Indeed, our present condition is dreadful, and death would be far more welcome to me than what I am now* *experiencing. But we need to be careful and consider what the Lord of the country to where we are going has said: you will do no murder. No, we are not to murder another man; much more, than, are we forbidden to kill ourselves.*

 Exodus 20:13

Besides, he who kills another and commits murder can be forgiven; but for one to kill himself is to kill body and soul at once.

Can this be forgiven?

Christian: *I do not know the answer to your question but you are right, we would be wise not to test it. My judgment betrays my understanding as I fear I am in a state of delirious **Mubblefubbles**.**

Hopeful: *And moreover, my brother, you talk about the ease in the grave; but have you forgotten that it is Hell where certain murderers go?*

For no murderer has eternal life.

 Galatians 5:21

And let us consider that all power is not in the hand of Giant-Despair. Others, so far as I can understand, have also been taken by him and yet have escaped out of his hands.

 Genesis 49:18

And if ever that should come to pass again, for my part, I am resolved to pluck up the heart of a man and to try my utmost to get out from under his hand.

---

* Mubblefubbles—Melancholy.

I was a fool not to try and do it before. But, my brother, let us be patient and endure a while longer. The time may come when we are released.

Christian: *You are right and I am persuaded that even if we are murdered, it will not be by our own hands.*

Faithless: With these words, Hopeful moderated the mind of his brother, Christian; so, they continued together in their sad and doleful condition through the darkness of that entire day.

Great-Heart: What happened next?

Well, in the evening the giant went down into the dungeon again to see if his prisoners had taken his counsel to do themselves in. But when he arrived he found them alive, although barely.

By this time the lack of bread and water, along with the wounds they had received, put them in a condition so terrible they could barely find the strength to breathe.

Great-Heart: Did he take pity on them?

Giant-Despair found them alive, but barely

Faithless: No, as a matter of fact, it put the Giant into a grievous rage, and he told them that seeing they had disobeyed his counsel, it would be worse for them than if they had never been born.

 Matthew 18:32-35

Hearing this news, they trembled greatly and I think Christian fell into a swoon. But coming a little to himself again, they renewed their discourse about the Giant's counsel and whether they had best take it or not.

Now Christian, again as before, seemed ready to take the advice of the Giant, but Hopeful made his second reply as follows:

> **Hopeful**: *My brother, remember how valiant you have been so far?*
>
> *Deuteronomy 15:15*

> *Apollyon could not crush you, nor could all that you heard, saw and felt in the Valley of the Shadow of Death destroy you. What hardship, terror, and amazement you have already gone through! Are you now nothing but a bundle of fears!*
>
> *1 Chronicles 16:12*

> *You see I am also in the dungeon, a far weaker man by nature than you. This Giant has wounded me and cut off the bread and water from my mouth as well. And, along with you, I mourn without the light. But let us exercise a little more patience.*
>
> *Genesis 49:18, Psalm 62:1*

> *You were not afraid of the chain, the cage, or a bloody death; therefore, let us bear up with patience as well as we can.*
>
> *Psalm 40:1, Psalm 25:5*

Faithless: Now when nightfall came and the Giant and his wife went to bed, she asked him again about the prisoners...

> **Dissidence**: *Have the two pilgrims heeded your counsel, Pippin?*

> **Giant-Despair**: *No, my Ladybird. They are sturdy rogues who choose to bear all hardships rather than to make away with themselves.*

Dissidence: *Do as I say, my best beloved.*

Tomorrow take them into the castle-yard and show them the bones and skulls of those whom you have already dispatched.Make them believe that before the week comes to an end, you will tear them in pieces, as you have done their fellows before them.

Faithless: So, when morning came, the Giant went to them again and took them into the castle-yard to show them the skulls and bones, just as his wife had asked him to do.

Christian and Hopeful
console each other
in the dark

Pointing at the skulls and bones the Giant said:

> **Giant-Despair**: *These were pilgrims once, just as you are. They trespassed on my grounds, as you have done and after I had beaten and starved them, as I have you, I tore them in pieces. Within ten days I will do the same to you. Now get down to your den!*

Faithless: And with that, he beat them both as they scrambled as best they could back to the dungeon. Christian and Hopeful lay there all day on Saturday in a lamentable case.

Now, after nightfall when Dissidence and her husband, the Giant, were in bed, they began to renew their discourse as they wondered why they could neither by grievous blows nor evil counsel bring these two pilgrims to an end.

Finally, his wife replied…

Dissidence: *I fear my Squire, that they live in hopes someone will come to rescue them, or that they have picklocks and can escape.*

Giant-Despair: *If you say so, my pet. I will search them in the morning.*

Faithless: Now I saw in my dream that on Saturday, about midnight, Christian and Hopeful began to pray and continued in prayer until almost the break of day.

 Acts 12:5

Now, a little before the sun came up, good Christian, as one half amazed, broke out into this passionate speech:

Christian: *What a fool I have been! Why am I laying in this stinking dungeon when I could be walking in liberty? I have a key in my bosom.*

 Psalm 18:2

Hopeful: *You have a key?*

What is it called?

Christian and Hopeful flee from Doubting Castle

Christian: *I have in my bosom the key called Promise which will, I am persuaded, open any lock in Doubting Castle.*

 Psalm 85:9

Hopeful: *That is good news! Take it out and see if it sets us free.*

Faithless: Then Christian pulled it out of his bosom and began to try to unlock the dungeon-door. As he turned the key, the bolt gave way and the door flew open with ease.

Then Christian and Hopeful both came out of the dungeon.

Christian then went to the outward door that leads into the castle-yard and with his key, he also opened that door.

Next, Christian went to the Iron Gate that would, once opened, grant them freedom from the Giant-Despair, Dissidence, and the terrible dungeon in the middle of Doubting Castle.

> **Christian**: *This lock is rusty and will not budge.*
>
> *Mark 9:29*

> **Hopeful**: *Keep trying, brother.*

> **Christian**: *Pray the Lord gives me the strength to open this lock.*

> **Hopeful**: *I need no prodding as I have been earnestly praying ever since you found the Key of Promise.*
>
> *Psalm 88:1, Isaiah 12:2*

Faithless: Then I saw in my dream that Christian lifted his eyes to the heavens and begged for help. Just then the rusty lock yielded to an unseen hand and finally opened.

 Psalm: 121:1-2, 7-8

> **Christian**: *Come, brother Hopeful, help me push open this gate.*

Faithless: Hopeful and Christian, with all the strength they had between the two of them, thrust open the gate to make their escape with speed. However, that gate made such a creaking sound as it opened that it woke up Giant-Despair.

Giant-Despair: *My sweet, I fear our prisoners are escaping!*

Dissidence: *Run hastily, my love, and pursue them. They must not get away.*

Faithless: I saw Giant-Despair leap from his bed, grab his cudgel and in a rage, head for the castle-yard.

By this time, Christian and Hopeful were running as best they could in their low condition. They were just outside the gate when they saw Giant-Despair enter the courtyard. I heard Christian say:

Christian: *We are done for!*

Hopeful: *Not so, my brother.*

Christian: *But that brute is coming for us faster than we can escape in our condition and there is no one to save us from certain death.*

Hopeful: *The Lord is my shepherd and my rock, He will save us from violence!*

 2 Samuel 22:3

Christian: *Lord, deliver us from our enemy as we have no strength to do it on our own!*

 Psalm 69:29

Great-Heart: And then what happened?

Faithless: It was a miracle! The sun had risen but it could not be seen because the sky was black with menacing, dark clouds.

Great Heart: And then?

Faithless: It was a miracle! I saw in my dream that the dark gloom was pulled apart by two mighty hands that appeared in the sky.

The sun came bursting forth out of the opening and then a beam of sunlight blinded Giant-Despair as if it was a thunderbolt sent from Heaven.

 I John 1:5-7

Great-Heart: And then what happened?

Faithless: Once the sunshine fell upon Giant-Despair, his limbs failed as he was overtaken by one of his fits and he fell to the ground, helpless as a newborn baby.

Next I saw Christian look back when he heard a loud thump, as if a large tree had fallen. Then I heard them speak:

Christian: *The Lord is my strength and help in time of need.*

 Psalm 121:1-2

Hopeful: *Thank You, Lord, a thousand times, thank you!*

Faithless: And for a moment I saw Christian fall to his knees, weeping and praising the King of the Highway Who had delivered him and made his way safe.

 Hosea 6:1

Great-Heart: What happened next?

Giant Despair pursues Christian and Hopeful who narrowly escape his grasp

Faithless: I could see that Hopeful was also overtaken with wonder and gratitude for the miracle he had just witnessed. However, he was also mindful that being within yards from the Giant, even though he was temporarily stricken, was not a place to linger.

Hopeful grabbed Christian by the arm and lifted him up. He would have dragged him forward but Christian was finally able to get his legs under him as he began to hobble and then to run.

Both pilgrims, after some faltering steps, took courage by both hands and made a dash for the stone fence, much like men escaping from a burning building.

They headed straight for the stile that had led them into the Giant's territory. Exhilarated and flush with fearlessness, the two pilgrims soon clamored over the stone fence, staining the steps as they went, with tears of wondrous joy and bitter sorrow.

Joy for the deliverance, sorrow for the need for it.

When Christian and Hopeful had made it over the stile, they began to talk between themselves about what they should do at that place where the ladder went over the fence. They wanted to prevent anyone else who should come along from falling into the hands of Giant-Despair.

They decided to erect a pillar and to engrave upon the side of it this sentence:

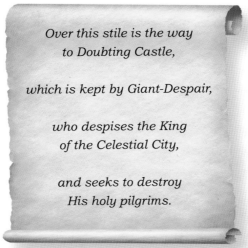

*Over this stile is the way
to Doubting Castle,*

which is kept by Giant-Despair,

*who despises the King
of the Celestial City,*

*and seeks to destroy
His holy pilgrims.*

Great-Heart: I imagine that the pilgrims who come after Christian and Hopeful, as they travel the King's Way, will read what is written on this sign and escape the danger of Giant-Despair and Doubting Castle.

What happened next?

Faithless: Christian sang a song.

Out of the way we went and found

No comfort on forbidden ground;

Let those who follow have a care,

They do not end up in the Giant's snare.

CHAPTER 23

Christian's Adventures in the Delectable Mountains

idelity, who had her hands busy preparing dinner, strained to hear the adventures of Christian and Hopeful. She stopped what she was doing, pulled up a chair and placed it just outside the view of the living room in order that she might hear how the two pilgrims escaped from the clutches of Giant-Despair and his wicked wife, Dissidence.

Coming to somewhat of a pause in the story, Fidelity quickly fixed a bowl of blackberries, sprinkled with honey, and a hot pot of tea.

Great-Heart beckoned Fidelity to come in and join them, half suspecting she was following with attention the last exciting adventure that unfolded in the dream of Faithless.

Faithless: Yes, we are glad to have your company and thank you for the tea and berries.

Faithless took a little rest from the dream-telling as he popped a couple of the blackberries into his mouth. Fidelity immediately noticed the one thing she had forgotten to bring and arrived a minute later with two damp towels, one for Faithless and one for her father.

Faithless smiled as he first licked and then cleaned his fingers that were covered with honey.

With everyone seated and silent, Faithless took one last sip of tea before he launched the next episode of the pilgrimage of Christian and Hopeful.

Faithless: Now I saw in my dream that Christian and Hopeful went along the stone wall, but this time they were back on the right side. The path was hard and the small stones that littered the way made the way difficult to pass. Christian and Hopeful, who had just a week before complained bitterly about the condition of the road, never uttered another word of complaint. After all, compared to the Giant-Despair's stinking dungeon, it was a walk-in paradise. Soon they were past the grounds of Doubting-Castle and entering the place Christian had longed to see, remembering the description of the place told to him when he was lodging at the House Beautiful.

> **Hopeful**: *This looks like a most welcoming place indeed!*
>
> *Proverbs 3:5-6*

> **Christian**: *By all accounts, it is that and more.*

> **Hopeful**: *Do you know about these beautiful, gentle hills and mountains?*

> **Christian**: *Yes, indeed I do!*

> **Hopeful**: *I think I hear the bleeting of sheep.*

> **Christian**: *And if I am not mistaken, we will soon find good company with The Shepherds who tend the sheep that graze on this hillside.*

Faithless: As they walked up the hill, lush with pasture grass and bordered by small brooks and well-kept orchards and vineyards, they spotted a group of men all holding staffs.

> **Hopeful**: *These men I see up ahead must be The Shepherds you spoke of.*

> **Christian**: *I think you are right.*

Faithless: The two pilgrims went up to the mountains where they beheld the gardens and orchards, the vineyards and fountains of water. From atop the mountain, they could clearly see the places they had stopped to drink, wash themselves and freely eat of the orchard's fruit and ripe delicious grapes of the vineyards.

Now on the tops of these mountains, they met with The Shepherds who were feeding their flocks. They were standing by the highway-side waiting for the two pilgrims to arrive.

The two pilgrims went to them, leaning upon their walking sticks (as is common with weary pilgrims). After some pleasantries had passed between The Shepherds and the pilgrims, Hopeful asked:

Hopeful: *Whose Delectable Mountains are these and who owns the sheep that are grazing on this lush pasture?*

Christian and Hopeful meet
The Shepherds on the
Delectable Mountains

The Shepherds: *These Mountains belong to the King and this is called Emmanuel's Land; you are within sight of His City. These sheep are also His; He laid down His life for them.*

 John 10:11-15

Christian: *Is this the way to the Celestial City?*

The Shepherds: *Yes. If that is your destination, then you are on the right path.*

Christian: *How much further is it?*

The Shepherds: *Too far for any except those who will be granted entry.*

Christian: *Is the way safe or dangerous?*

The Shepherds: *Safe for those for whom it is to be safe; but transgressors shall fall and never enter.*

 Hosea 14:9

Christian: *Is there in this place called Emmanuel's Land any relief for pilgrims who are weary and faint in the way?*

The Shepherds: *The Lord of these mountains has given us a charge not to be forgetful to entertain strangers. The bounty of this place is now yours for a season.*

 Hebrews 13:2

Then in my dream, I also saw that when The Shepherds perceived they were wayfaring pilgrims, they put questions to them (which Christian and Hopeful answered honestly as they had in other places).

The questions were not new to the two pilgrims.

The Shepherds: *Where did you come from? How did you get into the way? By what means have you survived all the tribulations along the way?*

 I Peter 3:15, Acts 14:22

Christian: *I am sure our answers are like the answers of other pilgrims who come into this land.*

The Shepherds encourage Christian and Hopeful

The Shepherds: *There are many who begin the journey to the Celestial City but they never arrive here to these mountains.*

Faithless: When The Shepherds heard how humbly and honestly the two pilgrims answered all their questions, they were pleased and from that moment on treated them like beloved brothers and said:

The Shepherds: *Welcome to the Delectable Mountains.*

Great-Heart: Do you remember their names?

Faithless thought for a moment and then spoke.

Faithless: One was named Understanding, another was called Experience, and I think I have forgotten the name of the third shepherd.

Fidelity: Was his name Watchful?

Faithless: Yes, that was his name. Do you know him?

Fidelity: We are near relatives of his as he is my father's second cousin and his daughter, whose name is Waiting-with-Patience, is a dear friend of mine.

Great-Heart: Weren't there four shepherds?

Faithless: Let me think. Yes, I think there was a fourth shepherd and a very ardent man whose name was...

Great-Heart: Might it be my friend, Sincere?

Faithless: Yes, that was his name. Let me see, there was Understanding, Experience, Watchful and Sincere. Anyway, these four shepherds led them by the hand to their tents where a meal had been prepared for them.

Great-Heart: Did Christian and Hopeful then continue on their way?

Faithless: They wanted to but The Shepherds told them they should stay and become acquainted with them while they rested and enjoyed the solace of the Delectable Mountains.

They then told them they were content to stay. So, it being very late, they went to their rest.

In my dream, I saw the following morning that The Shepherds called upon Christian and Hopeful and asked them to walk with them upon the mountains. So, the two pilgrims and The Shepherds set out for a walk.

Then the Shepherd, Watchful, said to Experience:

> **Watchful:** *Shall we show these pilgrims some wonders?*

> **Experience:** *I believe that would be very helpful to the pilgrims.*

So, after they were all in agreement to do it, they took Christian and Hopeful to the top of a hill called Error, which was very steep on the farthest side.

> **Experience:** *Christian and Hopeful, I want you to carefully watch your step as you go to the edge of this hill and look down to the bottom.*

> **Christian:** *Come, Brother Hopeful, let us do as Experience has asked.*

> **Hopeful:** *Yes, but carefully as he said.*

Faithless: So Christian and Hopeful carefully inched their way to the edge of the cliff where the hill had collapsed, and looked down.

> **Christian:** *I see more men than I can count who have been dashed all to pieces after falling off this hill.*

> **Hopeful:** *What does this mean?*

Understanding: *Have you not heard of those who were made to err, by hearkening to Hymenius and Philetus, concerning the faith of the resurrection of the body?*

 2 Timothy 2:17-18

Christian: *Yes.*

Hopeful: *Yes, indeed we have.*

Understanding: *Those whom you see dashed in pieces at the bottom of this Hill of Error are they. They have continued to this day to lay unburied, as you can see, as an example for others to take heed how they clamber too high, or how they come too near the brink of this mountain.*

Faithless: Next I saw that The Shepherds took Christian and Hopeful to the top of another mountain named Caution.

 I Timothy 1:19

Christian and Hopeful view the dangers they narrowly escaped

Understanding: *My dear pilgrims, look afar off in the distance.*

Hopeful: *I see several men walking up and down among the tombs.*

Christian: *It appears that the men are blind. I see them stumbling uponthe tombs.*

Hopeful: *All the tombs seem to be keeping them from escaping the cemetery.*

Christian: *What does this mean?*

Understanding: *Did you see a little below these mountains a stile that led into a meadow on the left hand of the way?*

Christian: *Yes.*

Watchful: *From that stile, there goes a path that leads directly to Doubting-Castle, which is kept by Giant-Despair. These men (pointing to those among the tombs) once came on a pilgrimage, as you do now, until they came to that stile.*

Understanding: *And because the right way was rough in that place, they chose to go out of the way and into that meadow where they were taken prisoner by Giant-Despair and cast into Doubting-Castle. After they had been kept in the dungeon, he at last put out their eyes and led them among those tombs where he has left them to wander to this very day that the saying of the wise man might be fulfilled, "He that wanders out of the way of understanding shall remain in the congregation of the dead."*

 Proverbs 21:16

The men were blind and stumbling upon the tombs

Faithless: Then I saw that Christian moaned and twitched in pain as Hopeful looked on. Soon they were both overcome by grief and pouring out their tears but said nothing to The Shepherds.

Sincere: *Let us take the pilgrims to another place at the bottom of the hill.*

Faithless: I saw in my dream that as they walked down the hill, they came around to the side of the hill in which there was a door.

Christian: *Where does this door lead?*

Sincere: *I bid you look inside the door.*

Christian opened the door.

Christian: *I can see it is dark and smoky.*

Hopeful: *I think I hear a rumbling sound that sounds like a raging fire.*

Christian: *I can hear the tormenting cries and wailing of a multitude of people.*

Hopeful: *I smell something vile and nauseating.*

Christian: *Yes, as do I. It has the scent of brimstone.*

What does this mean?

Understanding: *This is a by-way to Hell, a way that hypocrites go in. Namely, these are those who sell their birthright like Esau; those who sell their Master such as Judas; and those who blaspheme the Gospel such as Alexander.*

Hopeful: *I perceive all these had at one time the show of pilgrimage as we have now, had they not?*

 I John 2:19, II Timothy 3:5

The Shepherds: *Yes, and held up the pretense of it for a long time.*

Hopeful: *How far might they have gone on this pilgrimage in their day before they were cast away?*

The Shepherds: *Some farther, and some not so far as these mountains.*

Faithless: Then I heard the pilgrims say one to the other:

Christian and Hopeful: *We need to cry to the Strong for strength.*

The Shepherds: *Yes, and you will need all the strength you can get.*

Faithless: By this time, Christian and Hopeful had a desire to go forward and The Shepherds agreed they should depart to finish their pilgrimage.

The four Shepherds and the two pilgrims walked together towards the end of the mountains. Then The Shepherds said one to another:

The Shepherds: *Let us show the pilgrims the gates of the Celestial City, if they have the faith to look through our perspective glass.*

The pilgrims lovingly accepted the idea. So, The Shepherds took them to the top of a high hill, called Clear, and gave them the spyglass to look through.

Christian and Hopeful then tried to look, but remembering the last thing The Shepherds had shown them made their hands shake and so they could not look steadily through the glass. However, even though they were shaking, they did manage to see something like the gate, along with some of the glory of the Celestial City.

10 *Hebrews 4:11-15, I Corinthians 13:12*

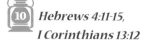

Looking through the spyglass, Christian and Hopeful glimpsed at the Celestial City

Then they went away, and sang:

Thus, by The Shepherds
secrets are revealed,

That which from all other men
are kept concealed.

Come to The Shepherds then,
if you would see

Things deep, things hid,
and that mysterious be.

Understanding, Experience,
Watchful and Sincere.

Faithless: When they were about to depart, they received the following instructions from The Shepherds:

Watchful: *Here, take these instructions about the way ahead.*

Experience: *And beware of the Flatterer.*

Understanding: *Take heed that you do not fall asleep on the Enchanted Ground.*

Sincere: *And I bid God-Speed.*

Faithless: Then I awoke from my dream.

CHAPTER 24

Christian and Ḥopeful Meet Ignorance

hen Faithless finished telling his dream, he got up, went over to the window and looked to see the sun's path overhead.

Faithless: It is getting late.

Great-Heart followed Faithless to the window, and peered out.

Great-Heart: It appears as if you have about 3 hours before **Dimpse.***

Fidelity: I can have dinner ready in a quarter of an hour.

Faithless: I am very grateful for your hospitality, but my wife will have dinner ready and waiting for me when I arrive home. It will not go well for me if I disappoint her.

Great-Heart: Nor should you. We bid you good day and please send our greetings to your dear wife.

With that, Faithless grabbed his coat and headed for the door.

Fidelity: Wait just a moment.

Fidelity went into the kitchen and returned with a large piece of bread smothered with blackberry jam.

---

* **Mubblefubbles**—Melancholy.

Faithless thanked Fidelity, balanced the toasted bread on the palm of his hand and headed out the door.

Great Heart and Fidelity watched Faithless bound down the meadow, stopping only to take a bite or two out of the toasted blackberry treat.

After a couple of minutes, they watched him stop and settle into the lap of a large Oak tree in order to finish eating his blackberry dessert.

Fidelity giggled at the sight of it.

Great-Heart, inspired by the obvious delight Faithless was having finishing off the toast and blackberry jam, turned to his daughter and smiled.

Great-Heart: Is this a treat only reserved for travelers?

Fidelity: I am so sorry, Father, I am fresh out of blackberry jam today.

Fidelity left her father peering out the window and returned a moment later with two slices of bread with more blackberry jam than would have ever been considered polite.

Great-Heart: I thought you said we were out of blackberry jam.

Fidelity: Actually, Father, I said we were fresh out of blackberry jam, today. And as you have always taught me to be precise and truthful in my speech, I must insist that you eat both slices right away, leaving not a trace of blackberry jam. Then we will be completely out as I told you and I will remain a daughter who always tells the truth.

Great-Heart laughed and caught himself before he spilled the contents of the plate on the floor.

Great-Heart: You have your mother's sense of humor.

Fidelity: Yes, and I can remember as a child that you always enjoyed her teasing, merry way, saying it kept you spry and on your toes.

With that, Fidelity gave her father a kiss on the cheek and went back to the kitchen to prepare the evening meal.

Great-Heart: Wait daughter, please take one slice of bread with my favorite jam on it as a reward for your generosity.

Fidelity returned to her father, peered for a moment as she put her nose within an inch of the blackberry delicacy, and then said:

Fidelity: You would never forgive me!

Great-Heart laughed again as Fidelity made her way singing back to the kitchen.

An hour later, Fidelity joined her father in the living room where together they talked and prayed for all their neighbors and friends, paying special attention to include Faithless in their prayers.

Fidelity: Father, I am miffed that Faithless has not entered the Narrow Path that leads to everlasting life in Christ.

With all the evidence that certain destruction will come on all who are not found in the comfort and safety of Christ, I wonder why he does not flee the City of Destruction.

Great-Heart: Fidelity, there are some men who will not be moved from their comfortable place in the city, even in the midst of the terror that is to come. Instead of repenting and believing, they continue in their rebellion while increasing their hatred for our King and His Son.

Fidelity: Yes, but do you think Faithless hates the King and His Son?

Great-Heart: There is no hint that he does, however, if he does not repent and believe, he will be lost just the same.

 *John 12:48, Luke 13:3*

Fidelity: Do you think it is his destiny to be lost forever?

Great-Heart: If he does not put his trust in Christ, then that will certainly be his fate because there is no other way but the Narrow Way and Door that is Christ, Himself. But I pray and hope for better things for our friend, Faithless.

Fidelity: What about the dream?

Great-Heart: There is no doubt in my mind that God has shown extraordinary grace in order to make it clear to Faithless that he needs to enter into the Narrow Gate or face certain doom.

Fidelity: I pray that he does, and soon!

Great-Heart: There is a season and a time in the affairs of men that will never be repeated. This is the time God has ordained for Faithless to either come to Him or reject Him. There is no other ground.

 Hebrews 3:15, Hebrews 12:25

Fidelity: That is both a wonderful and a terrible thing.

Great-Heart: Yes, terrible if he rejects Christ and the worse for it since he has been facing the truth; wonderful on the other hand if he comes to Christ in faith, believing in Him alone, and having lost all confidence in himself.

Faithless arrived home just in time to eat dinner with his family. During dinner, he shared with them his visit with Great-Heart and some of his dream before he bid them all a good night and went to his bed.

It was anything but a good night for Faithless who tossed and turned with visions both horrible and wondrous.

Would he end up like the man who awoke each morning with visions of being swallowed up by Hell?

Was he just like Passion, enjoying all the pleasures of this life while having no care for the life to come?

Was he trusting in a form of religion like Formalist without having the substance of it?

Was he like Hypocrisy saying one thing and doing another?

Was Talkative his schoolmaster, teaching him to say but not do the will of God?

Was he more like Pliable than Graceless who became a true Christian?

If he began a pilgrimage to the Celestial City, would he survive the many trials and tribulations?

Or would he end up in Doubting-Castle tormented by Dissidence and Giant-Despair?

Would he end up blind wandering among the tombs?

Would he perish on the Hill of Error, scattered among the rest of the dead souls who fell from that terrible place?

Would he enter the door that leads to everlasting ruin, where the worm never dies and the stench of sulfur and brimstone suffocates for eternity?

Or might he enter into the Door that leads to the rest and glory of the Eternal Kingdom ruled by the King of the Celestial City?

As all these questions swirled in his mind, he tossed and turned until, completely exhausted, he finally fell asleep. And while he slept, he dreamt again.

Faithless got up early the next morning.

Just as the path of the sun began reflecting off the east window at the King's Cottage, there was a familiar sound at the door.

Great-Heart, as was his custom, was already up early spending time in the King's Book and in prayer. He immediately answered the door and was not at all surprised to see Faithless, flush with enthusiasm and ready to narrate the latest episode in his dream.

All the usual hospitality was extended as Faithless soon found himself sitting across from Great-Heart, who had his Great Book in his hand, sitting at attention ready to hear how the dream continued.

Faithless did not waste a minute since, as he said, there was a lot to report and he was anxious to do it before it faded from his memory.

Faithless: In my dream, I saw Christian and Hopeful going down the mountains along the highway towards the Celestial City. Now, a little below these mountains, on the left-hand side, there was the country named Conceit, which comes over and across the way in which the pilgrims walked.

Christian noticed a little crooked lane just up ahead. When they arrived at the lane, they met with a very brisk lad who came out of the Country of Conceit and his name was Ignorance. And now I will report the conversation I heard:

  Christian: *Where have you come from and where are you going?*

  Ignorance: *Sir, I was born in the country just to your left and I am going to the Celestial City.*

Christian and Hopeful meet Ignorance

Christian: *But how do you think you will arrive at the gate without difficulty?*

Ignorance: *Just like other good people before have entered into the Celestial City without any difficulty.*

Christian: *But what have you to show at that gate, that the gate should be opened to you?*

Ignorance: *I know my Lord's will, and have lived a good life. I pay every man what I owe; I pray, fast, pay tithes, and give alms, and have left my country to enter the Celestial City.*

 Matthew 7:22, Proverbs 16:18

Christian: *But you did not enter the path to the Celestial City from the Narrow Gate that is at the head of The Way. You have come here through that crooked lane, and therefore I fear, in spite of what you think of yourself, that when the day of reckoning comes you will be charged with being a thief and a robber and will not be allowed to enter the Celestial City.*

Ignorance: *Gentlemen, you are strangers to me. I do not know you so be content to follow the religion of your country, and I will follow the religion of mine. I hope all will be well.*

And as for the Narrow Way and the gate that you talk about, everyone knows that it is right next to our country and everyone knows the way to find the Celestial City. I cannot think of anyone in my country who does not know how to enter into the Celestial City. Nor does it really matter if they do or don't since we live in a place that is very fine and pleasant with a green comfortable lane that comes down from our country and enters into the way to the Celestial City.

Faithless: When Christian saw that the man was wise in his own conceit, he said to Hopeful whisperingly:

 Romans 12:16

Christian: *There is more hope of a fool than of him.*

 Proverbs 26:12

And, moreover, when he that is a fool walks by his own way, his wisdom fails him, and that tells everyone he is a fool.

6 *Ecclesiastes 10:3*

Shall we talk further with him or part company for the present, and so leave him to think about what he has already heard?

We can then, after a while, stop and talk to him again to see if by degrees we can do him any good.

Ignorance challenged to trust in Christ alone

Hopeful: *Let's leave Ignorance alone to think about our warning. Let's pray he takes our counsel.*

It is better we do not tell him too much at once so let's go past him and talk to him later.

So, Christian and Hopeful went on their way, with Ignorance following behind.

CHAPTER 25

The Sad Tale of Little-Faith

Faithless: And then in my dream, I saw them enter into a very dark lane where they met a man whom seven devils had bound with seven strong cords. They were carrying him back to the door they saw on the side of the hill.

1 *Matthew 12:45, Proverbs 5:22*

Christian began to tremble, and so did Hopeful; yet, as the devils led the man away, Christian looked to see if he knew him.

Hopeful: *Do you know this poor man?*

Christian: *Yes, I think I recognized him.*

Mistrust

Hopeful: *Who is he?*

Christian: *I believe the man is Mr. Turn-away who dwelled in the town of Apostasy.*

But he did not perfectly see his face because he hung his head like a thief who had just been caught.

Faithless: I watched Hopeful look back and when he did, he saw a paper stitched to his back with this inscription, "Wanton professor, and damnable apostate."

Christian: *This reminds me of something a good man once told me about a man named Little-Faith.*

Hopeful: *That does not sound promising.*

Christian: *Do not be so quick to judge him by his name. He was a good man that lived in the town of Sincere. Let me tell you what I heard.*

 Proverbs 14:14

Upon entering the place we are now passing, there is a lane that comes down from Broadway-gate, a lane, called Dead-Man's lane; so-called because of the murders that are commonly done there; and Little-Faith going on a pilgrimage, just as we are now, chanced to sit down there and fall asleep.

Little Faith is assaulted by Faint-Heart, Mistrust and Guilt

Now, at that time, there happened to come down the lane from Broadway-gate three sturdy rogues named Faint-Heart, Mistrust and Guilt, all brothers.

They spied Little-Faith and came galloping up with speed. Now the good man was just awakened from his sleep and was getting up to go on his journey.

 II Corinthians 4:3-4

The three rogues, Faint-Heart, Mistrust, and Guilt, all came up to him and with threatening language asked him to stand. At this, Little-Faith looked as white as a sheet, having no power to either fight or flee.

Then Faint-Heart said, "Deliver your purse!"

Little-Faith, not wanting to lose his money, refused. So, Mistrust ran up to him, and thrusting his hand into his pocket, pulled out a bag of silver.

Then Little-Faith cried out, "Thieves, Thieves!" With that, Guilt, having a great club in his hand, struck Little-Faith on the head. The blow sent Little-Faith to the ground where he lay bleeding as one who would bleed to death, all this while the thieves stood by. But at last, they heard someone coming up the road and fearing it might be Great-Grace from the town of Good-Confidence, they suddenly left, leaving Little-Faith to shift for himself. After a while, Little-Faith regained consciousness, got up and went on his way.

Hopeful: *But did they take everything he had?*

Christian: *No. They didn't ransack the place where his jewels were hidden. But, as I was told, Little-Faith was much afflicted for his loss because the thieves got most of his spending-money. Even though they did not get his jewels, I was told he was left with a few* **Chinkers**,* *with which to continue his journey.*

Faint-heart, Mistrust and Guilt, rob Little-Faith

---

* **Chinkers**—Money, Coins.

I heard that just to keep himself alive, he was forced to beg as he went on his way because he would not sell his jewels. So, he went on his way begging as best he could, spending many days hungry and discouraged.

 1 Peter 4:18

 Hopeful: *I am amazed that the thieves did not steal his certificate of admittance to the Celestial City!*

Christian: *It was amazing. But it had nothing to do with Little-Faith, who had neither the power nor the skill to hide anything from the robbers. It was by God's providence that the robbers missed the precious things Little-Faith retained.*

2 Timothy 1:12-14, 2 Peter 2:9

Hopeful: *It must be a comfort to Little-Faith that they didn't steal his jewels.*

Christian: *It might have been a great comfort to him, had he used it as he should have. However, as the story goes, he made but little use of his jewels all the rest of the way because he was so dismayed that he had his money taken from him. He forgot about his jewels for most of the rest of his journey. Besides, when his possession of the jewels came into his mind and he began to be comforted, then fresh thoughts of his loss would come again, swallowing every other thought.*

Hopeful: *Poor man, I can imagine his grief.*

Christian: *Grief? Yes, a grief indeed! And it would have been the same for either of us had we been robbed and wounded in* a strange place as he was. It is a wonder he did not die with grief, the poor heart.

I was told he spent almost all the rest of the way bitterly complaining about what had happened to him, retelling the story of his narrow escape from death and his great loss to anyone who would listen.

Little-Faith

Hopeful: *But it is a wonder that his great need did not tempt him to sell or pawn some of his jewels in order to make his journey easier.*

Christian: *Hopeful, I am surprised that you are talking like you have a shell covering your eyes.*

For what should he pawn his jewels?

To whom should he sell them?

In all that country where he was robbed, his jewels were not considered to be worth anything.

Besides, had his jewels been missing at the gate of the Celestial City, he would have been excluded from an inheritance. That would have been much worse for him than the appearance and villainy of ten thousand thieves.

Hopeful: *Why are you so sharp with me, my brother?*

Esau sold his birthright, and that for a mess of pottage, and that birthright was his greatest jewel.

 Hebrews 12:16

If Esau sold his jewels, why wouldn't Little-Faith do the same thing?

Christian: *Esau did sell his birthright indeed, and so do many besides, and by so doing exclude themselves from the chief blessing.*

But there is a great difference between Esau and Little-Faith, as well as between their estates.

Esau's birthright was typical, but Little-Faith's jewels were not.

Esau's belly was his god, but Little-Faith's belly was not.

Esau only sought his fleshy appetite.

Little-Faith's appetite was for Heaven.

Besides, Esau could see no further than the fulfilling of his lusts: "For I am at the point to die," Esau said, "and what good will this birthright do me?"

 Genesis 25:32

But Little-Faith, though it was his lot to have but a little faith, was by his little faith kept from such extravagances. He prized his jewels and would not sell them, as Esau did his birthright.

 Romans 12:3

You will not read anywhere that Esau had faith, no, not even a little faith; therefore, don't marvel when the flesh controls our appetites and desires as it does in a man with no faith.

The man will sell his birthright and his soul together to the devil himself, when his mind is made up to please his flesh.

 Jeremiah 2:24

But Little-Faith was of another temper; his mind was on things divine. His livelihood was upon things that were spiritual and from above. Therefore, to what end should he sell his jewels to fill his mind with empty things?

 Matthew 6:19-21, Colossians 3:1-4

Will a man give a penny to fill his belly with hay? Or can you persuade the turtle-dove to live upon meat, like the crow?

Faithless ones can for carnal lusts, pawn, mortgage, or sell what they have, including themselves outright, to boot.

But those who have faith, even a little faith if it be saving faith, cannot do so. That, my brother, is your mistake.

At this point in the retelling of the dream, Faithless stopped and asked a question.

Faithless: Please forgive my ignorance, but I must ask, what is the meaning of the jewels?

Just at that moment, Fidelity entered the room with a tray full of freshly baked and buttered muffins and a small bowl of strawberry jam.

Great-Heart was glad for the interruption as he carefully considered how to answer the important question asked by Faithless.

After both Faithless and Great-Heart had smothered the muffins with jam and thanked Fidelity for her thoughtfulness, while nibbling on the edges of the well-timed treat, Great-Heart spoke.

Great-Heart: What do you suppose the jewels were?

Faithless: I thought I understood what they were until I heard, in my dream, Christian said Little-Faith considered them so valuable that he would not sell them. But at the same time, he revealed that those who live in the City of Destruction or one of its outlying towns or villages did not consider them valuable.

If I understand the words of Christian in my dream, these jewels seem to have great value inside the borders of the Celestial City. To answer truthfully, I am in a bit of a muddle and am finding it hard to figure out why these jewels have no value on the pilgrim's path and yet are so prized by the pilgrim?

Great-Heart: The answer to this mystery reveals itself in two parts. To unravel the puzzle you need to understand that the jewels have been deposited inside the Pilgrim.

Faithless: I do not understand.

Great-Heart: When the Gospel is believed, something enters the very heart and soul of man.

Faithless: The Gospel is deposited inside the believer?

Great-Heart: No, not exactly.

Faithless: This is becoming more and more of a mystery.

Great-Heart: Do you know what the Gospel of the age we now live in is?

Faithless: I suppose it is the good news about the King's Son.

Great-Heart: Yes, it is the good news about the King's Son in three particulars.

Faithless: What do you mean?

Great-Heart: It is the Good news that contains three everlasting truths, and without all three the Gospel is not active in the heart of a man.

Faithless: What are these three truths that make the Gospel active in the heart of man.

Great-Heart: The first is the bloody, sacrificial death of the King's Son on a wooden cross lifted up at just the right time in the place on this earth we call Calvary. This terrible event is the foundation of all true pilgrims' faith and profession.

Faithless: And what is the second truth?

Great-Heart: The second truth follows the first in what seems unremarkable at first glance, but is nevertheless a cornerstone of the Gospel and it is simply this: the King's Son not only bled on the wooden cross of Calvary but He died and was buried in a rich man's tomb as the king's prophets had foretold He would centuries earlier.

Faithless: And the third truth?

Great-Heart: Without the deposit of the third truth of the Gospel, man is left in his sin with no reason to hope in the future.

Faithless: I am now anxious to hear it!

Great-Heart: The King's Son raised Himself from the dead after three days and three nights in the tomb.

He is risen and now resides at the right hand of the King where He pleads for those who have trusted in Him, those who believed the Good News, the Gospel.

Faithless: So the three parts of the Gospel are the jewels?

Great-Heart: They are the jewels that have been deposited in the heart and very soul of Little-Faith and they are also his profession of that Gospel. The jewels are in his heart and cannot be stolen and they are also his testimony, even if it is a testimony propelled by little faith.

Do you understand now what the jewels represent?

Faithless: I think so.

Great-Heart was sure that Faithless was still in a bit of a muddle. He thought it best to give Faithless a space of time to allow the truth to take root in his mind and heart. With that in mind, Great-Heart took a large bite of the strawberry laden muffin and began to sip on his tea. Faithless did the same. The two sat silent for a few moments as they savored the treat and then Great-Heart, when he sensed the time was right, asked Faithless to continue the telling of his dream.

Faithless: The next thing I remember in my dream is that Hopeful became agitated as he considered the assault on Little-Faith.

This is what I heard him say:

> Hopeful: *The way Faint-Heart, Mistrust and Guilt attacked Little-Faith was cowardly. Why didn't Little-Faith pluck up his courage and resist?*
>
> *He might have stood one brush with them and have only yielded after putting up a good fight.*
>
> Christian: *Many have said they are cowards, but few have found it so in the time of trial.*
>
> *As for courage, Little-Faith had none; and I perceive by you, my brother, had you been the man concerned, you would have put up some resistance and only afterwards yielded. And since that is your opinion when the thieves are a great distance away from us, I wonder if they should appear presently if you might not have second thoughts?*
>
> *These three villains set upon me and in the beginning, I resisted like a valiant Christian, but when they could not overtake me they gave a shout and in came their master.*
>
> *I would, as the saying goes, have given my life for a penny, but as God would have it, I was clothed with armor. But even in full armor, I found it hard work to resist like a man.*

For no man can tell how he will conduct himself when in mortal combat until he has actually been in a battle.

The way Faint-Heart, Mistrust and Guilt attacked Little-Faith, was cowardly

Hopeful: *But they ran when they thought Great-Grace was coming to rescue Little-Faith.*

Christian: *True, they have often fled, both they and their master, when Great-Grace has appeared. But that is nothing to marvel at since he is the King's champion.*

But I know you will put some difference between Little-Faith and the King's champion. All the King's subjects are not his champions.

It is encouraging to think a little child should handle Goliath as David did. It is nice to think that there should be the strength of an ox in a dove. Some are strong, some are weak; some have great faith, some have little. This man was one of the weak, and therefore he was robbed and bruised.

Hopeful: *I wish it had been Great-Grace who encountered these three brothers.*

Christian: *If it had been him, he might have had his hands full. Even though Great-Grace is skillful with his weapons, and I must tell you that he has and can do well enough with them, so long as he keeps them at sword's point. However, if they get close to him and can throw him up on his heels, then it would not go well for even someone as courageous as Great-Grace. When a man is down there is little he can do to defend himself.*

Whoever looks closely at Great-Grace's face will see scars, cuts and bruises that have not yet healed and is proof that what I am saying is true.

I heard it from an honest witness that once Great-Grace was in such a battle and that he even despaired of life.

Consider how these sturdy rogues and their fellows made David groan, mourn, and roar!

Yes, and also Heman and Hezekiah, although champions, were forced to exert all their energy to fend off the attacks of these three thieves and robbers in their day.

 Psalm 88:1-4

Consider Peter who was the prince of the apostles. Remember how Faint-Heart, Mistrust, and Guilt, with little effort, made Peter afraid of a little girl.

Besides, these thieves have their prince at their beck and call. All they need do is whistle; he is never out of hearing and if at any time they are put to the worst, if possible, he comes in to help them.

Remember what God told Job about him:

"The sword of him that layeth at him cannot hold; the spear, the dart, nor the habergeon. He esteemeth iron as straw, and brass as rotten wood. The arrow cannot make him flee; sling-stones are turned with him into stubble. Darts are counted as stubble; he laugheth at the shaking of a spear."

 Job 41:26-29

But again, let me remind you that our enemy is no match for our frail frame, and we are lost without His strength and power.

Again, speaking of the enemy, Job said:

"Hast thou given the horse strength? hast thou clothed his neck with thunder? Canst thou make him afraid as a grasshopper? the glory of his nostrils is terrible. He paweth in the valley, and rejoiceth in his strength: he goeth on to meet the armed men. He mocketh at fear, and is not affrighted; neither turneth he back from the sword. The quiver rattleth against him, the glittering spear and the shield. He swalloweth the ground with fierceness and rage: neither believeth he that it is the sound of the trumpet. He saith among the trumpets, Ha, ha; and he smelleth the battle afar off, the thunder of the captains, and the shouting."

 Job 39:19-25

What can a man do in this case?

It is true, if a man could at every turn have Job's patience and courage, he might do notable things.

But for such footmen, as you and I are, let us never desire to meet with an enemy, nor puff ourselves up as if we could do better when we hear of others who have been foiled.

We should not be tricked at the thoughts of our own manhood; for those who do usually do the worst when tried.

Witness Peter, of whom I made mention before. He had swagger, yes, and he would, as his vain mind prompted him to say, do better and stand more for his Master than all men. But who besides Peter was so beaten down, humbled and run down by those three villains?

When we hear that such robberies as these take place on the King's Highway, there are two things we should do:

1. *We should make sure we have the shield of faith, for if that is lacking, the enemy has no fear of us at all. Remember what Paul the apostle to the church said, "Above all, take the shield of faith, wherewith ye shall be able to quench all the fiery darts of the wicked."*

 Ephesians 6:16

2. *We should desire the company of the King Himself. This made David rejoice when in the Valley of the Shadow of Death, and Moses would rather die where he stood than to go one step without his God.*

 Exodus 33:15

O, my brother, if the King, Himself, will go along with us, we need not ever be afraid of ten thousand who shall set themselves against us.

 Psalm 3:5-8, 27:1-3

Great-Grace, the King's champion

But without Him, the proud are slain.

 Isaiah 10:4

For my part, I have been in the battle; and through the goodness of the King, I am, as you see, alive. Still, I cannot boast of any manhood.

I would be glad if we never met another enemy such as the brutes who robbed Little-Faith but I fear that we are not past all the dangers yet.

My hope is that God will also deliver us from the next uncircumcised Philistine.

CHAPTER 26

The Flatterer & the Testimony of Hopeful

Great-Heart continued to listen intently to the dream of Faithless.

Faithless: So, Christian and Hopeful went on with Ignorance following. They went along until they came to a place where they saw another path that came their way which seemed, at first glance, to lay as straight as the way they were on. Soon the two paths intersected and the pilgrims had a hard time figuring out which of the two paths to take, for they both appeared to be straight.

As they stopped to consider which path to take, a man dressed in garb as black as coal, with a white hood covering his face and a shining white robe that covered his back, came up to them and began speaking.

> **Flatterer:** *Why are you standing still and not going forward on the path?*

> **Christian:** *We are going to the Celestial City, but know not which of these ways to take.*
>
> *Psalm 37:7*

> **Flatterer:** *Follow me, that is where I am going also.*

Faithless: So Christian and Hopeful followed him in the way that soon turned into a road that, by degrees, turned further and further away from the Celestial City.

It wasn't long before the two pilgrims were going in the opposite direction of the true straight and narrow way and yet they continued to follow the man.

But by and by, before they were aware, he led them both into the circle of a net that was sprung like a rabbit trap.

Christian and Hopeful were soon so entangled they didn't know what to do, and with that, the white robe fell off the man.

 II Corinthians 11:1-3, Matthew 5:11

Then Christian and Hopeful saw clearly where they were. Try as they might, they could not un-tangle themselves from the net and the more they struggled, the worse their condition became until they were finally just reduced to tears and prayers for help.

> **Christian**: *Now I see my error. Didn't The Shepherds tell us to beware of the Flatterer? As the wise saying goes, "A man that flattereth his neighbor, spreadeth a net for his feet."*
>
> *Proverbs 29:5*

> **Hopeful**: *The Shepherds also gave us a note with directions about the way in order that we do not stray off the true path.*

The Flatterer is exposed

But we have forgotten to read it, and have not kept ourselves from the paths of the destroyer.

Here David was wiser than we; for he said, "Concerning the works of men, by the word of thy lips I have kept me from the paths of the Destroyer."

 Psalm 17:4

Faithless: For some time, Christian and Hopeful berated themselves as they continued to struggle to get out of the net. At last, they spied a Shining One coming towards them with a whip of small cords in his hand. When he was come to the place where they were, he spoke:

Shining One: *Where have you come from, and what are you doing entangled in this net?*

Christian: *We are poor pilgrims going to Zion, but were led out of the Way by a man whose pitch-black garb was covered with a shining white robe. He led us into this trap.*

Shining One: *He is the Flatterer, a false apostle who has transformed himself into an angel of light.*

 Daniel 11:32, 2 Corinthians 11:13-14, Galatians 1:8-9

Faithless: I saw in my dream the Shining One tearing apart the net and letting the men out.

Shining One: *Where did you spend the last few nights?*

Hopeful: *With The Shepherds upon the Delectable Mountains.*

Shining One: *And did you not receive a note giving you instructions about the way you should go from The Shepherds?*

Christian: *Yes.*

Shining One: *Did you read it?*

Christian and Hopeful: *No.*

Shining One: *Why have you not read the directions given by The Shepherds for your protection on the way?*

 Hebrews 13:17

Christian and Hopeful: *We forgot.*

Shining One: *Didn't The Shepherds warn you to beware of the Flatterer?*

Hopeful: *Yes.*

Christian: *But we did not imagine that this fine-spoken man was the Flatterer.*

 Romans 16:17-18

Faithless: Then, in my dream, I saw the Shining One command both Christian and Hopeful to lay down, which they did. He then took the whip he held in his right hand and chastened them until they were sore. He did this to teach them to stay in the good way and not stray off the path into certain destruction.

 Deuteronomy 25:2, 2 Chronicles 6:27

Shining One: *As many as I love, I rebuke and chasten: be zealous therefore, and repent.*

 Revelation 3:19

Now go on your way and take heed to the directions you were given by The Shepherds.

Christian: *Thank you!*

Hopeful: *Yes, for your kindness to us and for delivering us from the snare.*

Faithless: So, they thanked the Shining One and went softly along the right way, singing:

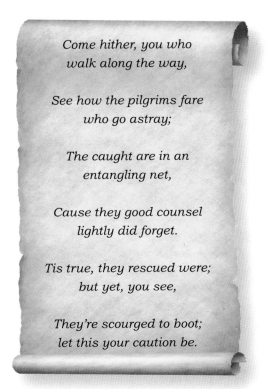

Come hither, you who walk along the way,

See how the pilgrims fare who go astray;

The caught are in an entangling net,

Cause they good counsel lightly did forget.

Tis true, they rescued were; but yet, you see,

They're scourged to boot; let this your caution be.

Now, after a while, Christian perceived afar off one coming softly, and alone, on the path to meet them. Then Christian said:

Christian: *Look, Hopeful, there is a man with his back towards Zion, and he is coming to meet us.*

Hopeful: *I see him; let us be very careful just in case he should prove to be another Flatterer.*

Faithless: The man walking away from Zion drew nearer and nearer, and at last came up to Christian and Hopeful. His name, as I learned, was Atheist, and he asked the two pilgrims where they were going.

Christian: *We are going to Mount Zion.*

Faithless: Then I saw in my dream that the man, Atheist, began to laugh heartily.

Christian: *Why are you laughing?*

Christian and Hopeful meet
Atheist, who mocks them
for their faith

Atheist: *I am laughing because I see before me two ignorant pilgrims taking on such a tedious journey for nothing.*

 Psalm 14:1

Christian: *Why? Do you think we shall not be received at the Celestial City?*

Atheist: *Received! There is not such a place as you dream of in all this world.*

Christian: *But there is in the world to come.*

Atheist: *When I was home in my own country, after hearing about this so-called Celestial City I decided to seek it out. I have been seeking this city these twenty years and have come to the conclusion that it simply does not exist.*

 Ecclesiastes 10:15, Jeremiah 17:15, Hebrews 11:6

Christian: *We have both heard, and believe, that there is such a place to be found.*

Atheist: *Had I not, when at home, believed, I would not have come this far to look for it. I have, I will wager, looked harder and longer than both of you for this imaginary place. I have never once found any evidence that it exists, not that it ever did exist. I am going back* *home now and will refresh myself with the things of this world that I can see and touch. Why would you cast away what is real to search in vain for something as fanciful as the Celestial City?*

Christian: *Do you think what this man is saying is true?*

Hopeful: *Take heed, he is one of the Flatterers. Remember what it cost us last time we listened to one of these fellows and besides did we not see Mount Zion with our own eyes from the Delectable Mountains? Didn't we see the gates to the Celestial City? Are we not now to walk by faith?*

 2 Corinthians 5:7

Let us keep going, just in case the Shining One with the whip overtakes us again. You should have learned your lesson and I for one, am not going to feel the whip again for listening to this foolish man. "Cease, my son, to hear the instruction that causeth to err from the words of knowledge." I say, my brother Christian, cease to hear him, and let us believe to the saving of our souls.

 Proverbs 19:27, Proverbs 3:11

Christian: *My brother, Hopeful, I did not put the question to you because I doubted the truth of our belief, but to prove you, and to fetch from you the fruit of honesty from your heart. As for this man, I know that he is blinded by the god of this world. Let you and I go onward, knowing that what we believe is true and not a lie.*

 1 John 5:21

Hopeful: *Now I rejoice in the hope of the glory of God.*

Faithless: So, they turned away from the man who laughed at them as he went on his way.

Then next in my dream, I saw Christian and Hopeful continue on until they came into a certain country whose air naturally tended to make all strangers who came into it, drowsy. And here Hopeful began to be very dull and sleepy. Hopeful said to Christian:

Hopeful: *I am beginning to grow so drowsy that I can scarcely keep my eyes open. Let us lie down here and take a short nap.*

Christian: *By no means, if we fall asleep here we may never wake up.*

Hopeful: *Why, my brother? Sleep is sweet to the laboring man; we may be refreshed if we take a nap.*

Christian: *Do you not remember that one of The Shepherds asked us to beware of the Enchanted Ground? He meant by that, that we should beware of sleeping; let us not sleep, as do others; but let us watch and be sober.*

 1 Thessalonians 5:6

Hopeful: *I acknowledge my error. Had I been here by myself, I may have fallen asleep and run the danger of death. I see it is true where the wise man says, two are better than one. For this long journey, your company has been a mercy to me, and you will have a good reward for your labor.*

 Ecclesiastes 4:9

Christian: *Now then, to prevent drowsiness in this place, let us fall into good discourse.*

Hopeful: *Yes, that is a good idea.*

Christian: *Where shall we begin?*

Hopeful: *Where God began with us. But you begin, if you please.*

Christian: *But first I will sing you this song:*

When saints do sleepy grow,
let them come hither,

And hear how these two
pilgrims talk together;

Yea, let them learn
of them in any wise,

Thus to keep open their drowsy,
slumbering eyes.

Saints fellowship,
if it be managed well,

Keeps them awake,
and that in spite of Hell.

Faithless: Then Christian began by asking Hopeful a question:

Christian: *When did you first think about taking this pilgrimage?*

Hopeful: *Do you mean, when did I first become concerned about my soul?*

Christian: *Yes, that is what I mean.*

Hopeful: *For all my life, I took delight in those things that were seen and sold in Vanity Fair; things I believe I would now have, had I continued seeking them. They were things that would have, once gained, drowned me in perdition and destruction.*

 *Philippians 3:8*

Christian: *What things were they?*

Hopeful: *All the treasures and riches of the world. Also, I delighted much in rioting, reveling, drinking, swearing, lying, uncleanness, Sabbath-breaking, and whatnot, that tended to destroy the soul.*

 I Corinthians 6:9-11

But at last, by hearing and considering things that are divine, which I heard from you and also from our brother, Faithful.

When Faithful was put to death for his faith, I began to think that the things I desired formerly would also end in death. And, that for these things sake, the wrath of God would soon come upon the children of disobedience.

 Romans 6:21-23, Ephesians 5:6

Christian: *And did you immediately fall under the power of this conviction?*

Hopeful: *No. At first, I was not willing to consider the evil of sin, nor the damnation that follows upon the commission of it.*

I endeavored, when my mind at first began to be shaken with the Word, to shut my eyes to the truth.

Christian: *Why were you not willing to change and when did you notice the first workings of God's blessed Spirit upon you?*

Hopeful:
1. I was ignorant that this was the work of God upon me. I never thought that awakenings for sin were a sign that God was beginning the conversion of a sinner.

2. Sin was yet very sweet to my flesh, and I was loath to leave it.

3. I did not want to part with my old companions, their presence and actions were something I still desired.

4. The hours in which I came under conviction were so trouble-some and frightening that I could not bear to remember them let them enter into my heart.

Christian: *So, it seemed like sometimes you could escape the conviction of sin?*

Hopeful: *Yes, but it was not long before it would come into my mind again, and when it did, it became worse and worse.*

Christian: *Why, what was it that brought your sins to mind again?*

Hopeful: *Many things such as:*

1. If I meet a good man in the streets; or,

2. If I have heard anyone read the Bible; or,

3. If I were told that some of my neighbors were sick; or,

4. If I heard the bell toll for someone who had died; or,

5. If I thought of dying myself; or,

6. If I heard that sudden death happened to others.

7. But especially when I thought of myself, that I must quickly come to judgment.

Christian: *And could you at any time, with ease, get rid of the guilt of sin, when you considered any of the things you have shared?*

Hopeful: *No, in fact, my sense of sin and guilt just got worse and worse.*

Christian: *And what did you do then?*

Hopeful: *At first, I thought I must endeavor to mend my life; or else, I am sure to be damned.*

Christian: *And did you endeavor to mend your life?*

Hopeful: *Yes. I fled not only from my own sins, but also from sinful company. I took on religious duties such as praying, reading, weeping for sin, speaking truth to my neighbors, etc.*

Christian: *And did this give you relief from the burden of sin and guilt?*

Hopeful: *Yes, for a while. But in the end, my trouble came tumbling back upon me once again, despite all my reformations.*

Christian: *How did that happen since you were now reformed in your ways and keeping good company?*

Hopeful: *There were several things that brought the sin and guilt upon me, especially those things written in the King's Book.*

Christian: *What particular things written in the King's Book brought you back under condemnation?*

Hopeful: *Sayings such as:*

All our righteousnesses are as filthy rags.

 Isaiah 64:6

By the works of the law shall no flesh be justified.

 Galatians 2:16

When ye have done all these things, say, we are unprofitable, and many, many more like it.

 Luke 17:10

So, Brother Christian, I began to reason with myself like so:

If all my righteousnesses are as filthy rags; if by the deeds of the law no man can be justified; and if, when we have done all, we are yet unprofitable, then it is folly to think you can obtain Heaven by the law.

I further thought thus: If a man runs a hundred pounds into the shopkeeper's debt and after that he pays cash for all his goods, there still is an old debt on the books that cannot be erased no matter how many times he pays cash for what he buys. The shopkeeper may sue him for what he is owing even though he is now paying for his purchases. The shopkeeper would be justified and could lawfully cast him into prison until all the debt is paid.

Christian: *Well, and how did you apply this to yourself?*

Hopeful: *Why, I thought to myself, by my sins I have run a great debt into God's Book and reforming, even if it was perfect which it was not, will not pay off that past debt.*

No matter how many good things I did, I could not by any means erase the bad things I had done and continued to do. So, I considered that while my righteousness may be greater than my neighbors, it would never be enough to satisfy the debt of sin I was under by God's reckoning.

So even though I reformed myself, it did not change my standing with God Who viewed me as a debtor to sin, unrighteous and unable by any means to save myself.

 *Hebrews 11:25*

Christian: *A very good application but pray, go on.*

Hopeful: *Another thing that has troubled me ever since I began to reform myself is that if I look carefully into the best of what I do now, I still see sin.*

I see new sin mixing itself with the best of what I do. So now I am forced to conclude that, notwithstanding my former conceited view of myself and my good deeds, I have committed enough sin in one day to send me to Hell, even if my former life had been faultless which unhappily, it was not.

Christian: *And what did you do then?*

Hopeful: *Do? I didn't know what to do until I shared my trouble with Faithful, for he and I were well acquainted. And he told me, that unless I could obtain the righteousness of a man who had never sinned, neither mine own nor all the righteousness of the world, could save me.*

Christian: *And did you think he was telling you the truth?*

Hopeful: *Had he told me this when I was pleased and satisfied with my own achievements, I would have called him a fool for his pains. However, since I now see my own infirmity, and the sin which over-comes my best performance, I have been forced to share his opinion.*

Christian: *But did you think, when Faithful first suggested it to you, that there was such a perfectly righteous man to be found? Did you know of a man who had never committed a sin?*

Hopeful: *I must confess, the words spoken by Faithful at first sounded strange. But after a little more talk and company with him, I concluded there was such a man.*

Christian: *And did you ask him what man this was, and how you must be justified by him?*

 **Romans 3:25-26**

Hopeful: *Yes, and he told me it was the Lord Jesus, Who dwelleth on the right hand of the Most High.*

 **Hebrews 10:12-21**

And he said you must be justified by Him, even by trusting in what He has done by Himself in the days of His flesh when He suffered hanging on the tree.

 26 **Romans 4:5, Colossians 1:14, 1 Peter 1:19**

I asked him further how that man's righteousness could accomplish my salvation, how it could justify another such as myself before God?

He told me the Lord Jesus was the mighty God and He did what He did, and also died the death not for Himself, but for me. He did it in order that His work, and the worthiness of them, should be imputed to me, if I only believed and trusted in Him and Him alone.

Christian: *And what did you do then?*

Hopeful: *I made my objections against believing, for I thought Jesus Christ was not willing to save me.*

Christian: *And then what did Faithful say to you?*

Hopeful: *He asked me to go to the Lord Jesus and see for myself. Then I said it was presumptuous. Faithful replied, "No, that is not true for I was invited to come."*

 27 **Matthew 11:28**

Then Faithful gave me a book that contained the testimony of and about Jesus to encourage me to come to Him. He said concerning that book, that every jot and tittle thereof stood firmer than Heaven and Earth.

 28 **Matthew 24:35**

Then I asked him what I must do when I came. He told me I must entreat upon my knees, with all my heart and soul, the Father to reveal His Son to me.

 29 **Psalm 95:6, Daniel 6:10, Jeremiah 29:12-13**

I asked him further how I must make my supplications to Him. He said, go, and you will find Him upon a mercy-seat, where He sits all the yearlong to give pardon and forgiveness to those who come.

 Exodus 25:22, 16:2, Numbers 7:89, Hebrews 4:16, Hebrews 7:25

I told Faithful that I didn't know what to say when I came, and he asked me to say something to this effect:

"God be merciful to me a sinner, and make me to know and believe in Jesus Christ; for I see, that if His righteousness had not been, or I have not faith in that righteousness, I am utterly cast away.

Lord, I have heard that You are a merciful God, and have ordained that Your Son, Jesus Christ should be the Savior of the world; and moreover, that You are willing to bestow His righteousness upon such a poor sinner as I am. And I am a sinner indeed.

Lord, take therefore this opportunity, and magnify Your grace in the salvation of my soul, through Your Son, Jesus Christ. Amen."

Christian: *And did you do as you were asked?*

Hopeful: *Yes, over, and over, and over.*

Christian: *And did the Father reveal the Son to you?*

Hopeful: *Not at the first, nor second, nor third, nor fourth, nor fifth, no, nor at the sixth time neither.*

Christian: *What did you do then?*

Hopeful: *What? I didn't know what to do.*

Christian: *Did you ever think of quitting, of no longer praying?*

Hopeful: *Yes, many times that thought came into my head.*

Christian: *And what was the reason you did not stop?*

 Luke 11:9

Hopeful: *I believed it was true that without the righteousness of Christ, all the world could not save me. Therefore, I thought to myself, if I leave off, I die, or I can die kneeling at the throne of grace.*

And then this came into my mind: if it tarries, wait for it; because it will surely come, and will not tarry.

 Habakkuk 2:3

So I continued praying until the Father showed me His Son.

Christian: *And how was He revealed unto you?*

Hopeful: *I did not see Him with my bodily eyes, but with the eyes of my understanding.*

 Ephesians 1:18-19

It happened like this: One day I was very sad, I think sadder than at any other time in my life. This sadness was caused by a fresh sight at the greatness and vileness of my sins. And as I was looking for nothing but Hell and the everlasting damnation of my soul, suddenly, as I was thinking, I saw the Lord Jesus looking down from Heaven upon me, and saying, "Believe on the Lord Jesus Christ, and you will be saved."

 Acts 16:31

But I replied, Lord, I am a great, a very great sinner: and He answered, "My grace is sufficient for you."

 2 Corinthians 12:9

Then I said, But, Lord, what is believing? And then I heard Him say, "He that cometh to me shall never hunger, and he that belie-veth on me shall never thirst."

 John 6:35

Then I understood that believing and coming was all one thing. And that he that came, that is, that ran out of a heart and affec-tions after salvation by Christ, he indeed believed in Christ.

Then I began to weep, and I asked further, but, Lord, may such a great sinner as I am be indeed accepted of You, and be saved by You? And I heard Him say, "...and him that cometh to me, I will in no wise cast out."

 John 6:37, Luke 5:32

Then I said, but how, Lord, must I consider You in my coming to You?

How may I place my faith upon You?

Then He said, "Christ Jesus came into the world to save sinners."

 1 Timothy 1:15

He is the end of the law for righteousness to everyone who believes.

 Romans 10:4

He died for our sins and rose again for our justification.

 Romans 4:25

He loved us and washed us from our sins in His own blood.

 Revelation 1:5

He is the Mediator between God and us.

 1 Timothy 2:5

He ever liveth to make intercession for us.

 Hebrews 7:25

From all this, I considered that I must look for righteousness in His person, and for satisfaction for my sins by His blood: that what He did in obedience to His Father's law, and in submitting to the penalty of sin, was not for Himself, but for him who will accept His salvation, and be thankful.

And now my heart is full of joy, my eyes full of tears, and my affections running over with love for the name, people, and ways of Jesus Christ.

Christian: *This was a revelation of Christ to your soul indeed. But tell me particularly what effect this had upon your spirit?*

Hopeful: *It made me see that all the world, notwithstanding all its so-called righteousness, is in a state of condemnation.*

It made me see that God the Father, though He is just, can justly justify the sinner that comes to Him through His Son.

It made me greatly ashamed of the vileness of my former life, and confounded me with the sense of mine own ignorance; for there never came a thought into my heart before that moment, I truly believe, that so clearly showed me the beauty of Jesus Christ.

It made me love a holy life, and long to do something for the honor and glory of the name of the Lord Jesus.

 John 3:19

I thought that if I had a thousand gallons of blood in my body, I could spill it all for the sake of the Lord Jesus.

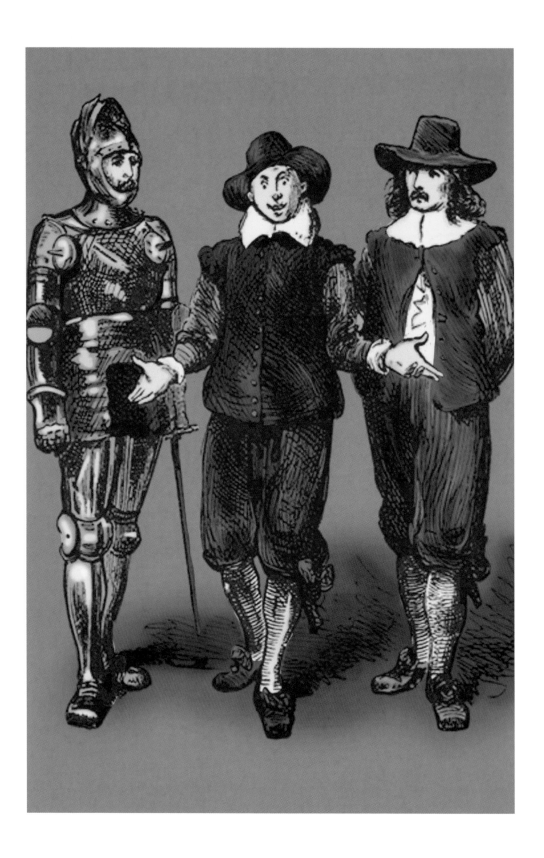

CHAPTER 27

Christian and Hopeful Re-encounter Ignorance

Faithless: In my dream, Hopeful looked back and saw Ignorance, whom they had left behind, coming up behind them.

Hopeful: *Look how far the youngster stays behind us.*

Christian: *Yes, I see him. He does not care for our company or our opinions as he has his own **Mumpsimus**.**

Hopeful: *It would have done him good to walk with us and consider our counsel.*

Christian: *That is true, but I am sure he thinks otherwise.*

Hopeful: *You're probably right, but let's wait for him.*

Faithless: So they did. Then Christian said to Ignorance:

Christian: *Come along, why do you stay so far behind?*

Ignorance: *I prefer to walk alone unless the company is good.*

Faithless: Christian then turned to Hopeful with a subtle nod.

Christian: *Did I not tell you he cared not for our company?*

---

* Mumpsimus—An incorrect view on something that a person refuses to let go of.

Come along Ignorance and let us pass the time in good conversation as we go through this solitary place.

Faithless: Christian then began to dialog with Ignorance.

Christian: *Come, how do you do? How stands it between God and your soul now?*

Ignorance: *I hope, well, since I am always full of good notions that come into my mind to comfort me as I walk.*

Christian: *What good notions? Please tell us.*

Ignorance: *Why, I think of God and Heaven.*

Christian: *So do the devils and damned souls.*

1 *James 2:19*

Ignorance: *But I think of them and desire them.*

Christian: *So do many who are never likely to come there. The soul of the sluggard desireth, and has nothing.*

2 *Proverbs 13:4*

Ignorance: *But I think of them and leave all for them.*

Christian: *That I doubt. To leave all is a very hard thing to do, harder than most people think. But why, or by what, are you persuaded that you have left all for God and Heaven?*

Ignorance: *My heart tells me so.*

Christian: *The wise man says, "He that trusteth in his own heart is a fool."*

3 *Proverbs 28:26, Proverbs 3:5-6*

Ignorance: *That is spoken of an evil heart, but mine is a good one.*

Christian: *But how do you know your heart is good?*

Ignorance: *It comforts me in hopes of heaven.*

Christian: *That may be through its deceitfulness for a man's heart may minister comfort to him without there being any grounds for hoping the thing desired will be attained.*

Ignorance: *But my heart and life agree together; therefore, my hope is well-grounded.*

Christian: *Who told you that your heart and life agree together?*

Ignorance: *My heart tells me so.*

Christian: *Unless the Word of God tells you so, your hope is in vain.*

Ignorance: *Doesn't a good heart have good thoughts? And is not a good life lived according to God's commandments?*

Christian: *Yes, it is a good heart that has good thoughts, and it is a good life that is lived according to God's commandments; but it is one thing to actually possess these, and another thing only to think you do.*

Ignorance: *Well then, tell me what are good thoughts and a life according to God's commandments?*

 Jeremiah 17:11

Christian: *There are good thoughts of many different kinds; some respecting ourselves, some having to do with God, some regarding Christ, and some other things.*

Ignorance: *What are good thoughts respecting ourselves?*

Christian: *Thoughts that agree with the Word of God.*

Ignorance: *When do our thoughts of ourselves agree with the Word of God?*

Christian: *When we pass the same judgment upon ourselves that the Word of God passes.*

To explain myself: the Word of God says of all persons in their natural condition, "There is none righteous, there is none that does good."

It says also that every imagination of the heart of man is only evil, and that continually.

 Genesis 6:5

And again, the imagination of man's heart is evil from his youth.

 Genesis 8:21

Now, then, when we think this of ourselves, when we think good thoughts of our heart, we can see that, according to the Word of God, it is not good, but evil.

Ignorance: *I will never believe that my heart is so bad.*

Christian: *Then you never have one good thought concerning yourself in your life.*

But let me go on. Just as the Word of God passes judgment upon our hearts, so it passes judgment upon our ways; and when the thoughts of our hearts and our ways agree with the judgment which the Word of God gives of both, then they are both good thoughts because they agree with God's Word.

Ignorance: *Explain what you mean.*

Christian: *Why, the Word of God says that man's ways are crooked ways, not good but perverse; it says they are naturally out of step with the good and right way, that they have not known it.*

 Psalm 125:5, Proverbs 2:15, Romans 3:12

Now, when a man thinks of his ways, I say, when he doth sensibly, and with heart-humiliation, think of his ways as God reveals, then has he good thoughts of his own ways, because his thoughts now agree with the judgment of the Word of God.

Ignorance: *What are good thoughts concerning God?*

Christian: *Just as I said concerning good thoughts of ourselves, when our thoughts of God agree with what the Word of God says of Him; that is, when we think of his being and attributes as the Word of God teaches, which is a topic we should spend our lives studying, then our thoughts are right thoughts of God.*

 Isaiah 55:8-9

To name a few, good thoughts of God to consider is that God knows us better than we know ourselves, and can see sin in us when we can see none in ourselves.

 John 2:25

A good thought about God, for example, is when we think that He knows our inmost thoughts and that our heart, with all its depths, is always open to His eyes.

 Psalm 11:4

A good thought about God is also when we think that all our righteousness stinks in His nostrils and that He cannot see us stand before Him with any confidence, even in all our best performances.

Ignorance: *Do you think that I am such a fool as to think that God can see no further than I; or that I would come to God in the best of my performances?*

 Isaiah 64:6

Christian: *Well, then, tell me what you think.*

Ignorance: *Why, to be short, I think I must believe in Christ for justification.*

Christian: *Why do you think you must believe in Christ when you do not see your need of Him?*

You have already admitted that you see no original nor actual infirmities, but have such a good opinion of yourself and all your deeds that you plainly do not see the necessity of Christ's personal righteousness to justify you before God.

How then can you say, "I believe in Christ?"

Ignorance: *I believe well enough, for all that.*

Christian: *How do you believe?*

Ignorance: *I believe that Christ died for sinners; and that I shall be justified before God from the curse through His gracious acceptance of my obedience to His laws.*

 James 2:10

I believe that Christ makes my duties, that are religious, acceptable to His Father by virtue of His merits, and so shall I be justified.

Christian: *Let me give you an answer to this confession of your faith.*

1. *You believe with a fantastical faith; for this faith is nowhere described in the Word of God.*

2. You believe with a false faith; becauseit taketh justification from the personal righteousness of Christ, and applies it to your own.

3. Your faith does not make Christ the justifier of your person, but of your actions; and of your person for your action's sake, which is false.

4. Therefore this faith is deceitful and will leave you under wrath on the Day of Judgment, for true justifying faith makes the soul sensible to its lost condition by the law.

True justifying faith sends the sinner fleeing for refuge to the righteousness of Christ.

The grace of God does not make you justified by your obedience to the law, nor will your obedience be accepted by God.

It is Christ's personal obedience to the law, in doing and suffering for us that produces a righteousness that is not our own, it is a gift of God that is only granted to those who have faith alone in the finished work of Jesus Christ on the Cross of Calvary.

 Ephesians 2:8-9, I Peter 2:24

You cannot think that mixing your righteousness, which God views as filthy rags, with the spotless righteousness of Christ is going to be accepted by God in the courtroom where works are not allowed, except for the finished work of His Son.

You have a false faith that does not conform to the Word of God. This kind of faith will not be accepted and will not deliver you from the wrath of God.

Ignorance: *What! Would you have us trust to what Christ in His own person has done without us?*

This conceit would loosen the reins of our lust, and tolerate us to live as we like; for what does it matter how we live, if we

may be justified by Christ's personal righteousness from all when we believe it?

Christian: *Ignorance is your name, and as your name is, so are you; even your answer demonstrates what I have told you.*

You are ignorant of what justifying righteousness is and just as ignorant as to how to secure your soul through the faith that you imagine needs your assistance.

 Hebrews 11:7

Yea, you also are ignorant of the true effects of saving faith in the righteousness of Christ, which is to bow and win over the heart to God in Christ, to love His name, His Word, ways, and people, and not as you ignorantly imagine.

Hopeful: *Ask him if ever he had Christ revealed to him from Heaven.*

Ignorance: *What! You are a man for revelations! I believe that both of you are suffering from some sort of brain fever and you have lost your wits as your explanation defies all worldly logic.*

Hopeful: *You're right about that. You have finally said something that is true. Christ is so hidden in God from the natural apprehensions of the flesh that without revelation from God no man can have or understand saving faith as it is unnatural and repulsive to his carnal mind.*

 I Corinthians 2:14

Ignorance: *That is your faith, but not mine. I am sure that my faith is as good as yours even though my head is not filled with such whimsical fantasies as you seem to be.*

Faithless: And with that, he wrinkled his face and began to ***Snirtle***.*

---

* **Snirtle**—To snicker.

Christian: *Let me leave you with one last warning. You should not lightly speak of this matter of which you have no experience or knowledge. For this, I will boldly affirm, even as my good companion has done, that no man can know Jesus Christ but by the revelation of the Father.*

The faith that is genuine saving faith, the faith that rests upon Christ alone is witness to the exceeding greatness and mighty power of God since it can be attained by no other means known to man.

 Matthew 11:27, 1 Corinthians 12:3, Ephesians 1:17-19

The faith that saves men from perishing and delivers them from the wrath of God is a faith that you do not have, poor Ignorance, you are ignorant of it. Wake up and see your own wretchedness and flee to the Lord Jesus; and by His righteousness, which is the righteousness of God (for He Himself is God), you will be delivered from condemnation.

Ignorance: *You are going too fast and I cannot keep pace with you. You go ahead as I prefer to stay behind.*

Christian: *Well, Ignorance, you will remain foolish. You have slighted the good counsel given to you ten times over. If you continue to refuse it, you will know before too long how evil your opinions are. I bid you, no I beg you, one last time to heed the counsel we have given you and turn away from your false notions that will lead you, despite all your lofty opinions, to the pit of Hell.*

CHAPTER 28
The Error of Ignorance

Faithless: I saw in my dream that Ignorance was falling farther and farther behind Christian and Hopeful on the path that leads to the Celestial City. He seemed to deliberately stop in order for the space between Christian, Hopeful and himself to increase until he could barely be seen hobbling behind them.

Christian: *Well, Hopeful, it looks like you and I must walk by ourselves again.*

I pity this poor man, Ignorance. It will certainly go ill with him at the end.

Hopeful: *Yes! There are many in our town in his condition, whole families, yes, entire streets, and some consider themselves true pilgrims; and if there are so many in our parts, how many do you think there must be in the place where Ignorance was born?*

Christian: *Indeed, the Word says, "He has blinded their eyes, just in case they should see..."*

 Isaiah 44:18, John 12:40

But, now that we are by ourselves, tell me what you think of such men? Have they at any time come under the conviction of sin and consequently been terrorized by fears that they are in a dangerous condition?

Hopeful: *You are my elder brother, please share what is on your mind.*

Christian: *I think that sometimes they may feel a twinge of conviction regarding their true condition, but being naturally ignorant they do not understand that such convictions are for their good. Therefore, they do desperately seek to stifle them, and then they presumptuously continue to flatter themselves in the way of their own hearts.*

Hopeful: *I do believe, as you say, that fear is instructive and meant for men's good, as well as to begin their pilgrimage on the right path.*

 Jude 1:23, II Corinthians 5:11

Christian: *And what path is that do you suppose?*

Hopeful: *The fear of the Lord is the beginning of wisdom.*

 Job 28:28, Psalm 111:10, Proverbs 1:7, 9:10

And the right path begins with the firm and true conviction that we are without hope in this world except by one path and one Man; and that path is Christ alone.

Christian: *And I will add that once on the path, they do not flatter themselves that they can ever add anything to what the Savior has done to put us on that path which leads to Eternal Life.*

Hopeful: *How do you describe right fear?*

Christian: *True or right fear is discovered by three things:*

1. By its beginning; it is caused by saving convictions for sin.

2. It drives the soul to lay fast hold of Christ alone for salvation.

3. It begins and continues to put our soul in great reverence of God, His Word, and ways; keeping it tender, and making it afraid to turn from them, to the right hand or to the left, or to anything that may dishonor God, break its peace, grieve the Spirit, or cause the enemy to speak reproachfully.

Hopeful: *Well said; I believe you have spoken the truth. Look, we are almost past the Enchanted Ground.*

Christian: *We have about two miles further to go. So, let's use the time to return to the matter we were considering.*

The ignorant do not know that such right convictions that make them fearful are for their good and as I said, they seek to stifle them.

 *Romans 1:18-20*

Hopeful: *How do they seek to stifle them?*

Christian:
1. They think those fears are wrought by the devil (though indeed they are wrought of God), and thinking so, they resist them as things that directly tend to their overthrow.

2. They also think these fears tend to the spoiling of their faith; when the problem is that the poor men have no faith at all in the first place, and so they harden their hearts against them.

3. They presume they should not fear and therefore, despite the fears, they become presumptuously confident.

4. They see that those fears tend to take away from them their pitiful, old self-holiness, therefore they resist them with all their might.

Hopeful: *I know something about this myself; before I came to the end of myself and threw myself, without anything to recommend me, at the mercy of the Savior.*

Faithless paused for a moment, then raised his hand in order to signal to Great-Heart that he had a question about what Christian said to Hopeful in his dream.

Great-Heart recognized the quizzical nod, as it was a familiar gesture that always preceded the need for further clarification.

Great-Heart: I can guess your question as it is something that has been the topic of much conversation and some confusion among pilgrims for hundreds of years.

Faithless bent forward to hear what Great-Heart had to say.

Great-Heart: You're wondering why God has blinded their eyes just in case they should see. I suppose you're asking yourself why God would not want them to see something that could save them from the terrors of eternal judgment?

Faithless: Indeed. This is what has been troubling me ever since I had this latest dream. Why is God hiding His truth on one hand, while doing everything He can to reveal His truth on the other hand?

Great-Heart: Let's take a look in the King's Book and see if we can find the answer.

Great-Heart opened his book and immediately found the page where God revealed this puzzling truth to the prophet Isaiah, who recorded it so that we might understand the mind of God.

Before Great-Heart began reading from the King's Book, he asked Faithless to find the passage written by John the fisherman and follower of the King's Son whose name means God's Salvation—the name we know as Jesus the Christ.

Great-Heart watched with patience as Faithless turned pages back and forth until he finally found the passage in the Book of John the 12th chapter and the 40th verse.

Great-Heart: Listen to what the prophet Isaiah said.

Faithless looked up, giving the matter before him his full attention.

Great-Heart: "They have not known nor understood: for he hath shut their eyes, that they cannot see; and their hearts, that they cannot understand."

Great-Heart looked up at Faithless who was now more confused than ever.

Faithless: It sounds like God is shutting their eyes and keeping their hearts from understanding. Is that right?

Great-Heart: Not exactly. Without knowing why God has shut their eyes, you will come to the wrong conclusion about God and why He does what He does.

Great-Heart looked at the open book Faithless had in his lap and asked him to read the passage from John 12:40.

Faithless found the place and began to read.

Faithless: "He hath blinded their eyes, and hardened their heart; that they should not see with their eyes, nor understand with their heart, and be converted, and I should heal them."

Faithless looked up more confused than ever.

Faithless: It says that God hardened their hearts! It sounds like God does not want them to believe.

Great-Heart: I have a question for you Faithless.

Faithless: I will try to answer it as best I can.

Great-Heart: Have you ever used bricks to build a building, or built a stone wall using concrete?

Faithless: Yes.

Great-Heart: When you put the concrete mortar between the bricks or stones, what condition is it in?

Faithless: It is pliable and wet.

Great-Heart: And when you return the next day, is it still pliable and wet?

Faithless: No, it is hard and brittle.

Great-Heart: Why is that?

Faithless: Well, I suppose because it is concrete, and concrete, once mixed up, soon becomes hard and brittle.

Great-Heart: So, you wouldn't use plum pudding as mortar, only concrete because it is the nature of concrete to become hard and dry?

Faithless: That's right.

Great-Heart: When the prophet Isaiah and the fisherman and follower of the King's Son talk about God hardening hearts, they are talking about the already existing condition of the heart. The heart, like concrete, may be wet and pliable but like concrete, given time, it is the nature to harden.

God is hardening the hearts of those who have rejected Him, He is not changing their hearts. He is simply strengthening and giving them courage to be what they are.

And do you know what that is?

Faithless gave Great-Heart a blank look.

Great-Heart opened the King's Book once more to 2 Corinthians 4:2-4.

Great-Heart: "But have renounced the hidden things of dishonesty, not walking in craftiness, nor handling the Word of God deceitfully; but by manifestation of the truth commending ourselves to every man's conscience in the sight of God. But if our gospel be hid, it is hid to them that are lost: In whom the god of this world hath blinded the minds of them which believe not, lest the light of the glorious gospel of Christ, who is the image of God, should shine unto them."

Faithless: So, who is doing the blinding, the false god of this world or the true and living God?

Great-Heart: The answer to your question is this. Men are in unbelief and as a result of the unbelief have been willingly blinded by the god of this world. God judges these unbelieving men by making their blindness permanent as long as they are in unbelief.

Faithless: So, the blindness is caused by unbelief?

Great-Heart: That's right.

Faithless: Can the blind then ever see again?

Great-Heart: If they repent of their unbelief and seek God with all their hearts, He will allow Himself to be found and He will remove the blindness and give them a new believing heart.

Faithless: And how does that happen?

Great-Heart: It happens when faith destroys the strongholds of the god of this world.

Faithless: And how do blind men with hardened hearts come to faith?

Great-Heart turned the pages of the King's Book until he found the book written to the Romans, chapter 10, and read verses 13-17.

Great-Heart: "For whosoever shall call upon the name of the Lord shall be saved. How then shall they call on him in whom they have not believed? and how shall they believe in him of whom they have not heard? and how shall they hear without a preacher? And how shall they preach, except they be sent? as it is written, How beautiful are the feet of them that preach the gospel of peace, and bring glad tidings of good things! But they have not all obeyed the gospel. For

Esaias saith, Lord, who hath believed our report? So then faith cometh by hearing, and hearing by the Word of God."

Faithless: So, it is possible to regain your sight?

Great-Heart: It is the miracle of God's grace.

Great-Heart then held out the King's Book and solemnly addressed Faithless with these words.

Great-Heart: Faithless, I declare to you in the sight of Almighty God that there is only one way to be saved. That way can only be found by putting your faith and trust in the Lord Jesus Christ. I bid you to call upon His name in faith, believing that His sacrifice can cleanse you from all unrighteousness, and His blood alone can gain you entry into the Celestial City.

Faithless was a little taken back and for a few uncomfortable moments sat silently in front of Great-Heart, who held his peace while waiting for Faithless to respond.

Sheepishly, Faithless finally spoke.

Faithless: Shall I continue telling you my dream?

Great-Heart paused for a moment, a little saddened that Faithless had not heeded the call to put his trust in Christ alone, but then cheerfully nodded to indicate his excitement to hear more.

Faithless: Christian then decided to ask Hopeful another question.

> **Christian**: *Shall we leave off discussing the condition of our neighbor, Ignorance, and begin another profitable question?*

> **Hopeful**: *Yes, that is a good idea. Please ask the question.*

> **Christian**: *Well then, did you not know someone named Temporary, who was bold in religion about ten years ago?*

Hopeful: *Yes; he dwelled in No-Faith, a town about two miles from Honesty, and he lived next door to a man named Turnback.*

Christian: *Right. Turnback and Temporary lived under the same roof. Well, Turnback was much awakened once and I believe back then he had some knowledge of his own sins and the wages those sins had earned.*

Hopeful: *Yes, I remember, for my house was only about three miles from his and he would often visit me with many tears.*

Truly I pitied the man, and was not altogether without hope of him; but as the King's Book says, not everyone who cries, "Lord, Lord!" is a true pilgrim.

Christian: *Yes. Turnback once told me that he was resolved to go on a pilgrimage, as we go now; but all of a sudden, he made the acquaintance of Save-self and never spoke to me again.*

Hopeful: *Now, since we are talking about him, let us inquire into the reason for his sudden backsliding, which is not only his condition but many others besides.*

Christian: *It sounds like a profitable lesson; please begin.*

Hopeful: *Well then, there are, in my judgment, four reasons that explain the actions of Turnback and all those who backslide and never recover:*

***1.** Though the consciences of such men are awakened, yet their minds are not changed: therefore, when the power of guilt wears away, that which provoked them to be religious ceases.*

It is then, once the power of guilt has run its course, that they naturally turn back to their old ways and habits.

We can see an illustration of this in a dog that is sick from what he has eaten. So long as his sickness prevails, he vomits; not that he does this of his own mind (if we may say a dog has a mind), but he does it because it troubles his stomach. But now, when his sickness is over and his stomach is eased, his desires, being not at all disgusted by his vomit, entices him to return to it and lick it all up; and so that which is written is true, "The dog is turned to his own vomit again."

 2 Peter 2:22

So, being hot for Heaven, by virtue of their sense and fear of the torments of Hell, so as their sense and fear of damnation chills and cools, so also do their desires for Heaven and salvation cool. Therefore, when it comes to pass that their guilt and fear is gone, their desires for Heaven and happiness die, and they return to their old way of life again.

2. *Another reason is, they have slavish fears that overtake them: I speak of the fears who they have of men; For the fear of man bringeth a snare.*

 Proverbs 29:25

So then, though they seem to be hot for Heaven so long as the flames of Hell are about their ears, yet, when that terror goes away, they have second thoughts. Namely, that it is good to be wise and not to run, for they do not want to lose what they have, or put themselves in unavoidable and unnecessary troubles. Consequently, they go back to the world.

3. *The shame that attends religion is a stumbling block to them; they are proud and haughty, and religion in their eyes is low and contemptible. Therefore, when they have lost their sense of Hell and the wrath to come, they return again to their former way of life.*

4. *They shun guilt and terror. It is grievous to them and they do not like to consider it or the misery they see before them. So, when the guilt and terror are gone, they harden their hearts* *toward God and once rid of the fear of God's wrath, they go right back to the world.*

Christian: *You have described the symptoms of a false pilgrim very well. Now can you tell me the root cause of the symptoms?*

Hopeful: *No, please go on.*

Christian: *The reason that lies at the bottom of all this is simple. Turnback, and all those like him, are terrorized temporarily by the consequences of their sin but they never change their mind or their will. And without that change, they are like the criminal standing before the judge who quakes and trembles and seems to repent most heartily, but it is all motivated by his fear of the hangman's rope.*

He is not disturbed by his sin, it is not an offense to him and he does not detest his sinful life. The evidence of this is that once the sentence for his sin is relieved and he has his liberty back, he will be a thief or rogue just like he was before.

If his mind, heart and will were truly changed, then he would be changed and not return to his old ways because they would be detestable to him.

Hopeful: *Please continue.*

Christian: *With great pleasure.*

Here is the natural course of such men:

1. From their own imagination they think about all they can regarding God, death and the judgment to come.

2. Then they neglect, by degrees, private duties such as closet prayer, curbing their lusts, watching, sorrow for sin, and the like.

3. They also shun the company of lively and warm Christians.

4. *After that, they grow cold to public duty: hearing, reading, godlyconference, and the like.*

5. *They also begin to criticize some of the godly, finding fault with the infirmities that are the burden of all men, including the truly redeemed.*

6. *Then they begin to seek the company of and associate themselves with carnal, loose, and wicked men.*

7. *They then give way to carnal and wicked discourses in secret, looking to see if they can find fault with any who are counted honest in order to justify their own behavior.*

8. *After this, they begin to play with little sins openly.*

9. *And then, being hardened, they show themselves as they truly are. Thus, being launched again into the gulf of misery, unless a miracle of grace prevents it, they everlastingly perish in their own deception.*

CHAPTER 29
CROSSING THE RIVER

Now Faithless continued to explain what he saw with the pilgrims. He gathered his thoughts and searched for words to describe what he had seen in his dream.

Faithless: Then I saw in my dream, that by this time the pilgrims had passed over the Enchanted Ground, and entered into the country of Beulah, whose air was very sweet and pleasant.

 Isaiah 62:4-12, Song of Solomon 2:10-12

The straightway went directly through Beulah and so Christian and Hopeful refreshed themselves for a season.

While traveling through this land, they heard the singing of birds and watched as every day new flowers appeared on the earth, and heard the voice of the turtle dove.

In this country, the sun shined both night and day. This land was beyond the reach of the Valley of the Shadow of Death, and also out of the reach of Giant-Despair; nor could they from this place see Doubting-Castle. Here they were within sight of the Celestial City.

Christian and Hopeful reach Beulah Land

Here they met some of the inhabitants of Beulah; for in this land the Shining Ones commonly walked, because it was upon the borders of Heaven.

In this land also, the contract between the Bride and the Bridegroom was renewed; yes, here, as the Bridegroom rejoiceth over the Bride, so doth God rejoice over them.

Here they had no want of corn and wine; for in this place they met with an abundance of what they had sought for in their pilgrimage.

Here they heard voices from out of the city, loud voices, saying, "say to the daughter of Zion, Behold, your salvation cometh! Behold, his reward is with him! Here all the inhabitants of the country called them the holy People, the redeemed of the Lord."

Now, as they walked through this land, they had more joy than they had ever had in any other part of the journey on the King's Narrow Way; and as they drew near to the Celestial City, they had a more perfect view than they had ever seen before.

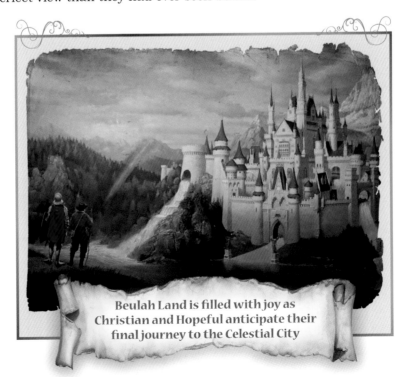

Beulah Land is filled with joy as Christian and Hopeful anticipate their final journey to the Celestial City

It was built of pearls and precious stones, also the streets of the city were paved with gold; so that, the natural glory of the city and the reflection of the sunbeams upon it made Christian feel sick with desire; Hopeful also had a fit or two of the same disease. Here they stayed for a while, crying out because of their great desire to enter the city.

As they walked on their way and came yet nearer and nearer to the Celestial City, they came upon orchards, vineyards, and gardens just off the path.

Now, as they came up to these places, behold the gardener stood in the way; to whom Christian asked:

> **Christian**: *Whose vineyards and gardens are these?*

> **Gardener**: *They are the King's, and are planted here for His own delight, and also for the refreshment of pilgrims.*

So, the gardener took Christian and Hopeful into the vineyards, and asked them to refresh themselves with the dainties, he also showed them the King's walks and arbors where he delighted to be: and here they stayed for a while and slept.

 Deuteronomy 23:24

Now I saw in my dream, that Christian and Hopeful talked in their sleep, more than they had done at any other place or time while on their journey.

Finally, the gardener spoke to them while they were talking during their slumber.

> **Gardener**: *It is the nature of the fruit of the grapes of these vineyards, to go down so sweetly as to cause the lips of them that are asleep to speak.*

 Song of Solomon 7:9

So, I saw that when they awoke, they made themselves ready to go up to the Celestial City.

But, as I said, the reflection of the sun upon the city (for the city was pure gold), was so extremely glorious, that they could not as yet with open face behold it, but could only see it through an instrument made for that very purpose.

 Revelation 21:18, 2 Corinthians 3:18

So, I saw, that as they went on, there met them two men in raiment that shone like gold, also their faces shone as the light.

> **Shining Ones**: *Where have you come from?*

> **Christian**: *I have come from the City of Destruction and entered the King's Way that has led us to this place through the Door that stands at the Narrow Way.*

> **Shining Ones**: *And you sir, where have you come from?*

> **Hopeful**: *I have come from the Town called Vanity Fair and have also entered the King's Highway through the Narrow Gate.*

Faithless: They also asked them where they had lodged, what difficulties and dangers, what comforts and pleasures, they had met within the way; and they told them.

> **Shining Ones**: *You have only two difficulties more to meet with, and then you will be in the Celestial City.*

> **Christian and Hopeful**: *Will you go along with us?*

> **Shining Ones**: *Yes, we will go along with you but you must overcome the two obstacles by your own faith.*

So, I saw in my dream, that they went on together until they came in sight of the gate.

Now I further saw, that between them and the gate was a river, but there was no bridge, and the river was very deep.

At the sight of this river, Christian and Hopeful were much stunned:

> **Christian**: *Is there not another way that we can go to arrive at the gate of the Celestial City?*

> **Shining Ones**: *You must go through the river or you cannot come to the gate of the Celestial City.*

> **Hopeful**: *Is there no other way to the gate?*

As Christian approaches the end of his life, he is haunted by his past failures and sin. Hopeful encourages Christian to trust in God's Word and the sure promises made to all those who have trusted in Jesus Christ

> **Shining Ones**: *Yes; but there are only two so far who have entered by another way and they were Enoch and Elijah. There will be a time coming when an untold number will be permitted to enter the city without going through the river.*

> **Christian**: *And when is that time?*

> **Shining Ones**: *We have not been told when that time is, no one knows the day or the hour of that event except the King, but that time has not come, so you must cross the river in order to enter the Celestial City.*

Christian: *Perhaps if we wait a while, we will be permitted to tread that path with the untold number.*

Shining Ones: *No one has been permitted to tread that path since the foundation of the world except for Enoch and Elijah, nor shall until the last trumpet shall sound.*

Faithless: I saw in my dream that the pilgrims, especially Christian, began to despair in their mind, and looked this way and that, but no way could be found by which they might escape the river.

Then I heard Hopeful asked one of the Shining Ones:

Hopeful: *Are the waters all the same depth?*

Shining Ones: *No; but we cannot help you with that since you shall find the water deeper or shallower depending upon your faith in the King of the place.*

Then Christian and Hopeful stepped up to the water, and upon entering, Christian began to sink. Christian cried out to his good friend Hopeful.

Christian: *I am sinking in deep waters; the billows go over my head; all his waves go over me. Selah.*

Hopeful: *Be of good cheer, my brother: I feel the bottom, and it is good.*

Christian: *Ah! my friend, the sorrows of death have compassed me about, I shall not see the land that flows with milk and honey.*

Faithless: And with that, it seemed that a great darkness and horror fell upon Christian so that he could not see anything in front of him.

Also, it was here that Christian lost his senses so that he could neither remember nor talk in an orderly manner or remember any of the sweet refreshments that he had met with in the way of his pilgrimage.

But all the words that he spoke displayed the horror of his mind, and the fears of his and heart, that he should die in that river, and never obtain entrance in at the gate to the Celestial City.

As Christian stood in the deep waters of the river, he was overcome with troublesome thoughts of the sins that he had committed, both since and before he became a pilgrim.

I also observed that he was troubled with apparitions of hobgoblins and evil spirits.

Hopeful had much difficulty to keep his brother's head above water; yes, sometimes Christian would go down head first into the water, and then, after a short while, he would rise up again half dead. Hopeful did all he could to comfort Christian, saying:

> **Hopeful**: *Brother Christian, I see the gate, and the Shining Ones standing by to receive us.*
>
> **Christian**: *It is you, it is you they wait for; for you have been hopeful ever since I knew you.*
>
> **Hopeful**: *And so have you, my dear brother.*
>
> **Christian**: *Ah, brother Hopeful, surely if all was right with my soul then He would now arise to help me; but because of my sins He has brought me into the snare, and has left me.*
>
> **Hopeful**: *My brother Christian, you have quite forgotten the text where it is said of the wicked, "There are no bands in their death, but their strength is firm; they are not troubled as other men, neither are they plagued like other men."*
>
> *Psalm 73:4-5*
>
> *These troubles and distresses that you go through in these waters, are not a sign that God has forsaken you; but are sent to test you, whether you will call to mind that which you*

have received of His goodness, and depend upon Him
in your distresses.

Then I saw in my dream, that Christian swooned for a while. Then I heard Hopeful say this:

Hopeful: *Be of good cheer, Jesus Christ makes you whole.*

Faithless: And with that, Christian brake out with a loud voice...

Christian: *Oh, I see Him again; and He tells me, "When you pass through the waters, I will be with you; and through the rivers, they shall not overflow you."*

 Isaiah 43:2

Then they both took courage, and the enemy was after that as still as a stone. Christian, therefore, presently found ground to stand upon, and so the rest of the river was shallow. Presently, Christian and Hopeful arrived safely on the other side of the river.

Standing upon the bank of the river they saw the two Shining Ones again, who were waiting for them. They saluted them, saying, we are ministering spirits, sent forth to minister for those that are the heirs of salvation. So, they went along towards the gate.

Now I saw in my dream that the city stood upon a mighty hill; but the pilgrims went up that hill with ease, because they had the Shining Ones to lead them up by the arms: they had left

Angels assist Christian and Hopeful as they approach the gates of the Celestial City

their mortal garments behind them in the river; for though they went in with them, they came out without them.

They went up with much agility and speed, though the foundation upon which the city was framed was higher than the clouds; they went up through the region of the air, sweetly talking as they went, being comforted because they had safely crossed over the river, and had such glorious companions to attend them.

As they briskly walked, they talked with the Shining Ones about the glory of the place; who told them that the beauty and glory of it were inexpressible. They told them that they would see Mount Zion, the heavenly Jerusalem, the innumerable company of angels, and the spirits of just men made perfect.

 Hebrews 12:22-24

You are going now, they said, to the Heaven of God, where you shall see the Tree of Life, and eat of the never-fading fruits thereof: and when you come there you shall have white robes given to you, and your walk and talk shall be every day with the King, even all the days of eternity.

 Revelation 2:7; 3:4-5; 22:5

There you shall not see again such things as you saw when you were in the lower region upon earth; to wit, sorrow, sickness, affliction, and death. For the former things are passed away.

 Revelation 21:4

You are going now to Abraham, to Isaac, and Jacob, and to the prophets, men that God has taken away from the evil to come, and that are now resting upon their beds, each one walking in His righteousness.

Christian and Hopeful then asked, "What must we do in the holy place?" To whom it was answered:

Shining Ones: *You must receive the comfort of all your toil, and have joy for all your sorrow; you must reap what you have sown, even the fruit of all your prayers, and tears, and sufferings for the King by the way.*

 Galatians 6:7-8

In that place, you will wear crowns of gold, and enjoy the perpetual sight and vision of the Holy One; for there you shall see Him as He is.

 1 John 3:2

There also you shall serve Him continually with praise, with shouting and thanksgiving, whom you desired to serve in the world, though with much difficulty, because of the infirmity of your flesh.

Your eyes shall be delighted with seeing, and your ears with hearing the pleasant voice of the Mighty One.

There you shall enjoy your friends that have gone before you, and there you shall with joy receive every one that follows into the holy place after you.

There also you shall be clothed with glory and majesty, and given a white horse fit to ride out with the King of Glory.

When He shall come with the sound of the trumpet in the clouds, as upon the wings of the wind, you shall come with Him; and when He shall sit upon the throne of judgment, you shall sit by Him; yes, and when He shall pass sentence upon all the workers of iniquity, let them be angels or men, you also shall have a voice in that judgment, because they were His and also your enemies.

Also, when He shall return again to Jerusalem, you shall go too with the sound of the trumpet, and be ever with Him.

 1 Thessalonians 4:14-17, Jude 14-15, Daniel 7:9-10, 1 Corinthians 6:2-3

Now, while they were drawing close to the gate, behold a company of the heavenly host came out to meet them: to whom it was said by the other two Shining Ones:

> **Shining Ones**: *These are the men that have loved our Lord when they were in the world, and that have left all for His holy name, and He has sent us to fetch them, and we have brought them this far on their desired journey so that they may go in and look their Redeemer in the face with joy.*

Then the heavenly host gave a great shout, saying, "Blessed are they that are called to the marriage-supper of the Lamb."

 Revelation 19:9

There came out also at this time to meet them several of the King's trumpeters, clothed in white and shining raiment, who, with melodious noises and loud, made the heavens echo with their sound. These trumpeters saluted Christian and his fellow pilgrim with ten thousand welcomes from the world; they did this with shouting and the sound of trumpeters.

This done, they compassed them round on every side; some went before, some behind, and some on the right hand, and some on the left (as if it were to guard them as they passed through the upper regions), continually sounding as they went, with melodious noise, in notes on high; it was as if Heaven itself was come down to meet them.

Christian and Hopeful walked on together and, as they walked, accompanied by trumpeters who made a joyful sound, mixing their music with looks and gestures, still signifying to Christian and his brother how welcome they were into their company, and with what gladness they came to meet them.

And now were these, Christian and Hopeful, as it were, in Heaven, before they ever came to it, being swallowed up with the sight of angels, and hearing all their melodious notes. Here also they had the city itself in view, and they thought they heard all the bells ring to welcome them thereto.

But, above all, the warm and joyful thoughts that they were going to be dwelling with this company of redeemed men and angels forever and ever was so overwhelming that it cannot be expressed by tongue or pen.

"Blessed are they that are called to the marriage-supper of the Lamb"

Finally, they came up to the gate.

Now when they were come up to the gate, there was written over it, in letters of gold, *blessed are they that do His commandments that they may have the right to the Tree of Life, and may enter in through the gates into the city.*

Then I saw in my dream, that the Shining Ones asked them to call at the gate: the which when they did, some men from above looked over the gate.

Christian and Hopeful immediately recognized Enoch, Moses, and Elijah among others to whom it was said, these pilgrims are come from the City of Destruction, for the love that they bear to the King of this place.

It was then that Christian and Hopeful gave them each their certificate that they had received at the beginning of their pilgrimage.

The certificates were carried to the King, who, when He had read them, asked, "Where are these men?" To whom it was answered, "They are standing without the gate."

The King then commanded to open the gate, "That the righteous nation that keepeth the truth may enter in."

 Isaiah 26:2

Now I saw in my dream, that these two men went in at the gate; and lo, as they entered, they were transfigured; and they had raiment put on that shone like gold.

There were also those that met them with harps and crowns, and gave them to them; the harps to praise withal, and the crowns in token of honor. Then I heard in my dream, that all the bells in the city rang again for joy, and that it was said unto them, enter ye into the joy of your Lord.

I also heard Christian and Hopeful sing with a loud voice, *saying, blessing, and honor, and glory, and power, be unto Him that sitteth upon the throne, and unto the Lamb, forever and ever.*

Now, just as the gates were opened to let in the men, I looked in after them, and behold the city shone like the sun; the streets also were paved with gold; and in them walked many men, with crowns on their heads, palms in their hands, and golden harps, to sing praises withal.

There were also of those that had wings, and they answered one another without intermission, saying, "Holy, Holy, Holy is the Lord." And after that they shut up the gates.

Great-Heart, hearing all this, began to tear up with great teardrops of joy.

Great-Heart: Faithless, what did you think of all this?

Faithless: I wished I myself was among them.

While I was gazing upon all these things, I turned my head to look back, and saw Ignorance come up to the riverside; he soon passed over to the other side without half the difficulty which Christian and Hopeful had met with. For it happened that there was in that place a Ferryman named Vain-Hope, that with his boat helped Ignorance over.

Then I saw Ignorance ascend the hill and come up to the gate, only he came alone without angels or anyone else to encourage him. When he came up to the gate, he looked up to the writing that was above his head, and then began to knock, supposing that he would immediately be invited in; but instead, he was asked by the men that looked over the top of the gate, where did you come from? And what would you have?

> **Ignorance**: *I have eaten and drank in the presence of the King, and He has taught in our streets.*

Then they asked him for his certificate, that they might go in and show it to the King: so, he fumbled in his bosom for one and found nothing.

Then said they, have you none? But the man answered never a word. So, they told the King, but He would not come down to see him but commanded the two Shining Ones, that conducted Christian and Hopeful to the city, to go out and take Ignorance, and bind him hand and foot, and take him away.

Then the angels took him up, and carried him through the air to the door that I saw in the side of the hill, and put him in there.

Great-Heart: Did you see a sign on the door on the side of the hill?

Faithless: Yes, the sign said; *this is the way to Hell.*

And then I awoke from my dream.

CHAPTER 30

FAITHLESS MAKES A LIFE OR DEATH DECISION

Great-Heart was silent for a moment as he reflected on the dream that had come to its final conclusion. After a moment, he looked up at Faithless and spoke.

Great-Heart: Do you know from whence this dream came?

Faithless: I have reflected on this very question for countless hours. I am not certain but I imagine that it might have come from the Celestial City.

Do you know the origin of this dream, and why I should be the one to receive it?

Great-Heart: I know the answer to your first question and may soon know the answer to the second.

Faithless: I pray sir, tell me.

Great-Heart: The dream you have had has a long history, it is not novel or new but rather an ancient prophecy that has been given to you from the very place the journey ends.

Faithless: You mean the Celestial City?

Great-Heart: That is the very place.

Faithless: And do you know why I received this message from the Celestial City?

Great-Heart: Can't you guess the reason?

Faithless: You suppose it was sent to me as an invitation?

Great-Heart: Perhaps.

Faithless: What other reason could there be?

Great-Heart: A warning!

Faithless: A warning?

Great-Heart: Your dream has revealed a great deal of information, which is now known by you. What you do with this information will have one of two outcomes.

The worst outcome, since you inquired, is frightening.

Faithless: How so?

Great-Heart: You have been given a view into the only question that matters when this life is over.

Faithless: What question is that?

Great-Heart: I think you know the answer to that question.

Will you receive or will you refuse the offer of salvation that God the Father has provided as a free gift of grace to you, at great expense to Himself? A revelation that you must agree, the King has gone to great lengths to disclose to you.

The Son of God has provided a way for you to escape the wrath that is going to come and destroy the City of Destruction and all them that dwell in it. All those that remain in that city will all sink lower than the grave into Hell itself unless they find a way to escape.

Jesus Christ is the only Door through which you can escape this certain dreadful fate.

So, Faithless, what will you do with Jesus the Christ?

Faithless bowed his head and thought for a moment.

Finally, he braced himself, raised his head and said:

Faithless: I must be getting back home as the hour is late.

At that, Faithless stood up and went to the door, said his goodbyes and made his way back to the City of Destruction.

Great-Heart and Fidelity watched with heavy but hopeful hearts. Each praying that the revelation given to the poor sinner, Faithless, would unwind his mind that was so fixed on the things of this present world and concentrate it on the world to come.

Fidelity: Has the vision of Faithless come to an end?

Great-Heart: I pray that he has one more vision.

Fidelity: And what vision is that father?

Great-Heart: The vision of the Son of God bleeding and dying in order that he might be delivered from the wrath to come.

Fidelity: Yes, let's pray toward that end.

As Great-Heart and Fidelity watched poor Faithless make his way back to the City of Destruction, they both began thanking the King of the Cottage for His grace and care. They humbly asked that the heart of Faithless would be forever changed by the Gospel truths that had been miraculously revealed to him.

Time passed and there was no further word from Faithless.

Weeks turned into months.

Three months later a poor pilgrim arrived at the Narrow Gate.

Goodwill heard the frantic knocks that he recognized as the signature pleas of a sinner who was desperate to enter the Narrow Gate.

As was his habit, he allowed the knocks to continue for a moment or two and then went to greet the poor pilgrim who was about to become the precious child of the King of his country.

At last, Goodwill came to the gate.

Goodwill: Who is there?

Where did you come from?

The man on the other side of the gate began to plead with Goodwill.

The Man at the Gate: I know that your name is Goodwill and that you are here to show God's gracious mercy to poor sinners.

Goodwill: You know my name?

The Man at the Gate: Oh yes, I know it very well.

Goodwill: What would you have me do for you, sir?

The Man at the Gate: Here stands a poor burdened sinner. I have come from the City of Destruction, but I desire to go to Mount Zion, that I may be delivered from the wrath to come.

I would, therefore, sir since I am informed that by this gate is the only way I may arrive safely at the Celestial City. So, I, if you are willing, desire with everything that is in me that you allow me to enter in.

Goodwill: I am willing with all my heart.

And with that, Goodwill opened the gate.

Just as the man was stepping in, Goodwill gave him a big pull, putting the man off his feet. Goodwill then slammed the door shut

Faithless comes to Christ trusting in His finished work on the Cross of Calvary. What about you?

and gently raised up the poor man who was not miffed at all by the sudden circumstances that left him on the floor on the other side of the Small Sheep Gate.

The Man at the Gate: I know why you pulled me in with such force.

At that, Goodwill smiled and asked him his name.

Faithless: My name is Faithless and I have come from the City of Destruction.

Goodwill: Indeed you are, Faithless. Who sent you here?

Faithless: I was beckoned to come by the King Himself, as He sent me a message inviting me to become His child.

Goodwill: A message? What sort of message?

Faithless: A dream that brought me to the King's Cottage where I met Great-Heart and his brother Evangelist and was given this Book to read.

Faithless held up the Book with the firebrand on the right corner.

Goodwill: This is the best of all books and contains the revelation that has sent thousands upon thousands of pilgrims to this Narrow Gate. And have you read this Book?

Faithless: Countless times.

Goodwill: And are the pages stained with your tears as you reflect on your lost condition outside of the Door you have just entered?

Faithless: Yes, I have wondered a hundred times why the Son of God would bother with such a one as I, but in the end, I believe His invitation to sinners as myself are a genuine and truthful account of the rich mercy of His heart. And so, I have come. And I thank you for letting me in.

Goodwill: You say that Great-Heart and Evangelist bid you enter the gate?

Faithless: Oh yes, a hundred times. And I would have come sooner but my love for the present world held me back as did the thoughts of my family which I at first would not leave behind.

Goodwill: Are they not willing to come with you?

Faithless: I do not know.

Goodwill: What do you mean, you do not know?

Faithless: They were not willing to come with me, even though I pleaded with them to come along. But they did have an earnest desire to take counsel from Evangelist. And have on several occasion in the last couple of months visited the King's Cottage where my dear wife took counsel from Fidelity and Great-Heart. And now I understand, Great-Heart is even now showing them their perilous condition and how they might remedy it by following me here to the Narrow Gate.

Goodwill: And do you think they will heed his advice and come to join you?

Faithless: Sir, I pray they will with all my heart. But if they do not, I must flee without their company as nothing is more important than to heed the call of the Gospel. But I am grieved to be here alone, as you can imagine.

Then Faithless began to weep tears of joy that he was now safely in Christ mingled with tears of grief that his wife and two children were still in the City of Destruction and facing the certain wrath of God if they did not escape as he had warned them to do.

Finally recovering from his tears, a little, he asked Goodwill...

Faithless: Great-Heart and his younger brother Evangelist who bid me come here and knock, said, that you, sir, would tell me what I must do next.

Goodwill nodded, smiled and said:

Goodwill: An open door is set before you, and no man can shut it.

Your name is no longer Faithless but Full-of-Faith.

Faithless: Full-of-Faith?

Full-of-Faith beamed with joy and repeated his new name several times.

Finally, he asked Goodwill:

Full-of-Faith: How did you know my birth name was Faithless?

Goodwill: I was notified by Evangelist that you might be entering the King's Highway on pilgrimage to the Celestial City. Great-Heart, who has escorted many pilgrims to the Celestial City, informs me that he will be joining you as a guide and companion. So, you are to wait here until he arrives.

Full-of-Faith beamed with excitement at the prospect of Great-Heart leading him on their pilgrimage to the Celestial City. He fell down on his knees and thanked God for His tireless entreaties and constant love that had led him to the only place that provided him peace and security for eternity in the everlasting arms of his Savior, the King's own Son, Jesus the Christ!

Just then Goodwill heard a commotion outside of the door. No one was knocking at first but he could hear the fiery darts and arrows of the enemy glancing off the door. Then he heard frantic and persistent knocking that sounded like the rat-a-tat of several drums.

Goodwill opened the little window to see what the hub-bub was all about. But instead of making inquiries, as was his usual practice, he flung upon the door.

Through the door sailed a little raggedy muff of a girl, followed by her older brother who tumbled on the floor and moaned a little, and then a young woman tripped and fell into the arms of Goodwill, and finally, dressed in full armor, in marched Great-Heart.

Full-of-Faith was beside himself with joy as he picked his children up off the ground, dusted them off and kissed them repeatedly and then embraced his wife and twirled her around until he was so dizzy he could hardly stand up. A little settled, he finally saluted Great-Heart and gave him a manly embrace and would have kissed him except the armor made it impossible.

I would tell you what happened next, but that is another story.

CHECK OUT OUR WEBSITE FOR OTHER TITLES!

www.lighthouse.pub

2015

Rest! What is the "rest" that Jesus proclaims in the Book of Matthew as He beckons the weary and burdened to come to Him? What is Heaven? How do we get there? What will we do there? What happens when we no longer need the grace of God? These questions, along with many others, are addressed in this brief but powerful book by writer C.J. Lovik.

2019

Author and editor C.J. Lovik spins a spectacular story of a family at the turn of the 20th century, full of adventure, mystery, life lessons, and solid biblical teachings. The mysteries surrounding Heaven are carefully revealed in both the plain text of Scripture and then amplified by the skillful unfolding of allegories. Families who read this book will be blessed beyond measure.

2019

Pastor and Author Buck L. Keely asks, "Are you trapped in a prison of addiction or an unhealthy relationship? Have you been a victim of an empty religious experience that promised you rest?" If so, you have found yourself in a snare set by Satan that promised rest but ended in a darkness that has robbed you of hope. Call on the name of Jesus and ask for freedom from your prison, and you will find rest.

2020

This delightful three-book box set, divided into Justification, Sanctification and Glorification, will be a true blessing to the reader. This devotional series, authored by Pastor Buck L. Keely, is perfect for the new believer, or for the long-time Christian who desires to dig deeper in knowing what the bible says about these three topics. This set will aid pilgrims along on their journey to the "Celestial City" from a biblical vantage point.

www.lighthouse.pub

Visit our website to purchase books, DVDs, and other Christ-centered media, and to preview upcoming titles.